R00200 81026

D1188500

Space Biology

THE HUMAN FACTORS IN SPACE FLIGHT

JAMES STEPHEN HANRAHAN *and* DAVID BUSHNELL

Space Biology

THE HUMAN FACTORS IN SPACE FLIGHT

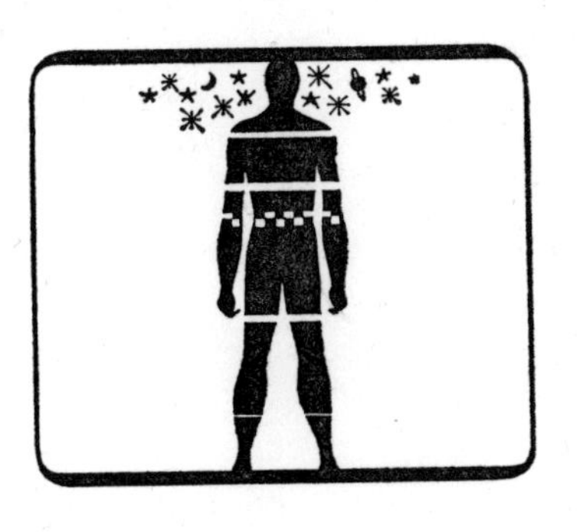

BASIC BOOKS, INC.
NEW YORK

All illustrations are official U. S. Air Force or National Aeronautics and Space Administration photographs and are used with their permission.

Library of Congress Catalog Card Number: 60-12021

PRINTED IN THE UNITED STATES OF AMERICA

DESIGNED BY LEWIS F. WHITE

Foreword

As MAN projects himself into the strange environment of the universe beyond the life-supporting atmosphere of his native planet, he will encounter physical and psychological forces alien to his experience. The success of his personal conquest of these extraterrestrial regions will depend in large measure upon his ability to identify these hazards and to neutralize them with protective devices. Space biology, in this pioneer generation of man's exploration of the limitless vertical frontier, is generally confined in definition to the study of these human factors of space flight. This limited use of the term is incorporated into the title and content of this volume.

This is not a textbook of space biology, in the sense of offering only a description of present knowledge concerning the physiological aspects of manned space flight. Instead it is an historical survey of research accomplishments from the earliest times which have led to our present state of sophistication in this revolutionary field. In addition to presenting the highlights of our present understanding of space-flight problems, ranging from waste disposal to weightlessness, it seeks to offer some indication of the steps by which we have reached our current level of accomplishment. More than this, it attempts to identify the individual scientists, both in the United States and abroad, who have made important contributions to this progress.

The authors take pleasure in acknowledging that many of these scientists have made direct contributions to this book. Three in particular deserve special thanks for their willingness to answer innumerable questions and to discuss in detail important developments related to their fields of specialized research. These individuals are Colonel John Paul Stapp, chief of the Aerospace Medical Laboratory at Wright Air Development Division; Lieutenant Colonel David G. Simons, now at the United States Air Force School of Aviation Medicine; and Dr. Harald J. von Beckh, Technical Advisor to the chief of the Aeromedical Field Laboratory at the Air Force Missile Development Center. Many others in the nation's universities, industry, branches of the military service and other government agencies—as well as their counterparts in other countries—who have been encountered in their laboratories or at various national and international symposia, have also helped in a similar manner. Although it is impossible to mention all by name in this brief foreword, they are identified as sources of information in the footnotes of each chapter.

We must also publicly confess our monumental debt to our wives, Virginia Bushnell and Jane Hanrahan—not only for their typing and proof-reading services, but for their toleration of the strange behavior often associated with the pangs of authorship.

James Stephen Hanrahan
David Bushnell

Table of Contents

PART ONE

Introduction

The Whim and the Wherewithal

MAN is beginning to venture forth into interplanetary space. Already material projections of his creativity have preceded him. Artificial satellites circumnavigate the earth. A man-made vehicle has impacted on the moon. Space probes have reached far outward and are now in perpetual orbit around the sun. Various agencies are planning to place instrumentation on Venus and Mars. And man will not be far behind.

Before living man can penetrate the hazardous vastness of space, many complex problems of space biology must be solved. But much has already been accomplished toward understanding the nature of these hazards and toward perfecting the protective devices which will neutralize the dangers. Space biology became a serious field of experimental research more than a dozen years ago, and the roots of these studies drift far back through time. The history of this scientific and technological endeavor is one of the boldest and most fruitful chapters in the story of human intellectual evolution.

Until man was actually faced with the possibility of space flight, there was slight practical justification for space biology. And before man could prepare to challenge the physical and mental forces to be encountered in space, two developments were required: the desire and the ability. The desire itself is age-old; it antedates recorded history. But the technical ability is new-found. Although the first significant achievements leading toward this ultimate accomplishment date from at least the seventeenth century, it was not until midpoint in the twentieth century that flight beyond the limits of the earth's atmosphere came within man's practical reach. And as the major powers of the world rush to win a foothold in the vastness of space, the human factors of space flight have become a field of intensive scientific research.

Some knowledge of the evolution of man's desire for interplanetary flight and of the development of his sciences and technology to the point where this is now possible is needed for an understanding of the new age of human history into which the world is moving. Each of these major prerequisites reached its necessary present stage through a series of historical steps. The early scientific and technological developments are a part of the recorded history of science and the practical arts. In later chapters there will be frequent reference to many of these early technical contributions. The evolution of the activating motivation, however, is less well documented and is worthy of brief consideration here.

The antiquity of man's desire to enlarge his personal cosmic environment and to escape the confines of the earth is impossible to ascertain. With the dawn of literature of any description, the concept is already well established. A recent book-promotion brochure was probably entirely correct when it referred poetically to man emerging from the cave to begin his journey to the stars.[1] The development of this desire, phase by phase, has been marked by major turning points in human intellectual evolution. This development of an idea is of particular importance for the final achievement of manned space flight, for it encouraged much of the technological advance required.

Marjorie Hope Nicolson, who for five years offered an English literature course at Smith College on "Science and Imagination" and continued her active exploration of the theme of cosmic travel at Columbia University, has brilliantly traced the development of this desire as reflected in the literature available to English readers of the seventeenth and eighteenth centuries.[2] Other individuals have brought parts of this history down to the present and have filled some of the gaps of the earlier story with examples from the literature of other languages. It is clear that throughout history, as recorded in any language, man has yearned for the stars as a young child reaches for the moon.

Because science and technology are always strongly influenced by prevailing social, religious, economic and political circumstances,[3] it is not possible to ignore completely any consideration of mythology, superstitious beliefs or religion. Speculations of this nature, however, have contributed comparatively little to the historical development of the determination to conquer space, and will be considered only as they have stimulated purposeful thought on the subject.

The first serious phase of man's desire for space flight was hampered by ignorance of basic astronomical and meteorological facts. Ancient thinkers had no reason to believe that the atmosphere did not extend upward to the stars, and so it seemed reasonable to contemplate using large birds, winged chariots, golden arrows and similar devices as vehicles for interplanetary travel. It was not until the sixteenth and seventeenth centuries that European scientists began to suspect the limitations of the atmosphere, although natives of the American highlands and of central Asia had long been aware of the adverse effects of great heights. In 1590 the Jesuit padre José de Acosta published his conviction that the thinning atmosphere had been responsible for his affliction in the Andes. Early in the same century Leonardo da Vinci and others undertook Alpine expeditions to observe the mysterious climate at high altitude, as well as for other aesthetic and scientific reasons.[4] But the thinning of the atmosphere was not confirmed scientifically until 1648, when Périer ascended the Puy-de-Dôme in Auvergne with a primitive Torricelli-type barometer and verified Blaise Pascal's deduction that atmospheric substance and pressure decreased with altitude.[5] As late as 1875 the balloonists J. E. Crocé-Spinelli and H. T. Sivel were martyrs in exploring altitude physiology as a field of scientific investigation.[6]

Ancient speculation on space travel which did not consider problems of space biology was yet practical within its own context, and forms an interesting part of the prehistory of astronautics. It was as realistic, in a sense, as the belief, after the famous *Man-High* balloon flights of 1957, that radiation hazards would probably not prove a serious obstacle to space flight[7]—a theory exploded a few months later when the Explorer satellites disclosed the existence of the Van Allen radiation belts.[8]

The earliest anthropological or historical evidence of modern man discovered to date is that of a *Homo sapiens* species already widely dispersed over a great part of the world.[9] And it is from many widely separated sources that the earliest extant traces of astronautical thought appear. Early Babylonian literature, transmitted to us by Persian intermediaries, includes this sort of speculation.[10] Winged anthropomorphic statuary and legends from early civilizations attest to the desire which caused the earth-weary Psalmist to cry "Oh that I had wings like a dove!" and which motivated the ancient Chinese emperor Shun to attempt flight and, with interesting foresight, dabble with the equivalent of parachutes.[11] Solomon, who historically led Israel to the height of its greatness and studded Jerusalem with a temple and public buildings, unhistorically is said to have given the Queen of Sheba "a vessel whence she could traverse the air," which he had made by the wisdom God had given him.[12]

Five hundred years later Anaxagoras, who brought Ionian philosophy to Athens and who remained there some 30 years to teach pupils such as Pericles, Euripides and possibly Socrates, reached the daring pre-telescope conclusion that the moon was a body much like the earth, with plains and ravines, and was inhabited.[13] He also sought to depose the god Helios by maintaining that the sun was a physical entity, probably a burning stone.[14] Charged with impiety and banished from Athens for life, he nevertheless left behind a more rational concept of cosmology and has continued to stimulate thought down to modern times concerning the physical and social environment that will be encountered on heavenly bodies by visiting earthlings.

The intellectual genius of Greece permitted an Anaxagoras to develop a rational concept of the physical nature of planets and stars. It produced an Anaximandros who conceived of man as the product of an organic evolution which originated in simple form and developed a creature who came up from the ooze to stand erect upon land.[15] It stimulated a Democritus to range mentally from the atomic theory of the structure of matter to a vast concept of a universe in which worlds collided—worlds which might or might not have water and flora and fauna.[16] It developed a Plato who could perversely speculate upon political theory or play with myths of souls rising and falling through heavenly regions.[17] It conceived an Aristotle who defined a sharp division between earth and heaven, who had the first glimmerings of an understanding of gravity, who insisted upon the necessity of studying the stars, but who could not admit of the concept of space travel at all.[18] Ultimately, some centuries later, a flickering of this genius produced a Lucian, the leading figure of the revival of Greek literature which flourished under the Roman Empire. And it was with the so-called *True History* of Lucian, composed in the third century of the modern era, that a tale of supernatural travel to other worlds was first fully developed and implanted in true literature.[19]

From that moment on, through Roman times to the present, tales of interplanetary or intergalactic travel have stimulated man's desire. More than this, they have encouraged him to expand his scientific knowledge and to enlarge his technology to the point that the National Aeronautics and Space Administration is already carefully preparing the first true astronauts to penetrate space in Project Mercury.[20] But before modern science and technology could accept as valid a concept so staggering, a long evolution of human desire to explore other worlds followed a long trail through a maze of fanciful stories, gradually acquiring greater validity as the fiction became more scientific, becoming more practical as new technologies developed.

Lucian, a serious philosopher and prolific writer upon matters philosophical, was the first to compose a full story of extraterrestrial adventure. He was bolder in imagination than Diodorus of Sicily, who three centuries before had told of Abaris and his flight around the world on a golden arrow; or than Cicero, who used a dream to provide the elevation necessary for a view of the entire universe; or than Plutarch, who pondered the moon and the possibility of life existing there.[21] Lucian ranged far through space and encountered near-human life in remote regions of the universe. He sought rational explanations of the problems involved in such a journey, and established a pattern followed by writers of later centuries.[22]

Even on far-flung frontiers of civilization during the so-called Dark Ages, man sought to add a third dimension to his existence. The legends of Britain, for example, tell of a ninth-century king named Bladud who flew on feathered wings. Elmer of Malmesbury was another who would take leave of the earth's surface, and John Damian, abbot of Tungland, would fly from Sterling Castle to France. All of these tales had important effects, for they continued to excite imagination through the writings of Geoffrey of Monmouth, John Stow,

Michael Drayton, John Taylor, John Milton, John Lesly, and William Dunbar.[23] But none of them seems to have matched the intellectual boldness of Lucian. It was not until the great period of fifteenth-century geographical exploration and the overseas expansion of western Europe, beginning with the work of Portugal's Henry the Navigator, that men again seemed to have the imagination to leap off mentally into the unknown with the courage of Polynesian seafarers.

Explorations in Africa, the discovery of the Americas, and the definitive rediscovery of the Far East brought unknown worlds into the ken of Europeans. And shortly thereafter, Lodovico Ariosto, in his *Orlando Furioso,* sent Astolfo, inspired by a visionary suggestion of St. John the Evangelist, on a trip to the moon.[24] Even the followers of John Calvin, who vehemently opposed the concept of human flight as being contrary to God's deliberate withholding of that power,[25] added fuel to the desire by their public deliberations upon the subject.

The real turning point in the development of man's desire to penetrate the seemingly limitless regions of the universe came with an equally important turning point in the history of science. This was the scientific revolution which began about the time of Nicolaus Copernicus and the anatomist Andreas Vesalius, both of whom published their scientific bombshells in 1539. During the next two and one-half centuries the pioneers of the new revolution overturned traditional authority and established science as a methodical, inductive investigation of nature. As one historian of science, A. R. Hall, has written:

> Much more has been learnt about Nature, from the structure of matter to the physiology of man, in the last century and a half than in all preceding time. Of this there can be no doubt. But the scientific revolution ends when this vastly detailed exploration began, for it was that which made such investigation possible.[26]

The trail-blazing giants of the new science, men like Galileo Galilei and Johannes Kepler, provided solid knowledge about natural laws and distant worlds which churned man's desire to explore those remote regions. True, traditional fantasies continued to appear in print, like the earlier speculation of Francis Bacon, who wondered about the possibility of human flight by means of fowls, or that of Francis Godwin, who sent Gonsales to the moon. Miguel Cervantes referred to a flight near that orb by Torralba and his lackey Zaquiel, and the Satan of John Milton performed the last of the truly supernatural cosmic voyages. But with Galileo's confirmation of Anaxagoras' concept of lunar topography, with the heliocentric theories of Copernicus, and with Kepler's formulation of the laws of planetary motion, scientific elements began to be added to the tales. Kepler himself wrote one of the best tales of cosmic travel ever written.[27] Yet this was also the period when William Shakespeare not only struggled with the legacy of 44 spelling variations of his family surname[28] but also touched in his works upon every conceivable subject except space flight.[29]

This was the transition period between the supernatural and the scientific. John Donne, a great poet and true humanitarian (and author of a later Hemingway title), demonstrated his debt to Kepler. But Athanasius Kircher, the German Hebrew-teaching Jesuit, gave up teaching to invent the magic lantern, study hieroglyphics and archaeology, and write in Latin his *Itinerarium Extaticum,* which included a grand tour of the heavens in the old style with an angel guide. Robert Burton put to one side his contemplation of the causes, symptoms, and cures of melancholy and wrote in his *Satyre Menyspée* of a trip to the moon. Cyrano de Bergerac—who published fantasies in 1656 and 1662 on the nations and empires to be found on the moon and sun, and who also provided inspiration for Rostand's later tragedy about the person with the soul of a poet but a nose of astronomical proportions—conceived the first literary journey into space by means of rocket ship. And during this same transition period in the development of astronautical thought, John Wilkins, a founder of the Royal Society, influenced by the recent translation of Lucian's *True History* and the works of Kepler and Godwin, turned romance toward science by writing a treatise with the lengthy title: *Discovery of a New World: Or, a Discourse Tending to Prove, that it is Probable there may be another Inhabited World in the Moon.*[30]

After this period, especially after Newton published his *Principia,* the pattern was set. More than ever, man desired to incorporate the universe within his personal realm, but now he began to struggle with reality instead of pure fantasy, and to seek the means of making his age-old dream come true. With only a few backsliders, a phalanx of pseudoscientific and semiscientific writers began to pave the way to the science fiction writers and astronautical planners of today, all expressing the desire to reach beyond the confines of the earth. They even began to suspect and take into consideration some of the human-factor problems inherent in such projects. Kepler had already toyed with the problem of breathing in an airless environment, and both Kepler and Wilkins had already considered the problem of physical motion in a subgravity field.[31]

This transition period, when the traditional considerations of the physical world yielded to the radically new concepts concerning the nature of man and his universe, was also a period of great religious ferment. Science affected religion, and religious speculation in turn affected astronautical thought. The egocentric nature of man had survived its Copernican shift from the center of our solar system to a whirling orbit somewhat removed from the center. It had adjusted, too, to a mechanical universe in which fixed, unchanging physical laws relieved the heavenly host of the responsibility for the proper regulation of planetary and stellar motions.

The effect of these new ideas upon religion is apparent, and their direct effect upon astronautics was reinforced indirectly by spiritual speculation. Deeply religious Christian Huygens—who announced the existence of the rings of Saturn, discovered improved methods of grinding lenses, harnessed the pendulum to regulate clocks, determined acceleration due to gravity, and proposed the wave theory of light—also stated that he could not but "sometimes think that it's not improbable that the rest of the Planets have their Dress and Furniture, and perhaps their Inhabitants too as well as this Earth of ours."[32] Emanuel Swedenborg, the Swedish mathematician, scientist, philosopher, and founder of the religious sect bearing his name, wrote in his *Earths in the Universe* that there are "very many earths inhabited by man . . . thousands, yea, tens of thousands of earths, all full of inhabitants."[33]

Voltaire, high priest of the onrushing Enlightenment, that delightful period when, in theory, reason ruled, reversed the theme of Kircher's *Itinerarium Extaticum* with his satirical *Micromégas.* According to his story, a gigantic traveler from a planet of the star Sirius visited Earth in the company of a friend from Saturn. As they looked about in the midst of sophisticated mid-eighteenth-century European civilization, they commented sardonically upon existing customs and behavior.[34] Thomas D'Urbey had already adapted Godwin's *Man in the Moon* to the comic opera *Wonders in the Sun.*[35] On into the first half of the nineteenth century the theme of interplanetary or interstellar travel flowed from the pens of earth-bound men, including that of Edgar Allan Poe.[36]

About midway through the nineteenth century a major new period of astronautical thought evolved. It was signaled by the birth of both modern science fiction and serious consideration of the technical problems of space flight. Jules Verne blazed the trail for the modern extraterrestrial excursion within a seemingly scientific context, and Konstantin Eduardovich Tsiolkovsky took the first, deliberate, purely scientific step into space. Jules Verne, born the very year that the famous military rocket specialist William Congreve died,[37] sharpened his literary skill on plays and librettos. He then abandoned drama to write in rapid succession an enormously successful series of semiscientific adventures in which he foretold with astonishing correctness a number of later technological developments. The first of his astronautical romances, *From the Earth to the Moon,* was published in 1865.

Calling upon his brother-in-law, a professor of astronomy, to provide technically correct background for his story, Verne was able to include precise calculations of the trajectory and velocities involved in the takeoff and other aspects of the lunar journey.[38] The method of propulsion was bizarre—a giant cannon 900 feet long weighing 68,000 tons. But it showed that Verne understood the magnitude of initial thrust necessary to overcome the force of gravity to the extent required to reach the moon. The space vehicle itself was an aluminum projectile equipped with various emergency survival devices—a literary forerunner of the Mercury capsule to be used in the United States manned-satellite program.[39]

In 1957 a periodical devoted to furthering the conquest of space published a short article calling attention to a series of Verne's predictions which are both fantastic in their accuracy and amusing in their implications. Almost a hundred years before Vanguard I, Verne wrote of a journey into space in a vehicle weighing 20,000 pounds, launched from a site in Florida at latitude 28° N., and fired aloft by a "Baltimore Gun Club." Vanguard I, in 1957, was planned to weigh 24,000 pounds and would be launched from the Air Force Missile Test Center in Florida at latitude 28½° N. The Missile Test

Center is one of the main installations of the Air Research and Development Command, whose headquarters at the time of the launching were in Baltimore.[40]

The year in which Verne's first story of space flight appeared was also marked by the publication of *Alice in Wonderland* by Charles Lutwidge Dodgson (Lewis Carroll), which Marjorie Hope Nicolson has called her favorite cosmic-adventure in English literature,[41] although it is not a space-flight story in the literal sense. It is interesting, too, that a modern weapon gets its name from another tale by the same author—Dodgson's *The Hunting of the Snark.* Snark is the name of a near-sonic United States guided missile of intercontinental range. (This, in turn, has given rise to the tongue-in-cheek renaming of the ocean off the eastern coast of Florida as the "Snark-infested waters.")

Nineteenth-century science fiction reached its climax with the publication in 1898 of H. G. Wells's *War of the Worlds.* Combining scientific speculation with sociological idealism, Wells initiated a new era in such spectacular stories. In his tale, civilization on earth is saved when otherwise invincible creatures from Mars are destroyed by microbes alien to their native planet. This theme is reminiscent of the history of the European conquest of the Americas, when diseases strange to the New World, such as smallpox, practically annihilated entire aboriginal population groups.[42]

The late nineteenth century was far more of a turning point for astronautical thought, however, than the new fiction of the Verne-Wells school would suggest. For during this period the true science and technology of astronautics were born. Probably as early as 1876, Konstantin Tsiolkovsky began his scientific speculation upon the concept of interplanetary travel.[43] Later he became involved with technical considerations related to the aeronautics of lighter-than-air vehicles, such as balloons and dirigibles. He also dabbled in science fiction. Between 1893 and 1896 he published a series of articles and stories including *An Imaginary Journey to the Moon* and *Is There Life on Other Worlds?*

In 1898, the same year that Wells's *War of the Worlds* appeared, Tsiolkovsky completed a manuscript entitled the *Exploration of Cosmic Space by Rocket*. This work can be considered as marking the birth of astronautics as a science. Published in 1903, it has been termed the first basic treatise on space travel by rocket. It far surpasses scientifically the contribution of earlier speculators, such as Hermann Ganswindt. Tsiolkovsky, today one of the heroes of the Soviet Union, and of astronautics in general, is honored by a simple memorial in the Russian town of Kaluga, where he taught school. Engraved on the monument are his own words: "Mankind will not remain on earth forever."

In the twentieth century, man's desire to extend his personal influence beyond his earth-bound natural habitat has reached the final phase of its evolution necessary to achieve reality. Only within our lifetime has the flame of this urge, fanned by man's increasing technical knowledge, reached such intensity that he is deliberately forcing the final development of his sciences and technology to close the gap between theoretical possibility and actual accomplishment. This quickening technical interest and the creation of the necessary favorable environment have been influenced by the ever more sophisticated expression of the desire in the writings of both scientists and science fictionists.

With the advent of high-altitude rocket experimentation—first by Robert H. Goddard and then by others—the theme of space flight began to invade other media besides the novel and short story. The genuine literary effort, of course, continued with the work of C. S. Lewis, John Livingston Lowes, Aldous Huxley, Robert A. Heinlein, Fredric Brown, and George Orwell. Even full-fledged scientists, mathematicians, and engineers scratched their ballpoints or pounded their typewriters to swell the flood of literary space flight—men like E. T. Bell, Isaac Asimov, Harry Stubbs, Robert S. Richardson, John R. Pierce and G. Harry Stine.[44] But the theme now began to appear in comic strips such as Buck Rogers and Flash Gordon, which greatly assisted its dissemination. This is also the period when Orson Welles, like Lucian almost 2000 years before, warned his public that pure fantasy was to follow and then staggered the imagination of his contemporaries with "The Invasion from Mars," a radio script by Howard Koch.[45] A similar broadcast in Moscow in 1955 prompted a similar public reaction within the Soviet Union.[46] Newspapers, too, began to comment editorially upon man's desire to explore the universe,[47] and organized religion accepted the challenge of space flight as "legitimate before God."[48] And even the "Stranger in Paradise," musically inspired by Alexander Borodin and revived for the musical *Kismet* in the 1950s,[49] found himself suspended in space suffering no biological difficulties—only the agony of delay in experiencing love's fulfillment.

In short, after World War II, governments began consciously to plot the conquest of space. Both man's desire to accomplish this and his technical ability to achieve it had reached the stage where space flight was not only possible but mandatory. And it was at this point, because of the rather awesome problems of human survival in space, that space biology became firmly established as a recognized field of scientific investigation.

PART TWO

The Space Vehicle

2

The Question of Air Pressure

MAN has evolved over eons of time within the gradually changing environment on the surface of the earth. He has developed his physical identity and his intelligence within what he calls a unity field of gravity, within the lowest level of the peculiar atmosphere that surrounds his native planet, within the familiar natural cycles—hydrographic, food-waste, carbon-oxygen, and others—that maintain a near equilibrium of his earth-bound environment. And when man leaves this natural habitat to travel to alien portions of the universe, he will have to enclose himself in a small earth-like environment—one which will permit him to eat and breathe, to eliminate body wastes, to operate physically and mentally within a tolerable field of gravitational forces, and to survive the meteoritic and radiation hazards of space.

From the point of view of Hubertus Strughold, pioneer dean of space medicine and Research Adviser to the Commandant of the School of Aviation Medicine of the United States Air Force, the problem of creating and maintaining such an artificial environment is not as esoteric as it appears to many of his fellow scientists and engineers. Dr. Strughold has pointed out that since man first evolved he has been orbiting through the universe aboard the equivalent of a space ship—a vehicle almost infinitely large in mass compared to the life-supporting environment it carries along on its journey.[1] When man leaves this vehicle, Mother Earth, to explore space in a machine of his own creation, he need only capture a small segment of his familiar environment within the smaller vehicle and devise relatively simple methods of maintaining it as a close approximation of the original. Dr. Strughold concedes that this requirement imposes difficult tasks upon science and engineering, but his approach eliminates much of the psychological fog that has made the problem appear so formidable.

Difficult problems arise in each of the major aspects involved in creating a life-supporting environment for space travel. The need for an atmosphere is only one of the demands upon the ecological subsystem of a manned space vehicle. Yet this single aspect includes many problems, related to the selection and maintenance of a suitable gaseous chemical medium, the careful control of its temperature, and the regulation of its pressure within severely narrow limits.

The importance of atmospheric pressure can be understood when one considers the effect upon man of exceeding the rather narrow limits to which he is accustomed. Caisson disease, or bends,[2] is one of the effects resulting from exposure to pressures significantly greater than the normal 15 pounds per square inch. The disease derives its name from the compressed-air chamber first used in 1851 by Sir William Cubitt and John Wright for constructing bridge piers 61 feet below the surface of the Medway River at Rochester, England. The greatest depth at which men can work in such a chamber without adverse effects, even in very short shifts, is about 120 feet, where the air pressure is 52 pounds per square inch. In 1870, during the construction of the Eads Bridge at St. Louis, Missouri, men worked below the hundred-foot level under 45 pounds of pressure in half-hour shifts. Because the physiological causes and effects of caisson disease were largely unknown, these men were allowed only two or three minutes for decompression, so that 14 died of caisson disease and there were many near-fatalities.[3]

The affliction is also familiar to sandhogs driving tunnels beneath rivers, to miners clawing at mineral resources deep within the earth, and to deep-sea divers descending in search of scientific knowledge or sunken treasure. During the construction of the first Hudson River tunnel between New York and Jersey City, which took from 1874 to

1908 to complete, men worked under 35 pounds of pressure and suffered considerably from caisson disease. To cope with this situation, the contractors built what was probably the first medical airlock; with this device they recompressed afflicted men until the painful symptoms subsided and then decompressed them very gradually.[4]

The symptoms of caisson disease, other than ear pain, do not usually appear until minutes or even hours after a return to lesser pressure. But they arise from physiological changes that take place while the body is under pressure. Under a pressure of two or three atmospheres, the blood absorbs increased amounts of oxygen and nitrogen and distributes them to the fluids in various parts of the body. Unless decompression takes place gradually, permitting the circulation to return these extra quantities of gases to the lungs for exhalation, nitrogen bubbles will form in the blood and body tissues. Physiological damage begins with numerous capillary emboli, which can produce lesions in the brain or spinal cord. In severe cases unconsciousness and death result, although much more frequently the symptoms are acute pain in the extremities or abdomen, vertigo, deafness, and occasional hemorrhaging. Similar effects are experienced when one is subjected to rapid, but not explosive, decompression while flying at fairly high altitudes. For this reason, among others, the problems of underwater operations are of interest to aviation and space medicine.

Too little pressure will bring on another variety of dangers. Sea-level man can obtain sufficient oxygen from the surrounding atmosphere without difficulty only to an altitude of about 10,000 feet, although with physiological conditioning he can adjust to elevations several thousand feet higher. One can breathe pure oxygen from a mask up to about 40,000 feet, and from a pressurized mask up to about 42,000 feet. At about 49,000 feet, however, the pressure of the ambient atmosphere is equal only to the pressure of carbon dioxide and water vapor within the lungs. Above this altitude the normal process of respiration will bring none of the oxygen, even pure oxygen from a pressurized container, into the lungs, and man can survive only within a mechanically pressurized environment.

At about 62,000 feet, where the atmospheric pressure is only about half that at 42,000 feet, unprotected exposure would result in the boiling of the blood and other body fluids. These threats can be met by pressurization of the cabin with air compressed from the exterior ambient atmosphere, but beyond about 80,000 feet, only a sealed cabin carrying its own supply of air is practicable.[5] As a creature of his terrestrial environment, man cannot exist if the pressure conditions are altered much beyond certain narrow limits. Physiological conditioning can stretch these limits to a slight, though significant, degree, but to travel through space he must be encapsulated within an atmosphere approximating that in which *Homo sapiens* evolved.

The first scientific demonstration of the variation of atmospheric pressure in relation to altitude occurred in 1648, when Périer carried his barometer up the Puy-de-Dôme to prove the theory of Blaise Pascal that the pressure would decrease with increase in elevation.[6] Half a century earlier, the Jesuit padre José de Acosta had concluded that the mysterious illness which had afflicted him in the Colombian highlands was a result of the rarefied atmosphere at those elevations.[7] Two or three generations before Acosta published his speculation, Spanish conquistadores had observed that it was practically impossible for their horses to reproduce in the mining communities of the high Peruvian and Bolivian Andes, a fact which gave rise to an historically important mule trade with Argentina.[8] Even earlier, Leonardo da Vinci, during a semiscientific expedition to observe the flora and fauna of the high Alps, had noted the mysterious thinning of the atmosphere as he progressed higher and higher.[9] And one of the earliest recorded observations of this phenomenon appears in a Chinese tale published in 981 A.D. as part of the classic collection *T'aip'ing Kuangchi.*[10]

There is twofold importance for manned space flight in these early observations. The most obvious deduction is that the limits of atmospheric pressure within which man can survive are narrow. More interesting is the fact that physiological conditioning can extend these limits to a small but significant degree, which materially eases the exactness of the requirements in space-cabin design.

MOUNTAIN STUDIES

"Alpine" physiology, including valuable studies of natives in the Andes and mountain climbers in the Himalayas and recent experiments in this field by scientists and volunteer airmen of the School of Aviation Medicine of the United States Air Force, has contributed a great deal to understanding of the human factors in space flight.

Long before the physiological influence of altitude was studied by scientists, it was exerting a pronounced influence upon the distribution of man over the surface of the earth. One leading authority in cultural geography considers the physiological effects of altitude a major force in determining the population pattern of much of Spanish America.[11] This region is famous for the high elevations of many of its major cities, and its ancient semicivilizations are usually considered mountain or high-plateau cultures. But actually, although the natives lived at altitudes which were high compared to the home cities of European conquerors, they avoided extreme elevations and left vast areas unsettled.

It appears that the highest permanent human habitation in the world is in Peru. A small mining camp in that country is reported to be located at 17,500 feet, and a stone-walled, thatched-roof shepherd's hut was definitely measured at 17,100 feet above sea level. But these are exceptions and involve only a handful of people.[12] When the famous Institute of Andean Biology in Peru embarked upon a long and fruitful study of man at high altitudes, it selected as its subjects the natives of a mining town called Morococha, at an altitude of 14,900 feet, where the air density is about two-thirds that at sea level. These investigations compared the physiology of the mountain dwellers with that of the inhabitants of Lima, who reside at only 500 feet, or practically at sea level.[13]

The first significant studies of mountain physiology dealt with the phenomenon known as mountain sickness—called *soroche, veta, la puna* or *mareo de la cordillera* in the American highlands, *bis, tunk, dum, mundara,* or *seran* in various parts of central Asia, and *ikak* in Borneo.[14] Most commonly, the symptoms are nausea and dizziness, caused by an inadequate supply of oxygen, which may prelude serious results.

Among the first Europeans to attempt identification of the physiological mechanism of mountain sickness was Alexander von Humboldt. In 1799 while exploring the Andes, he measured the pressure and oxygen content of the atmosphere.[15] In the mid-nineteenth century another pioneer named Jourdanet, studied high-altitude effects in Mexico and coined the word *anoxemia* to describe the causative condition.[16] Then in 1879-80 Edward Whymper, during a mountain-climbing expedition in Ecuador, combined historical research on mountain sickness with scientific observations of the physical conditions of the atmosphere in which it occurred and the symptoms that announced its onset.[17] By that time the cause of mountain sickness was understood, although not until much later was its physiology reasonably explained.

Physiological research conducted during a series of expeditions to the Himalayas in the 1930's called the attention of German flight surgeons to the importance of acclimatization for high-altitude flying. The result was a series of studies in altitude laboratories in the Alps.[18] After World War II the United States Air Force—still interested only in flight within the atmosphere—began experiments in mountain physiology in the Colorado Rockies and contracted with the Institute of Andean Biology in Peru for related investigations. Some of the results, such as changes in lung volume during exposure to high elevations, were to be of particular interest later to scientists studying the problems of flight beyond the atmosphere.[19]

Research in mountain physiology now deals with the problems man will face when he leaves his familiar environment on earth for outer space. Preliminary findings of scientists working with the Institute of Andean Biology indicate that one of the major characteristics of natural acclimatization to high elevations is an amazing capacity to perform physical work in the hypoxic condition—an ability which newcomers to the region generally lack even after a prolonged residence.[20] After several weeks of physical conditioning, visitors from Lima are able to approximate the work rate of highland natives for extensive periods, but to do so they must have twice the lung activity of the natives, for the latter are twice as efficient in extracting oxygen from the rarefied atmosphere.[21]

High-altitude man generally appears capable of unusual economy in the use of oxygen.[22] One outstanding characteristic seems to be more efficient ventilation of all lung areas where gas transfer occurs.[23] And there is evidence to support a theory of chemical adaptation at the tissue level which may influence oxygen utilization.[24] Institute scientists are also investigating the possible contributions of modifications in the oxygen transport system, of tissue-vascular adjustments, and of chemical and anatomical cellular changes.[25]

If a native of Morococha in Peru were selected as the first astronaut to invade space, the task of space scientists and engineers would be considerably eased, so far as atmospheric pressure requirements within the space vehicle are concerned. But neither the Soviet Union nor the United States is likely to recruit key manpower from the South American highlands, and the first astronauts will probably be natives of regions at much lower altitudes than Morococha. There are indications, however, that physiological conditioning can endow lowlanders with many, if not all, of the abilities enjoyed naturally by natives of the high Andes. The findings of experimental programs in physiological conditioning conducted by the Air Force's School of Aviation Medicine provide a firm basis for this optimism.

In the summer of 1958 a seven-man team from the School of Aviation Medicine arrived at Mount Evans in Colorado to carry out a rugged program of physiological conditioning to the high mountain environment and to evaluate the benefits of such conditioning to astronauts. The results were spectacular. Five subjects, all volunteer airmen, were led through the program by task scientist Bruno Balke, once a research physician in the German Army Mountain Corps and now in the School's Department of Physiology and Biophysics. James A. Green, of the same department, was the team physician.

The experiment called for comparing the data collected at Mount Evans with data gathered during a three-month period of physical conditioning and testing in the environment of near-sea-level San Antonio, Tex. Tests were designed to ascertain what effect, if any, the period of active mountaineering would have upon the ability of these men to withstand much higher elevations in a space-cabin simulator. Another goal was to find methods of increasing the time of consciousness after loss of oxygen at extreme altitude. And all the data would be useful in deciding what sort of man would make the best astronaut.[26]

Beginning their 42-day mission at the 11,000-foot level, the team launched an active schedule of cross-country runs, long-distance hikes under heavy loads, and rock climbing. Gradually the men spent a greater proportion of their time at higher and higher elevations, until they finally shifted their camp to the rustic buildings of the Inter-University High Altitude Laboratory at the top of the 14,260-foot, wind-swept peak.[27] In early August the team suffered its only serious casualty: Dr. Green fell and broke his leg.[28]

Of significance for space flight is the fact that this program of conditioning led to an increased ability to function physically and mentally at ultrahigh altitudes and at abnormally low atmospheric pressures. In pressure chambers at the top of Mt. Evans and later at the School in Texas, tests indicated that the men were able to withstand simulated altitudes of 55,000 feet for varying periods, whereas previously, even after a program of altitude conditioning at the School, none had been able to go higher than 49,000 feet.[29] Dr. Balke, for example, could spend a full 30 minutes at 30,000 feet without additional oxygen (an unacclimatized man would last less than two minutes), and all of the team could far exceed 30 minutes at a simulated altitude of 25,000 feet.[30] This would mean that in a space-flight emergency, such as puncture of the cabin by a meteorite, the conditioned man would have a much longer time to don a pressure suit and take corrective action before becoming unconscious.

Another result of the conditioning program was a much greater tolerance to carbon dioxide and humidity. Team members found that they could retain full consciousness until the carbon dioxide level built up to 12 per cent—much higher than the normal sea-level concentration of about one-thirtieth of one per cent. Again, the conditioned man would have a greater period of time to take corrective measures if something went wrong with the atmospheric cycling mechanism of his space craft.[31] Dr. Balke has determined that, once acclimatized up to a 14,000-foot elevation, man can retain the effect at sea level for up to 12 weeks by spending an hour or two each day in a chamber pressurized to simulate that altitude.[32]

Conditioning of crews at high mountain elevations, then, considerably eases the problem of designing vehicles for space flight. Such conditioning also increases the survival potential of the crew members. As for selecting crew members, 52-year-old Dr. Balke says that the age limits should be 30 and 45 years. He bases the upper limit upon the results of his experiments. The lower limit is imposed, he says, because it will take that long for a man "to get all the necessary training and education."[33]

SUBMARINE STUDIES

Long before man began to experiment with the physiological problems of flight in the atmosphere, he was coming to grips with similar problems in underwater activity. Hermann Oberth, a pioneer of astronautics, is one of many space technologists who have acknowledged the contributions of submarine medicine to space medicine, because of its concern with the problems of a sealed-cabin environment.[34]

At the December, 1957, annual meeting of the American Rocket Society, Commander C. C. Brock of the United States Navy delivered a paper, "Space Flight in the Undersea," in which he emphasized the similarity of human problems in space to those encountered in cruising under the Arctic icecap in a submarine. The naval officer was so bold as to suggest that whereas a conventional aircraft and a space vehicle are cousins, a space ship and a long-range submarine are brothers. Dr. Strughold, in commenting upon this paper, suggested that the first true space ship should be named the *Astronautilus.*[35]

Commander Brock's claim is reinforced by the underwater voyages of the nuclear submarines *Skate* and *Seawolf.*[36] Even before the *Skate* surfaced from its month-long voyage, some 200 of the world's leading specialists in environmental medicine had gathered at the submarine base in New London, Conn., for an international symposium on the "Ecological Problems Related to Confinement in the True Submersible or Sealed Space Cabin." The meeting was sponsored by the American Institute of Biological Sciences and supported by the Advanced Research Projects Agency of the Department of Defense.[37]

Underwater medicine dates from the beginning of the sixteenth century and the invention by Sturmius of the diving bell, a device which filled only partly with water when lowered to the bottom, thus leaving an air space in which men could work. The trapped air, however, rapidly became foul, and the pressure increased greatly as water rose within the chamber. Edmund Halley, the English physician, later contributed a partial solution by inventing a helmet into which compressed air from the surface could be pumped. This extended the working time and allowed the workmen to leave the bell while under water.[38]

From these early beginnings evolved the carefully controlled cabin of the first atomic-powered submarine, the *Nautilus.* Navigated by an inertial guidance system originally developed for the Air Force's Navaho missile, the *Nautilus* passed under the icecap of the North Pole shortly before midnight on August 3, 1958, for its pioneer underwater transit of the Arctic Ocean.[39] About 150 years before this event the original *Nautilus,* a submarine designed and built by Robert Fulton of steamboat fame, had evoked the passing interest of Napoleon (though not of his own country's officials). But the problems of maintaining a life-supporting environment within a submarine hull had begun to attract serious attention during the American Revolution, when David Bushnell built his pioneering submarine, *Turtle,* and tried (unsuccessfully) to attack the British fleet in New York harbor.[40] Submarine medicine finally became a significant field of research in 1900, when the United States Navy adopted John P. Holland's porpoise-dive vehicle—the prototype of later operational submarines throughout the world.[41]

Today there are other types of underwater vehicles with far more exacting environmental requirements than the conventional submarine. Whereas submarines cannot operate much below 750 feet, Auguste Piccard's bathyscaphe *Trieste* (recently purchased by the United States Navy) can descend thousands of feet[42] and has already reached the bottom of one of the deepest Pacific Ocean trenches, more than seven miles down[43]

The thesis that the submarine has fathered most of our ideas about space-ship requirements[44] is only partly correct. It is true that submarine voyages have anticipated some of the problems that will arise in space flight—the question of how much or how little oxygen a man can tolerate, the problem of boredom on a long voyage (of months or years), the problem of becoming accustomed to an artificial wake-sleep cycle. During the 60-day underwater cruise of the *Seawolf,* men were required to breathe mechanically purified air, to cope with the psychological problems of boredom, to adjust to an artificial day-and-night pattern, and to entertain the risk of structural failure. They also had to be shielded against radiation (from the ship's nuclear power plant). But these are only a few of the problems facing astronauts. The *Seawolf* had no difficulties of food supply (or waste disposal); its crew feasted on steaks, roast beef, turkey, leg of lamb, Chinese dinners, Italian cooking, and snacks of cold cuts from a well-stocked refrigerator.[45] On an interplanetary voyage, this type of payload would be a multimillion-dollar luxury, if not absolutely prohibitive. Submarine medicine certainly has contributed much to understanding the problems of maintaining an artificial environment, and man has made progress toward outer space by his underwater voyages, but space medicine is still left with many problems to solve.

BEGINNINGS OF AVIATION PHYSIOLOGY

Aeromedical research has contributed directly to many problems of space flight: the problems of subgravity and weightlessness, multigravitational acceleration and abrupt deceleration, the windblast of escape within the atmosphere and the tumbling of atmospheric reentry, and the hazards of cosmic rays and other extraterrestrial radiation, as well as cabin pressures, oxygen starvation, explosive decompression, and various atmospheric and food-waste cycling devices.

Man's personal conquest of the limitless vertical frontier was launched on October 15, 1783, when a French scientist named J. F. Pilâtre de Rozier piloted the first manned balloon flight. Carefully tethered at a height of 84 feet, de Rozier remained aloft for 4 minutes, 24 seconds and made the first observations concerning man's reactions to flight. He later assured his friends that he had not experienced the least inconvenience; there had been no giddiness, no incommoding motion, no shock whatever.[46] For the next 20 months this intrepid aeronaut continued flying. But on June 15, 1785, de Rozier became the first flier to die when he and a companion attempted a cross-channel flight in a vehicle combining the features of a hydrogen balloon with those of the original hot-air variety. The balloon burned in the sky and they crashed to the ground.[47]

Biological experimentation in atmospheric flight actually began a month before de Rozier's first flight. On September 19, 1783, Joseph and Jacques Montgolfier, the inventors of the balloon, entertained Louis XVI and his court at Versailles by sending a sheep, a rooster, and a duck to an altitude of about 1,500 feet in their new hot-air balloon. Upon landing, the animals underwent inspection, and all was well except for an injury to the rooster's right wing. Some suggested that the injury was an effect of flying, but the Montgolfiers were able to show that it was "the consequence of a kick . . . received from the sheep, at least half an hour before, in the presence of at least ten witnesses."[48]

A model hot-air balloon had been demonstrated successfully in Lisboa as early as August 8, 1709 by Bartholomeu Lourenço de Gusmao, a Brazilian Jesuit,[49] but the Montgolfiers achieved the first full-scale balloon flight (on June 5, 1783). Later that year, on August 27, Jacques A. C. Charles, a distinguished physicist, demonstrated an important technological improvement: the substitution of hydrogen gas (recently discovered by Henry Cavendish) for the hot air in the envelope. Benjamin Franklin, then representative to France of the successfully rebellious English colonies of North America, who 31 years before had experimented with kite flying and electricity, watched this experimental flight from a carriage. When asked, "What is the use of the balloon?" Franklin is said to have replied, "Of what use is a new-born baby?"[50] Three days later he described the event in considerable detail to Sir Joseph Banks, president of the Royal Society in London, and in November was speculating as to the military value of flight.[51]

Charles was also the first to make genuinely scientific observations concerning the physiological effects of flight upon man. In a free ascent on December 1, 1783, he reached an altitude of about 9,000 feet. Experiencing a severe pain in his right ear, he correctly diagnosed the cause as being the expansion of air within his ear. And with this observation, aviation physiology was born.[52]

In the interesting historical introduction to his *Principles & Practice of Aviation Medicine,* Harry G. Armstrong, then Surgeon General of the United States Air Force, covers much of the early physiological observations and experimentation made possible by the invention of lighter-than-air vehicles.[53] He sketches the career of the American John Jeffries, who conducted balloon-borne experiments on atmospheric temperatures and pressure, and who collected samples of the upper air for later analysis. He records the fact that the first thesis concerning the possible medical benefits of flight was presented before the Faculty of Medicine of Montpellier by Louis Leullier-Duche less than a year after the first balloon flight.

Gradually the hazards of high-altitude flight were identified, their causes partially understood, and primitive protective devices developed. In 1803, for example, three Italians ascended to elevations so high that two, after repeated vomiting, lost consciousness. The third remained conscious but could not read the instrumentation, because in the rarefied atmosphere the lantern's candle became dimmer and dimmer and finally went out.[54] It is probable that air currents, rather than lack of oxygen, snuffed the struggling flame, for in still air a candle does not go out until an altitude of about 59,000 feet, and it is doubtful that the trio could have survived if the balloon had gone as high as 30,000 feet.[55] The men descended into the Adriatic, and fortunately all three were rescued, though their extremities were frozen and one required the amputation of three fingers.[56]

In 1862 the British Association for the Advancement of Science conducted a long series of scientific flights, one of which produced a graphic description of near-fatal anoxemia—almost a point-by-point account of how man responds to the decreasing pressure and lack of oxygen during a flight to nearly 30,000 feet.[57] In 1875 two of three scientists died in a flight to 28,820 feet when they suddenly lost the ability to move and thus could not make use of the oxygen they had carried for the final portion of the ascent.[58] As late as 1920, Rudolph W. Schroeder, a commissioned aviator of the United States Army and a World War I ace, went to 38,180 feet in a plane without proper high-altitude equipment; his eyelids froze shut, and the plane fell six miles before he recovered.[59]

To avoid such accidents and to permit man to fly ever higher, practitioners of aviation medicine have created complex laboratories and conducted elaborate programs of scientific research. The first large-scale support came during World War I, primarily to aid in the more efficient selection of potential pilots and other crew members. Since then the research has been extended to a vast number of fundamental phenomena and problems, not the least of which is the matter of atmospheric pressure.

LOSS OF PRESSURE

Probably the most drastic change in environment that may occur during space flight will be the sudden loss of cabin pressure due to meteoritic damage or other types of structural failure. Even a gradual escape of the cabin's atmosphere because of a leak would eventually rob the astronaut of his oxygen supply and the atmospheric pressure upon which his life depends. One way or the other, he would find himself exposed to the alien, vacuum-equivalent conditions of outer space. Should this situation occur almost instantaneously, the result would be what is usually termed explosive decompression.[60] Whether the decompression was explosive or gradual, death would be inescapable unless emergency actions were taken.

If the structural damage produces an opening wide enough, the sudden blast of the cabin's escaping air through the aperture may blow unrestrained occupants into outer space. There have already been numerous unfortunate accidents of this kind in pressurized commercial and military aircraft, with persons ejected through windows or gun turrets. Other effects of space-cabin decompression include not only anoxia (lack of oxygen) but also physical damage to various parts of the body due to the pressure change, which produces tearing, hemorrhaging, bubbling in the blood stream, and other reactions.

The problem of explosive or rapid decompression did not really exist until 1935. In that year the XC-35 substratosphere aircraft, designed and built by the Lockheed Aircraft Corporation for the Army Air Corps, became the first successful pressure-cabin airplane.[61] The introduction of pressurized aircraft was a significant contribution to the conquest of the vertical frontier: it raised the theoretical limit for prolonged flight to altitudes of 80,000 to 100,000 feet. The practical ceiling for pressurized aircraft is lower than the theoretical one, however, for several reasons. One is the adiabatic heating of compressed air, which would cause the temperature in the cabin to reach 550° C. if the ambient atmosphere at 100,000 feet were compressed to an equivalent of just under 10,000 feet.[62] The weight of refrigeration equipment needed to cope with this condition would be virtually prohibitive. Also, the atmosphere between 65,000 and 98,000 feet is enriched with ozone—a heavy concentration of this gas, compressed to normal pressure, is toxic.[63] Measures and equipment to counter this hazard are impracticable. These are some of the reasons that most scientists and engineers place an arbitrary limit of about 80,000 feet for prolonged flight in pressurized aircraft; above this altitude the true sealed cabin becomes necessary.

The advent of pressurized aircraft was greeted with great apprehension, because the dangers of explosive decompression seemed appalling. As late as 1939, Harry G. Armstrong considered a pressure change equivalent to a rise in altitude of 5,000 feet per minute to be within the classification of "explosive." By 1944, however, H. H. Sweeney had exposed a human subject to a pressure drop equivalent to rising from 40,000 to 50,000 feet in 0.005 of a second and from 10,500 to 35,000 feet in about 0.02 of a second without producing physical injury.[64] But rapid decompression to a 50,000-foot equivalent and unprotected exposure for more than a brief period of seconds would lead to unconsciousness and death in spite of a remaining atmosphere of pure oxygen.[65] The alveolar pressure of carbon dioxide and water vapor in the lungs would be at least as great as the oxygen pressure in the ambient atmosphere, and a person would literally drown in his own water vapor.

The chances of a meteoritic impact which would produce explosive decompression during space flight are serious enough but rather slight. This is not because space is really empty, for the Soviet scientist B. S. Orlov conservatively considers the total weight of meteoritic matter falling on the earth alone to be between ten and 15 tons per day.[66] From data available when he was employed by the Air Force Cambridge Research Center, Maurice Dublin, now with the National Aeronautics and Space Administration, calculated that the total could be far greater—as much as 3,000 tons daily.[67] And in 1946 Fletcher Watson of Harvard predicted in *Science* that pioneer moon voyagers would run a sizeable risk of destruction by cosmic flak and that at least one of every 25 space ships on this relatively short haul would be destroyed. Operations to nearby Venus would suffer even greater losses.[68]

With the benefit of actual space operations, such estimates of danger have now been revised drastically downward. Only seven micrometeorite hits during a period of a month were recorded by *Explorer I,* and apparently none of these penetrated the satellite's shell.[69] The abortive *Vanguard* attempt of May 27, 1958, however, recorded 17 hits by these tiny flecks of matter during the first ten-minute period after its third-stage separation, and this led Navy scientists to multiply their estimate of micrometeorite bombardment by a factor of five.[70] And the radio transmitters of *Explorer III* were silenced some two weeks ahead of schedule when the 31-pound vehicle traversed the Eta Aquarids meteorite swarm.[71]

In spite of the presence of considerable cosmic matter in space, it should be possible for space vehicles to avoid known swarms of meteorites. A Soviet scientist has accepted the calculation that the probability of a space ship with an area of 93 square meters being hit by a meteorite the size of a drop of water or larger is such that there would be about 38,000 years between such impacts.[72] *Sputnik III* data seem to indicate that a vehicle with an area of 100 square meters will encounter a meteorite of one gram or larger only once in every 14,000 hours.[73] And *Explorer VI,* the paddlewheel satellite, has reported back that dust specks were encountered only 28 times in its first two days in orbit—an impact rate which would indicate the presence of only one such particle in a volume of space the size of the Empire State Building.[74]

Nevertheless, the possibility of encountering destructive hits does exist. It is a mistake, however, to assume that the escape of air would necessarily be instantaneous. Hubertus Strughold has indicated that if the holes punched in the cabin amounted to one square centimeter per cubic meter of cabin volume, it would take nine seconds for the atmospheric pressure to drop to the critical level of 300 mm. Hg.[75] Eric Burgess also calculates that the time for pressure to fall to a given level is directly proportional to the relationship between the area of the hole and the volume of the cabin. If the relationship is $\frac{1}{1000}$ to 1, interior pressure will fall to one-tenth its original value in five seconds; if the ratio is $\frac{1}{10{,}000}$ to 1, the time is 30 seconds.[76] In any case, barring a head-on collision with a massive object which would literally bisect the cabin, there remains a critically brief moment of falling pressure in which crew members could take emergency action, especially if aided by servomechanisms.

There is also the additional brief period of seconds which Strughold has termed the "time of useful consciousness" in which the crew could continue emergency measures. This time interval, before aeroembolism, the so-called boiling of body fluids,[77] the expansion of gas-filled cavities within the body, and finally alveolar drowning, is about 15 seconds[78]—enough time for automatic mechanisms to activate emergency pressure suits.

Much thought has been given, of course, to shielding space vehicles against meteorites. As far back as 1938 the British Interplanetary Society proposed a double-walled hull for this purpose in its space-ship design, and the idea was further developed by the astronomer Fred L. Whipple in the mid-1940's.[79] Recent research at the Armour Foundation has indicated that heat and dust erosion is so great that much thicker shields may be required than the thin outer hull suggested by Whipple.[80]

OPTIMUM SPACE-CABIN PRESSURES

As to what pressure to maintain within the crew compartment, there is a conflict of opinion among experts. Most research in this area is predicated upon the approach of reducing the engineering problems by using lower-than-normal pressure, to which the crew could be conditioned. With a lower interior pressure there would be less outward strain on the vehicle hull, a smaller possibility of leakage, and a slighter workload on the atmospheric regenerative system. Other scientists and engineers believe that providing normal pressure in the vehicle is a relatively minor structural problem, on the ground that this requirement is overshadowed by the structural load imposed on the vehicle by the multi-g acceleration of its takeoff.

The Project *Mercury* capsule is designed to maintain an altitude-equivalent of about 27,000 feet, and compartments for other major man-in-space proposals generally include such lower pressures.[81] The ultimate goal, however, will be to achieve "shirtsleeve" space flight under completely normal physical conditions. Chance Vought Aircraft Corporation is working on a Navy-sponsored capsule for aircraft with this capability.[82] And Douglas Aircraft Company scientists, headed by Eugene B. Konecci, are strong advocates of terrestrial-equivalent environments for space vehicles. They point out that space men of the near future will probably include highly trained scientists and technical observers, who may not be as physically fit as the astronauts selected for Project *Mercury* and who may not respond as well to suboptimum environments or the long period of physiological conditioning required to increase tolerance to reduced pressures.[83]

3

The Cabin Atmosphere

THE matter of selecting and maintaining a life-supporting environment within a space ship is more complex than even science-fictionists may suspect. Scientists and engineers recognize that they must control the pressure, temperature and humidity; they must keep the atmosphere purified and in equilibrium; for long expeditions they must devise a food-waste cycle.

More than 300 years ago Johannes Kepler—the mathematical genius upon whose work much of the astronautical science of today is based—wrote a fictional account of space flight entitled *Somnium*. His hero was transported to the moon by supernatural means. Although this was written some years before Torricelli invented the barometer and even longer before this instrument was used to prove the limitations of the earth's atmosphere, Kepler seems to have suspected the existence of the airless void between these heavenly bodies; in his story the lack of an atmosphere helped, for the transporting "deamons" needed only initial thrust to make the journey. And Kepler solved the problems of space biology in an airless world with the simple technique of artificial breathing via sponges moistened and applied to the nostrils of his hero.[1]

Scientists and engineers today, cursed with the knowledge of a few additional facts—and possibly a lesser degree of genius—are unable to write off the biological problems of space flight so simply. The first of these problems is to select a combination of gaseous elements which will safely support human life and yet not require too complicated a system for its maintenance. The second is to devise the system for keeping this atmosphere at a constant composition, purity, and pressure.

The problem really boils down to creating a set of cycles rather similar to those that maintain man's environment on earth in a reasonably precise equilibrium. Hubertus Strughold of the Air Force's School of Aviation Medicine has rightly identified our native planet as a mother space ship aboard which we are spinning through space. Surrounding our earth is an atmosphere of certain chemicals, such as oxygen and nitrogen, and various chemical mixtures and compounds, such as water vapor and carbon dioxide. This atmosphere is only a portion of man's environment. It is meshed with the other portions in a gigantic system in which, for the most part, each assists in maintaining the whole nearly constant.

An example of one of these important subcycles is the cycle of rain, run-off, and evaporation that maintains the water balance in our environment—what geographers and climatologists refer to as the hydrologic cycle.[2] On earth, there is a fixed supply of water which is used over and over again. In one phase of the hydrologic cycle, this supply takes the form of the familiar bodies of water, such as oceans, rivers, and lakes; in another phase it is the moisture in the earth's exposed crust; in its third phase it is water vapor in the atmosphere. Another example is the oxygen-carbon dioxide cycle. Men and animals breathe oxygen from the atmosphere, exhaling carbon dioxide; plants remove the carbon dioxide from the air and then through photosynthesis restore oxygen to the atmosphere.[3] Man's existence on earth depends on these and many other subcycles of a similar nature. And his existence on long-duration space voyages will depend upon his ability to create and maintain an artificial environmental cycle which will approximate the environmental system of the earth.

SELECTION OF AN ARTIFICIAL ATMOSPHERE

Men began experimenting with artificial atmospheres when they began to probe the narrow limits of their natural earth-surface environment. As mentioned in the previous chapter, such research was an early part of activities in deep-level mining, underwater operations, and high-altitude balloon ascents. And a great amount of time and effort has been invested in related problems of purifying the air in factory workshops or attempting to cope with metropolitan smog. But with the advent of prolonged high-altitude flight and long-range submarine operations, and especially with the dawning of the age of space, efforts to select and maintain artificial atmospheres were greatly intensified.

There are various possibilities for the composition of a space-cabin atmosphere. But all must contain at least a certain amount of oxygen. The simplest formula would be pure oxygen. More closely approximating the earth's atmosphere would be a mixture of oxygen and nitrogen. Oxygen with helium offers certain advantages. And there are many other interesting possible combinations.

Aviators have long been accustomed to taking supplies of oxygen aloft for high-altitude flight. Before the end of World War I, military flyers of all the principal belligerents had been provided with early types of oxygen equipment.[4] Indeed, an oxygen supply had been a vital item of balloonist gear for generations. And so it was natural that many of the early considerations of this major environmental problem for space flight specified an atmosphere of pure oxygen and then moved on to tackle the difficulties of keeping it pure. As late as 1946, for example, H. E. Ross of England predicated an atmosphere of oxygen alone and worked out the quantities required for voyages to the moon and the nearer planets under certain conditions. He concentrated chiefly upon the removal of the carbon dioxide and water vapor produced by the crew, which would otherwise rapidly foul the atmosphere.[5]

Laboratory research, however, has established that there are hazards in the use of a pure oxygen atmosphere for space voyages of more than relatively brief duration. Prolonged breathing of pure oxygen at a partial pressure greater than about 425 millimeters of mercury, or the equivalent of total atmospheric pressure at about 15,000 feet altitude, can be toxic. Men sealed in a cabin for seven days at a simulated altitude of 10,000 feet experienced a decline in vital capacity and reported distress which seemed to arise beneath the breastbone. In one case, X-ray studies at the end of the experiment revealed the existence of an area in the lungs that lacked air.[6] This hazard, however, is of no concern in a sealed cabin maintained at a pressure equivalent to an altitude of greater than 15,000 feet for a short flight. In Project Mercury, for instance, the pressure will be the equivalent of about 27,000 feet,[7] and the flight will be brief, calling for only a 28-hour supply of pure oxygen,[8] so that there will be no hazard from this point of view. For animal satellites, AiResearch Manufacturing Division of the Garrett Corporation has constructed a five-pound capsule which will provide a tiny rodent with a 30-day supply of pure oxygen.[9]

But in more sophisticated space vehicles of the future, using normal atmospheric pressure, the toxic effect may be serious enough to rule out a pure-oxygen atmosphere. Although two scientists were apparently unharmed after three days in an oxygen-filled chamber at a simulated altitude of 30,000 feet,[10] other evidence seems to establish that prolonged exposure to a pure-oxygen atmosphere has a depressing effect.[11] For long-duration expeditions, some nitrogen may have to be introduced into the microatmosphere of the space vehicle if for no other reason than that small quantities of this element appear to play a role in metabolism.[12]

There are additional reasons why a pure-oxygen atmosphere may be undesirable. As Soviet and United States scientists have pointed out, in such an environment there is the increased danger of fire and the speed-up of other oxidation processes which cause food spoilage.[13] Certain hydrocarbons, for instance, can ignite spontaneously when exposed to an atmosphere of pure oxygen at sea-level pressure. A series of burning tests performed in the Aeromedical Field Laboratory at the Air Force Missile Development Center has indicated that anything which will burn in an earth-surface environment will burn much more rapidly in reduced atmospheric pressure if the amount of oxygen is maintained at the original level. Fortunately, the same experiments also demonstrated that at reduced partial pressures of oxygen—which will be likely at least in some of the early space vehicles—the process of combustion is somewhat inhibited. The burning rate at an oxygen partial pressure equivalent to 18,000 feet is just half as great as that at 5,000 feet.[14]

Exhaustive research by George J. Kidera, president of the Aerospace Medical Association, and John P. Marbarger, an early worker in the field of space medicine, has demonstrated that at the reduced cabin pressures of commercial jet aircraft, hydrocarbons such as freshly applied lipstick and chapstick or the fats and oils of the human skin will not burst into flame in a flow of pure oxygen.[15]

Furthermore, removal of most of the highly combustible substances or introduction of a quantity of inert gas such as helium, neon, argon, krypton, or xenon into the cabin atmosphere would further minimize the hazard of fire. And if the terrestrial-equivalent cabin atmosphere proposed by Eugene B. Konecci and other Douglas Aircraft Company officials proves feasible, the hazard of fire in a space vehicle will be no greater than in the atmospheric environment of Tulsa, Okla., or Santa Monica, Calif.[16]

Many suggested space-ship atmospheres call for the inclusion of nitrogen. This colorless, tasteless, and odorless element constitutes about four-fifths of the earth's atmosphere by volume. French chemists refer to it as *azote,* because by itself it is incapable of supporting life. But a certain small amount does seem to play a role in metabolism. Because the presence of nitrogen permits, among other things, an increase in breath-holding time by individuals, some scientists have recommended a heavy concentration of this element in any sealed-cabin environment, especially for long-duration flight.[17] Some engineers also lean to nitrogen rather than rare gases because its rate of leakage through small orifices is less than that of neon or helium. This is an important consideration for the preservation of an atmosphere in the case of slight structural failure or penetration by small meteoritic particles. But while nitrogen is better than neon or helium for this reason, the Soviet writer Ari Shternfeld points out that both argon and krypton are considerably better than nitrogen.[18] Nitrogen is clearly a compromise. In the Bell Aircraft Corporation X-1 rocket plane, in which Frank J. Everest, Jr., established new altitude and speed records in 1949, nitrogen was used to maintain pressure within the cockpit compartment while his oxygen supply was provided through a mask.[19]

There are certain adverse factors in the use of nitrogen in a space-vehicle compartment. One of these is the fact that nitrogen dissolves in the blood and therefore would produce bends, or caisson disease, in the event of a sudden reduction of cabin pressure. Other atmospheric gases are less likely to do this. In the famous *Man-High* balloon ascents to space-equivalent altitudes, a large quantity of helium was substituted for nitrogen, because it is far less soluble in either blood or the fatty and nonfatty tissues. The person making the flight entered the capsule several hours before takeoff and began breathing the artificial atmosphere to remove much of the nitrogen from his bloodstream. The object was to prevent a severe attack of disabling bends should decompression occur at high altitude.[20]

But helium also has its disadvantages. Like other inert gases (except argon), it alters the velocity of sound propagation. This, in turn, affects the intelligibility of human speech and could have important adverse psychological effects upon the crew or interfere with voice communication between the vehicle and the earth or extraterrestrial stations.[21] In addition, helium's comparatively high thermal conductivity speeds the rate of heat loss from objects, and so there is a tendency to feel cold in such an atmosphere.[22]

Less research has been carried out on the effects of the inert gases than on those of oxygen and nitrogen. One reason is that the inert gases were discovered more recently, and another is that they are relatively rare. It has been known for some time that they have narcotic effects, and this gave concern to those who considered their use in artificial atmospheres for space flight. In 1959, however, S. F. Cook of the University of California at Berkeley, under contract with the Air Force Missile Development Center, completed research which indicates that the narcotic effect is caused by purely physical properties of the gases. Furthermore, their ability to narcotize is related to the pressure—the greater the pressure, the greater the narcotic effect. It has been established that at normal or less than normal atmospheric pressures the effect is not of major importance.[23] The effects of the inert gases upon metabolism and heat exchange, however, vary considerably, so more intensive investigation under simulated space-flight conditions is needed.

Meanwhile, opinions vary concerning the most advantageous composition for space-vehicle atmospheres. Some recommend heavy oxygen concentrations; others support the use of large amounts of inert gases; still others insist that the artificial environment of a space ship should duplicate the one that has supported man until now. Since scientific research has established the feasibility of various atmospheres, the final answer for any particular mission will probably be largely determined by the relative sophistication of engineering technology at that time. One of the deciding factors will be ability to maintain the purity and equilibrium of the chosen atmosphere.

CONTROL OF ATMOSPHERIC FACTORS

Picture a musician volunteering to aid scientific research by entering a sealed test chamber. Inside the chamber the atmosphere to start with is identical to that at the surface of the earth. He has a comfortable chair and a copy of the libretto to Giuseppe Verdi's opera *Aïda* to amuse him during the experiment. He seats himself and begins to read about the enslaved Ethiopian princess who has fallen in love with the Egyptian Radamès.

But this chamber has no atmospheric control system. If left sealed in the chamber, the musician would soon be as dead as Verdi's lovers, who were entombed alive. For with his first breath he begins to alter his microatmosphere. His presence rapidly lowers the free-oxygen content, raises the level of carbon dioxide, increases the relative humidity, and produces other alterations of his environment.

The result would be no different for crew members of a space ship if their atmospheric regenerative system should malfunction—except that in their case no monitoring scientist observing their predicament could open the doors to let fresh air flood the compartment. In short, it is vital to have a reliable, automatic system to maintain a stable atmosphere. Because of the many complications involved, this is also one of the most difficult engineering assignments.

A complete atmospheric control system, such as that required for prolonged space flight, must accomplish two major tasks. First of all, it must remove additives from the atmosphere as they appear. Secondly, it must reclaim and restore all the original constituents necessary to support life.

One problem that received early attention was the question of how much oxygen is required to sustain life. If maintaining human life is the only requirement, the range between the absolute minimum and maximum oxygen concentration is very broad. For instance, man can live in a pure oxygen atmosphere at pressures ranging from slightly over 47 millimeters of mercury, or slightly less than an equivalent of 52,000 feet altitude, to considerably more than 760 millimeters of mercury, which is the standard sea-level pressure at 32° F. Or he can live in an atmosphere having a fairly low percentage of oxygen if the atmospheric pressure is normal or higher than normal. At sea level, for example, oxygen is only 23 per cent of the earth's atmosphere by weight or 21 per cent by volume.

But simple maintenance of life is not the only requirement with respect to the oxygen content of the microatmosphere. Crew members must be able to perform involved physical and mental tasks with a high degree of efficiency. And if they are to perform complex integrative functions, the oxygen content in their bloodstream must be maintained at about 80 to 85 per cent of saturation to provide adequate oxygenation for the cerebrum and other nervous tissues, the first to be affected by hypoxia.[24] Still, the tolerances are fairly wide. A recent proposal for a manned-satellite atmospheric control system calls for maintaining the oxygen content between 20 and 60 per cent at a pressure equivalent to about 18,000 feet altitude.[25]

Another substance in the cabin atmosphere of a space ship—one that requires greater precision in its control—is carbon dioxide. This is the gas that makes a champagne cork pop and causes the tickling in the nostrils as the bubbles issue from the wine. It is also a familiar ingredient in the earth's atmosphere, its concentration ranging from about 0.043 per cent by weight in open country to about 0.1 per cent in cities. In a poorly ventilated and crowded room the carbon dioxide will build up to higher levels. In the completely sealed cabin of a space vehicle an uncontrolled build-up of carbon dioxide would rapidly reach critical proportions, causing headaches, nausea, and vomiting. The gas is not in itself a fatal poison, but as the oxygen in the microatmosphere is depleted (and converted to carbon dioxide) death may result from asphyxiation.

According to V. V. Rozenblat of the Soviet Union, the average human body would discharge about 950 grams of carbon dioxide per day into the space-cabin atmosphere.[26] F. A. Hitchcock of Ohio State University warns that the build-up at an acceptable cabin pressure must not exceed a partial pressure of eight to ten millimeters of mercury.[27] This would be a very small amount within the relatively small volume of the crew compartment of a space craft. Physiological conditioning to a chronic subnormal amount of air in the lungs produces a lower sensitivity to carbon dioxide; the pearl diver who holds his breath for two or three minutes, the cross-country runner, or the iron-lung patient can tolerate a somewhat higher percentage of this gas in the air. But even conditioning does not do away with the need for limiting the concentration of carbon dioxide to a small percentage of the total atmosphere. Bruno Balke of the Air Force's School of Aviation Medicine found that four weeks of conditioning atop Mount Evans in Colorado enabled his subjects to tolerate as much as 4.5 per cent carbon dioxide in the atmosphere of a low-pressure chamber—a "most severe" trial.[28] The research of Clayton S. White of the Lovelace Foundation indicates that, while man cannot withstand a sudden exposure to an atmosphere of 5 per cent carbon dioxide for more than a few minutes, he can tolerate it for considerably longer periods if the build-up is very gradual and if the individual is at rest or indulging in only moderate exercise.[29] This toleration, however, does not permit effective performance of involved functions.

Control of excess water is another major problem in maintaining atmospheric equilibrium for long-duration space flight. Space scientists refer to this problem as the "water barrier." It arises from the simple fact that the human body discharges more water than it takes in (in the form of water itself). A man doing strenuous work may give off water in vapor form at the rate of two pounds per hour.

An astronaut drinking two liters of water each day would return to the cabin environment not only these two liters but also about 350 grams more produced by his body's metabolism of food substances. Approximately one and a half liters would be discharged by the kidneys, half a liter through the skin as perspiration and another four tenths of a liter via the lungs.[30] In mid-1957, Hans G. Clamann of the School of Aviation Medicine called attention to the problem of biological oxidation, which converts oxygen and food into carbon dioxide and water. Over an extended time, the excess of water would eventually convert the sealed cabin into a swimming pool, or perhaps even into an aquarium. Hubertus Strughold has remarked that man must either find a method of converting metabolic water back into energy-containing carbohydrates or revert to the paleological stage of being an amphibian.[31]

Even for a short journey the water balance must be controlled. For instance, the discomfort of a stuffy atmosphere is generally more the result of excess water vapor than of excess carbon dioxide. According to Hitchcock, the relative humidity of cabin air must not exceed 40 per cent for more than a brief period; otherwise it will interfere with the efficiency of crew members.[32] Without adequate control, the relative humidity would rapidly increase and produce an impossible situation. The time it would take to reach this point depends upon such factors as the volume of the cabin, the number of the crew, the extent of their physical activity, and the temperature.

In addition to regulating the oxygen, carbon dioxide, and humidity of the microatmosphere, the recycling system must perform many other functions. It must recover water for drinking and washing. It must eliminate the deadly carbon monoxide produced by over-heating equipment or by the algae of a biological recycling system; a carbon monoxide concentration as low as one-fifth of one per cent can cause death in a relatively short time. The system must also deal with the ammonia entering the atmosphere from urine, the methane and hydrogen in perspiration and glandular excretions of the skin, the indole, skatole, phenol, and various amines in the feces. And it must control the atmospheric temperature and eliminate offensive odors.[33]

Maintenance of the cabin's atmosphere in near equilibrium will be complicated enough without introducing the burdens imposed by tobacco smoking or certain types of cooking. As early as 1938 the British Interplanetary Society vetoed smoking during space flight, for the reason that "every cubic inch of oxygen will be needed for human consumption."[34] Even with an atmospheric regenerative system, spaceship designers still frown upon smoking, because it would greatly complicate the system, although the Russian Ari Shternfeld adds that the tars and other products could be condensed on cold surfaces, as would the gases formed by cooking.[35]

These engineering problems, however, are not the primary reasons the "No Smoking" rule will be in force for space flight. Eugene B. Konecci points out that smoking, in addition to adding to the problem of environmental control, would definitely augment the hazard of carbon monoxide, which may already be present to some degree from other sources.[36] More to the point, probably, is the fact that, in the low atmospheric pressures of space-vehicle cabins, respiration would have to speed up, and the presence of tobacco smoke would contribute to sensitization of the nose and throat. It would also add to the respiratory distress called chokes, which often accompanies altitude sickness in high atmospheric flight and probably would do so in the reduced pressures of the astronaut's compartment.[37]

THE SEARCH FOR SOLUTIONS

Intensive research on the complex problem of controlling the cabin atmosphere is being pursued along various avenues of approach. There is considerable optimism that this difficult task will be fulfilled. Already solutions to many of the major aspects of the overall problem have been found. Nevertheless, scientific or technological breakthroughs are still required to devise a workable environmental regenerative system for long voyages. In many ways the task looks almost as difficult as the hopeless proposition of making a perpetual-motion machine.

There are three primary methods of regulating portions of a confined atmosphere, each with its particular advantages and disadvantages, and each with its enthuiastic champions. One approach is chemical: the wastes or unwanted substances in the atmosphere would be absorbed and reconverted to the original ingredients by chemical action. The second approach is the mechanical one: recycling would be accomplished by physical processes such as condensation, distillation, and so on. More popular by far than either of these, however, is the biological approach: namely, recycling by processes such as photosynthesis, whereby plants remove carbon dioxide from the air and liberate oxygen. Of course, aspects of all three approaches may be combined.

Sputnik II, which was the first biosatellite by virtue of its canine passenger Laika, used chemical compounds to absorb carbon dioxide and water vapor and to give off enough oxygen for respiration.[38] This method had been employed previously in submarines. Compounds such as sodium hydroxide or soda lime have long been used for identical purposes in rebreathing appliances in connection with anesthesia[39] and also in gas masks for chemical warfare. Sodium hydroxide, in fact, was specified in the 1938 British Interplanetary Society investigation of the feasibility of a lunar expedition.[40] Mario Pezzi, the Italian aviator who broke the altitude record that year by going above 55,000 feet in a sealed cockpit, also used sodium hydroxide as an absorber.[41]

Other chemical compounds, such as nonregenerative lithium oxide, have gained popularity as effective absorbers for short flights in space. For relatively long periods calcium oxide is recommended, because this reagent can be regenerated by heating the carbonate formed by the absorbing action.[42] Even the latter compound, however, is not practical for lengthy voyages, for it does not completely reverse the chemical changes that have occurred in the atmosphere and, therefore, does not maintain the atmosphere in its original state of equilibrium.

As a move toward perfecting a chemical system which will be practical for journeys lasting up to three years, the Battelle Memorial Institute is investigating methods of chemical reduction to reverse the basic oxidation process of human metabolism and thus recover oxygen from carbon dioxide. According to research director John F. Foster, the plan is to use a reducing agent to convert carbon dioxide into solid carbon and obtain oxygen as a gas.[43] Such a system would be extremely valuable for short space missions. It would not suffice, however, for extended voyages, even to the distant planets of our own solar system.

Mechanical methods can be very effective in removing excess carbon dioxide and water vapor from the space-cabin atmosphere. A small refrigeration unit is all that is required. If the air is circulated past a container of liquid oxygen, for example, the water vapor and then the carbon dioxide will freeze out. Tars and some other by-products of cooking or smoking also can be condensed on cold surfaces. Or high temperatures, instead of low, may be used to convert water vapor into usable water by distillation. But these simple mechanical methods, too, are useful only for brief periods. They do not reconvert waste products to their original form or restore them to the environment for reuse. Theoretically, extreme heat can promote the thermal decomposition of carbon dioxide. But so far such mechanical concepts have not appeared either particularly efficient or practical for space flight, because the weight of required equipment would be virtually prohibitive.

BIOLOGICAL CONTROL

So far the approach that has made the most progress toward the goal of reversing the metabolic process is the biological one. It entails harnessing the photosynthetic process, using green plants—especially algae—to convert carbon dioxide from the atmosphere into oxygen and food. Actually, such a system is rather complicated, and serious problems must yet be solved before it will be practical for long-term space flight.

Photosynthesis is a process of constructive metabolism which takes place in the chlorophyll-containing leaves of plants when they are exposed to light. The entire process is not yet completely understood, but basically what appears to take place is that by means of the radiant energy absorbed by the chlorophyll, the plant converts carbon dioxide from the air into carbon monoxide, breaks up water molecules, and then combines the carbon monoxide with the hydrogen from the water, freeing oxygen and forming formaldehyde, which eventually becomes various sugars through polymerization. And the carbohydrates, as plant physiologists point out, are the fuel that maintains human life. In reality, photosynthesis is far more complex than this oversimplified account would indicate, but the end products of pure oxygen and food make the process very attractive to scientists and engineers concerned with the problems of human flight through space.

The possibility of using a biological system for maintaining the atmosphere of a space vehicle is not a recent concept. Fairly early in this century, Konstantin E. Tsiolkovsky—called the father of modern space technology—suggested the use of plants for this purpose.[44] And since the early post-World War II period, many scientists have undertaken intensive research in this important area.

For several years Jack Myers of the Department of Algal Physiology in the University of Texas and scientists at the Air Force's School of Aviation Medicine have cooperated in research on the use of plants to regenerate air in a closed ecological system. Their investigations began with *Chlorella pyrenoidosa,* a small, round blue-green alga a little larger than a red blood cell. Five pounds (fresh weight) of this strain of algae, they announced, can provide one man with a continuing supply of oxygen and absorb his exhaled carbon dioxide. More recently they have investigated a much smaller, bacteria-like microorganism, *Anacystis nidulans,* which appears much more efficient: one and one-half pounds are enough to meet a man's respiration needs.[45]

Scientists from other universities and various industrial firms have also been active in this area of research. Russell O. Bowman of Vought Astronautics has maintained mice in an algae-controlled atmosphere for extended periods. He uses a system of pumps and fluorescent lights to circulate and activate an algae brew which absorbs carbon dioxide and gives off oxygen.[46] James G. Baume, chief of the Space Medicine group at the Martin Company plant in Denver, has conducted related experiments with mice.[47] Both of these projects are similar to earlier experiments conducted at the University of Texas by Myers, who managed to maintain dwarf mice on algae-produced oxygen for 37 days.[48]

Preliminary successes such as these have generated enthusiasm in many quarters. T. A. Gaucher of General Dynamics Corporation's Electric Boat Division, cooperating with Dean Burk and George Hobby of the National Institutes of Health, has reported upon the use of a fast-growing new strain of algae, discovered by C. Sorokin of the University of Texas. This organism multiplies 1,000-fold per day, compared to only eight-fold for the earlier types. According to Gaucher's report, a very dense culture of the alga is pumped rapidly past an extremely intense source of light, thus providing the advantages of intermittent illumination and giving the algae a brief rest period for recovery. The efficiency of this system is such that only about one-twentieth the amount of algae is required, compared to earlier techniques.[49] Chapter 4 will discuss other experiments with algae as a source of food.

There are many still unsolved problems in using algae or other plants for regenerating the cabin atmosphere. One is the matter of weight—the weight of the necessary water (which makes up the bulk of the algal culture), of the culture tanks, and of the other required equipment. The weight problem, of course, may eventually be overcome either by miniaturization of the system or by advances in propulsion.

Other adverse aspects, however, may prove more difficult to solve. As H. E. Ross pointed out in 1947,[50] the green plants used in such systems are simply carbon dioxide-oxygen interchangers. And no matter how efficiently they work in breaking down the carbon dioxide in the atmosphere, they can never replace the oxygen that remains in the body to sustain certain metabolic processes. Even if all the oxygen in the carbon dioxide could be recovered, some additional oxygen would have to be supplied to keep the atmosphere in equilibrium. Furthermore, plants themselves give forth carbon dioxide and require some oxygen for life, though they do liberate more oxygen than they use. And plants cannot remove or reconvert all the unwanted products that will develop in the atmosphere of a space cabin. Another important problem has been identified by Syrrel S. Wilks of the School of Aviation Medicine.[51] Plants damaged so that the normal process of photosynthesis is disrupted may liberate deadly carbon monoxide instead of oxygen. Moreover, dead plants contain carbon monoxide.

In spite of the unsolved problems, there is reason to believe that a workable system will be perfected. Possibly it will be a composite system, using the advantageous aspects of highly sophisticated chemical and mechanical systems as well as biological. Or it may be that scientists will achieve the capability of producing artificial photosynthesis, for in 1951 they managed to duplicate a large portion of the natural photosynthetic process.[52] Still another possibility is photolysis; that is, decomposition of carbon dioxide by the use of ultraviolet radiation and a catalyst.[53] Certainly one of the greatest causes for optimism is that the atmospheric control system will not have to be totally self-contained, for energy will be available from the sun.

A further complication is that the solution of the atmospheric control problem has to be coordinated with other aspects of the environmental system, such as the food-waste cycle. However, the latter problem is so closely related to the former that a common solution seems likely.

4

Food, Water, and Wastes

For obvious reasons, food, water, and disposal of human waste in space flight will present difficult problems. Food is a problem for one primary reason—weight. The space vehicle's propulsion system will require several hundred pounds of fuel for each pound of payload, and just to carry the amount of food and water needed for the relatively short 516-day round trip to Mars would call for a ship of prohibitive weight. As officials of Chance Vought Aircraft, Inc., point out, a man would normally require at least five pounds of water and two to three pounds of food each day—a total of about 4,000 pounds per person for a trip to Mars. Without the radical substitution of highly concentrated food for more familiar fare and a recycling system to cut drastically the initial cargo of food and water, these needs would require blasting a supermarket into space.[1]

There are, of course, many other problems complicating the feeding of space travelers. Some are physiological, such as the nature of the food required under confined conditions of interplanetary flight. Some are psychological; for example, how bizarre a diet can be tolerated by men engaged in an endeavor of high emotional and intellectual stress? What will be the problems of eating and digestion under subgravity conditions? How will the food be affected by radiation and the cabin's atmospheric composition?

The basic problem of weight has been recognized from the beginning. More than 20 years ago Maurice K. Hanson, reporting for a British Interplanetary Society team which had investigated the problems involved in a three-week round trip to the moon, announced that the pioneer astronauts would have to undergo a period of specialized exercise and diet before departing—"a fattening for the slaughter, as it were."[2] This preconditioning would eliminate the need for bulky protein-yielding foods, make vitamins relatively unimportant, and reduce the necessary diet to carbohydrates and fats of high-energy yield per unit weight. Luxuries as light in weight as pepper and mustard would be prohibited, although a small supply of alcoholic beverages might be permitted "to celebrate the landing on the moon."

Some 17 years later V. V. Rozenblat of the Soviet Union expressed views in general agreement with this British study. He specified that the food payload should be mainly carbohydrate—four and one-half times as much carbohydrate as protein. The Soviet scientist added, however, that a reasonable supply of supplemental vitamins and mineral salts was essential and emphasized his conviction that the food for space flight must be palatable.[3] More recently, both in the United States and the Soviet Union, the trend appears to be in favor of a heavier protein percentage. And there is an even greater emphasis upon achieving a gourmet quality for the menu.

On the weight problem there are several approaches under exploration which may yield at least partial solutions. Yu. S. Khebtsevich of the U.S.S.R. has suggested rocketing advance food supplies in unmanned transports to the moon for trips to that destination,[4] but this of course does not solve the more general problem of long flights in space. Among the specific ideas under study are: using highly concentrated foods (packed in edible containers); making the atmospheric regenerative system do double duty by growing algae for food as well as renewal of the air; and even recovering food and water from the human wastes.

The most exotic suggestion of all is that the astronauts' need for food and water might be eliminated altogether. John Lyman of the Biotechnology Laboratory at the University of California at Los Angeles has conducted experiments on suspended animation, searching for a "frozen sleep" which would allow man to travel in space for generations of time without depleting his biological substance.

This stratagem not only would do away with the need for food, water and oxygen but would eliminate boredom and the other mental and emotional stresses of space flight. Furthermore, there would be no biological aging, so that the original crew could survive for several life spans.[5]

Experiments indicate that the biochemical processes of life continue in frozen animals even after the heartbeat stops, and that these processes must all be stopped simultaneously if the subject is to revive successfully. This may be accomplished by almost instantaneous freezing. Thus the astronauts would be frozen solid before takeoff and would remain ice-like statues until they neared their destination, whereupon an automatically triggered warming device would restore them to the state of animation.

Experiments have shown that the body temperature of monkeys can be reduced to 39.2° F. for as long as two hours without detectable after-effects. This, of course, does not produce anything like the sought-after condition of frozen sleep, but rather a form of hibernation. It may, however, prove a step toward achieving the condition of complete anabiosis (suspended animation). Lyman's plans early in 1959 called for a series of experiments which would include dunking mice in a dry-ice-and-alcohol bath to reduce their temperatures to levels as low as minus 100 degrees.

A. S. Parkes and Audrey U. Smith of the National Institute for Medical Research at Mill Hill in Great Britain have also been working on anabiosis. In a paper entitled "Space Transport of Life in the Dried or Frozen State,"[6] they point out that spores and seeds have remained viable for centuries, even millennia, under highly adverse conditions. They also call attention to our growing knowledge of the long-term preservation of animal organisms and their germ cells at low temperatures. Interesting examples of natural anabiosis are shown by some Alaskan and Siberian insects, which revive after passing months in the solid state during Arctic winters. Intertidal molluscs survive in some regions although they are frozen and thawed twice each day during winter months. In laboratory experiments, Parkes and Smith continue, moth larvae have been successfully revived after being frozen and stored in liquid air.

Although the freezing or supercooling of warm-blooded animals has produced remarkable results, scientists have not yet been able to reduce a physically unharmed, living animal to the extreme temperatures required to halt all biochemical processes and derived physical changes. But if this can eventually be accomplished in man, as some biologists believe, our personal universe will be extended far beyond our solar system and the nearby star or two which an astronaut might reach in an ordinary lifetime.

Still another suggested possibility leading toward the elimination of the need for food and other life-supporting commodities is attributed to James B. Edson, assistant to the United States Army's Director of Research and Development. According to newspaper reports, Edson has referred to efforts underway to develop a synthetic nutrient which, injected into the bloodstream, would make breathing, eating, and drinking unnecessary.[7]

POSSIBLE FOODS

Of great practical value for journeys within the central portion of the solar system are projects designed to reduce the weight and size of food cargoes by devising concentrated foods and edible food containers. Albert Olevitch, chief of the Packaging Division at Wright Air Development Division, announced at a meeting of the Society of Industrial Packaging and Materials Handling Engineers that the Air Force has a project to develop flexible, high-strength, vitamin-packed, and edible films as containers for food. Rigid containers, too, could be made of nutritious substances.[8] Like the casing already used on frankfurters, these containers could be eaten directly or used as plant food or converted into useful gases. A fringe benefit of the use of such containers, as the British journal *Aeronautics* was quick to point out, is that "the last thing you are going to see round an American lunar base will be a junk heap of empty tin cans."[9] Similar projects are underway elsewhere. Chemists at the Southwest Research Institute, in addition to developing a type of "K ration" in capsule form which could be dispensed into the mouth by a slot-machine device, are trying to make the capsule shell not only soluble but also of nutritive value.[10]

A number of programs are concentrating on developing and manufacturing high-energy foods of a fairly conventional type. At the Culinary Arts Show in New York during the autumn of 1958, visitors were confronted by a "buffet table on the moon," containing chicken or beef dinners, sweet-and-sour pork, apple sauce and other items, all in toothpaste-type tubes. An advantage of food in this form is that it can be squeezed into the mouth while both the astronaut and his meal are in a subgravity state. These epicurean delights were the products of investigation by members of the Aerospace Medical Laboratory at Wright Air Development Division and the Army's Food Container Institute in Chicago.[11] A further development of this interesting technique is a straw-like tube, one end of which is screwed onto the container and the other end inserted into the mouth through an airlock in the face plate of the spacesuit helmet.[12]

As early as April 1957, the National Research and Development Corporation of Atlanta, Ga., announced a concentrated food called Multi-Meal-Tube, consisting of semisolid concentrates which could be squeezed from soft metal tubes into the mouth.[13] Nine months later the same corporation had shifted to lightweight plastic tubes with a special mouthpiece and had developed a large number of tube menus, each containing about 720 calories plus certain bulk-producing substances, and none of which required refrigeration.[14] The Soviets have been experimenting along much the same lines. Acording to reports, they have developed a semisolid mixture of high-energy liquefied meats and milk products, with the consistency of thick chocolate-malted milk, which is carried in a can with a feeding tube attached. Another of their developments is a mixture of ham, cheese, and bread packed in a squeezable tube.[15]

The Aerospace Medical Laboratory at Wright Field has projects seeking to develop solid-food "lipstick" rods of highly nourishing mixtures in various flavors. Bite-size solid foods, such as bacon, cheese, or malted milk tablets, are another approach. And the experimental use of dehydrated foods, including casserole dishes, to which the space traveler would add only water and stir, is still another project.[16] One expert from the National Aeronautics and Space Administration has even suggested that parts of the space ship itself, such as bulkheads and fuel tanks, be constructed of foodstuffs. After their primary functions were fulfilled, these components could be processed and eaten.[17]

GROWING FOOD IN SPACE

When man ventures on journeys beyond the nearest planets, even "magic pellets," providing a six-course meal in a single pill, will come to too much weight as the entire trip's food supply. Concentrated stored food, in fact, will be practicable only for orbital flight about the earth or for very brief visits to the moon. For travel even to nearby Venus or Mars, the generation of a food supply as a by-product of the cabin atmosphere regenerative system, by recycling human waste, or from a combination of these methods, becomes virtually mandatory.

As the preceding chapter pointed out, considerable attention has centered upon the use of photosynthesis as a means of recycling the oxygen supply of a space vehicle. Many space technologists believe that algae, single-cell green plants which are particularly efficient for this purpose, could serve also as the primary source of food. Activated by the energy of light, these tiny plants—the familiar green scum found in almost any pond—absorb carbon dioxide and give off oxygen. Some algae can tolerate extreme environmental conditions: one type thrives in Yellowstone geyser pools at temperatures of 185° F. Their wants are simple: inorganic salts, water, carbon dioxide, and a fixed source of nitrogen. In return for these substances, some varieties can more than double their number in a day, and the harvested surplus yields a food substance about 50 per cent protein, and also rich in carbohydrates, minerals and vitamins.

One variety of algae, *Chlorella,* has attracted particular interest among United States and Soviet experimenters. In an article published in *Sovetskaya aviatsia,* entitled "The Cosmic Breakfast," Lieutenant Colonel I. Krestousky refers to experimentation with *Chlorella* underway at the Institute of Physiology of the Ukrainian Academy of Sciences. One of its menus for astronauts calls for a high ratio of *Chlorella* combined with a small quantity of mushrooms.[18] Sydney S. Greenfield, an associate professor of biology at Rutgers University, has also been working with this alga. He points out that *Chlorella* is almost all food: it contains little inedible tissue. On the other hand, he has also discovered by sampling a crop harvested from his apparatus that, by itself, *Chlorella* would hardly please a gourmet.[19]

Russell O. Bowman, an astrobiologist with Vought Astronautics, a division of Chance Vought Aircraft, has attempted to overcome this objection by combining algae with a very thin cookie mix. He used a formula containing 20 per cent dehydrated algae by weight to produce a delectable batch of green cookies. After trying them on his wife and Vice Admiral R. B. Pirie, Deputy Chief of Naval Operations for Air, he fed them to members of the National Aeronautics and Space Administration, the Advanced Research Projects Agency, and the television and press corps. The cookies were also distributed at the 1959 convention of the Air Force Association, but a request for a huge quantity for the November 1959 meeting of the American Rocket Society could not be filled because of the magnitude of the manufacturing problem.[20]

Of course, the addition of cookie mix or mushrooms is hardly a solution for space flight, because such taste appeasers would add to the cargo weight. However, Dr. Bowman points out that algae can be treated to taste like steak, roast beef, kebabs, fish, coffee, tea, desserts, or (and this might appeal especially to our Soviet colleagues) caviar. But there are psychological problems, and Bowman admits that—even though tiny amounts of spices might impart the flavors of a Roman banquet—science cannot give alga steak the right consistency. Getting rid of the green color, too, is so difficult that it is impracticable. On the other hand, Japanese experimenters have used algae in various forms to supply up to 50 per cent of the diet, and in certain South American countries it has been fed to hungry people as a soup, providing about one-third of their total diet.[21]

The lack of bulky roughage in algae may or may not prove a detriment to the use of these plants as food. Syrrel S. Wilks of the Air Force's School of Aviation Medicine has discovered that green plants such as algae give off deadly carbon monoxide along with pure oxygen, and this may raise a serious problem.[22] Bruce W. Pinc of the Air Force Ballistic Missile Division has cited many adverse aspects of algal culture, including the problem of power, weight, and volume requirements.[23] But the possibilities are promising enough to support a great deal of continuing research on algae.

Under Air Force sponsorship the Department of Food Technology at the Massachusetts Institute of Technology is investigating the generation of food in closed ecological systems.[24] The Arthur D. Little Company is operating a pilot plant of 600 square feet which uses some 1,200 gallons of culture to produce slightly more than three-quarters of a pound of dried algae per day. Independent studies indicate that an algal system large enough to supply the total food and oxygen requirements in a space ship would weigh at least 500 pounds per man.[25] Carsbie C. Adams of the National Research and Development Corporation, considering these figures, believes that algae will be useful as a food supply only if grown aboard a space vehicle of tremendous size.[26] Nevertheless, in spite of the questions and all the unknowns, Dean Burk of the National Institutes of Health contends that it would be worth while to quadruple the funds spent on algal research, to one million dollars yearly, in order to have such a recycling system ready in time for manned space flight.[27]

Somewhat related to experimentation with algae is another project of considerable interest—the investigations into the possibility of growing more conventional plant food in alien environments. Republic Aviation scientists, for example, are working under an Air Force contract to judge the feasibility of raising crops at a lunar base from an initial supply of light-weight seed transported from the earth.[28] This food would be useful either to support operations on the moon or to supply stores for voyages to other planets from a lunar base. In one experiment, research specialists have attempted to grow carrots and turnips under conditions simulating an altitude of 46,000 feet. So far they have had little success in germinating seeds under these conditions. On the other hand, some plants grow with unusual speed at an atmospheric pressure equivalent of 10,000 to 15,000 feet above sea level.[29]

The Naval Research Laboratory recently sent seeds aloft on a Stratoscope balloon flight for exposure to cosmic radiation before planting them in Republic Aviation's "lunar garden." The purpose was to assist in the study of germination abnormalities and the potential usefulness of such food for astronautical menus.[30] The Martin Company in Denver is experimenting with the design of an enclosed lunar base which will provide room for agrarian pursuits, as well as for a certain amount of barnyard endeavor.[31] This reminds one of an interesting suggestion by Norman Lee Barr of Republic Aviation: he proposes an intensive study of the digestive system of the cow, in order to design a simulated apparatus for a space ship which would convert plant stalks, leaves, roots, and tough fibers into a meat-like food.[32]

RECOVERING WASTES

All these devices—concentrated food, cultivating algae, and the others—could be dispensed with or reduced to mere supplements to the diet if a system for recycling human wastes could be devised. At the annual meeting of the Aerospace Medical Association in 1958, C. C. Clark of the Naval Air Development Center at Johnsville, Pa., proposed a chemical-mechanical-biological system to produce food and water from these wastes.[33] The solid residue from urine, for example, would provide fixed nitrogen for cultivation of algae or other plants, which would serve for food and oxygen regeneration. The processing of human waste could also yield glucose, in the form of a sugary water thickened to the consistency of Pablum by cellulose fiber. The heavy power requirements of Clark's system—about 1,000 times the energy provided to the astronaut from the final food product—would be obtained from solar energy.[34] He estimated that the weight saving on food and water requirements would amount to about 3,000 pounds per crew member per year.

The American Machine & Foundry Company, under an Air Force contract, is developing a waste-collection unit for such systems, and the Massachusetts Institute of Technology, also with sponsorship by the Air Force, is studying other methods of recycling solid waste products.[35] Such systems, of course, are not required for short-duration orbital flights, such as are planned for Project Mercury. The pilots on those flights will have a concentrated low-residue food which will eliminate the need for disposal of solid wastes.[36] For example, the Quartermaster Food and Container Institute in Chicago has developed a high-calorie, high-protein, high-fat chocolate drink yielding no solid residue whatever.[37]

Albert Taylor, chief of the Biomedical Division of the Air Research and Development Command's Directorate of Life Sciences, has called for more intensive research on waste regeneration as a solution to the biologistics problems of space flight. He has also proposed establishing a small, isolated human community on earth to study the efficacy of biological or chemical-mechanical recycling systems. After the problems of maintaining the group in the terrestrial laboratory were solved, engineers could then approach the problems in miniaturization to make the system for space flight.[38]

Providing a water supply for astronauts appears less of a problem than getting rid of the excess water produced by the body's metabolic processes, which, as we have seen in the preceding chapter, will soon make the cabin too humid. Research at Ohio State University has indicated that the relative humidity of the cabin must not exceed 40 per cent.[39] But Dr. Clark at Johnsville states that the excess water produced by metabolism amounts to some 300 cubic centimeters per man per day[40]—enough to saturate the atmosphere quickly far beyond tolerance.

More than 20 years ago it was recognized that the unpleasantness of a stuffy atmosphere was more the result of humidity than of too much carbon dioxide, and that, in space flight, the oversupply of water vapor would have to be removed by absorption with soda-lime or other suitable chemicals.[41] This process, however, would be feasible only for short-duration journeys. After World War II, attention shifted mainly to condensing the excess water vapor by refrigeration.[42] This would permit purification and reuse of the water.

Another obvious source of water in a closed ecological system is urine and the moisture of feces. R. A. Bembenek and J. D. Zeff have discussed and evaluated various laboratory-tested methods of recovering usable water from urine; they include absorption, filtration, ion exchange, refrigeration, electrodialysis, freeze-drying, and distillation.[43] The Douglas Aircraft Company human-factors team, headed by Eugene B. Konecci, confirms that water purified in this way would not only be drinkable but would contain no pathogens and would have a lower bacterial count than most tap water consumed in our homes.[44] The Aeronautical Division of the Minneapolis-Honeywell Regulator Company has actually constructed for the Air Force's School of Aviation Medicine a seven-ton space simulator in which urine and all other waste water are purified by a system including chemical treatment, filtering, superheating, freezing, and a final filtering through activated carbon.[45]

THE FEEDING OF ASTRONAUTS

How will space-flight conditions affect food, eating, and digestion? Carsbie C. Adams, surveying research to date on these problems,[46] points out that so far no direct physiological connection has been established between a reduced oxygen supply and appetite, although appetite may be influenced by moods such as boredom, frequently encountered at low pressures. Appetite may also be stimulated by an imaginary requirement for food, resulting from the reduction of body temperature associated with mild hypoxia. Prolonged, moderate hypoxia, on the other hand, would tend to be psychologically depressing and, therefore, adversely affect the appetite. Ingestion of food, Adams also concludes, should not be a problem at any pressure that the unprotected body can endure. Tests made during parabolic flight in jet aircraft indicate that with proper equipment eating and drinking are feasible even during weightlessness. As for elimination of wastes, this should be affected only slightly, if at all, by the subnormal cabin air pressure.

Cosmic radiation, Adams continues, has been established to be completely harmless to food, although certainly its direct effects upon the human body are another matter. Cosmic-ray sickness, with symptoms similar to those of atomic radiation sickness, would have adverse effects upon the alimentary processes. Over-irradiation produces vomiting, fever, diarrhea, weakness, progressive anemia, hemorrhaging, and a reduced white blood count, which lowers resistance to disease. The solution to this major problem lies in shielding (discussed later in the chapters devoted to the hazards of radiation).

Experimental results cited by Adams indicate that a high carbohydrate diet may have a slightly beneficial effect upon human tolerance to reduced atmospheric pressure. There are two schools of thought about the ability to get along on bulkless, low-residue foods; one school holds that some bulk is essential.

Living on strange foods with unusual textures, flavors, aromas, and colors may generate psychological problems of considerable magnitude. Nor is it pleasant to contemplate ingesting food and water retrieved from one's own urine and feces. Careful selection of the crew members and appropriate conditioning, however, will help to overcome these psychological problems, and much attention will have to be given to the eye-and-nose appeal of the processed foods.

A closed ecological system which would return every atom of human waste to the nutrition cycle is included in the theoretical proposal advanced by Dr. Clark of the Naval Air Development Center. Such a system, however, is not likely to be perfected in the near future, nor would it be needed for short expeditions. Meanwhile, we have the problem of waste disposal on the pioneer flights.

In 1938 the best answer that anyone thought of was to put the refuse in an air lock and let the air remaining there blow it away from the ship, or else to store the waste and abandon it on the moon or other stopping point during the journey.[47] But the air-lock discharge, of course, would gradually deplete the cabin's supply of air. New York University scientists later suggested that the wastes might be useful as fuel or to help grow food.[48] Harry C. Dyme, chief of the

Nutrition Section of Wright Field's Aerospace Medical Laboratory, has pointed out that the latter use is hardly different from the use of fertilizers in terrestrial agriculture.[49] The space-cabin simulator at Brooks Air Force Base will dispose of much of the waste residue by incineration, burning the gases thus produced in an afterburner and ending with nothing more than a bit of fine ash.[50]

Even the problem of disposal of deceased crew members, inevitably to be encountered during flights lasting from months to more than a generation, has been considered. In 1943, while all other units at the Peenemunde Rocket Research Institute were pushing the V-2 missile to operational status, the Preliminary Design Group speculated on futuristic satellite and space-station projects. As they dreamed of lunar expeditions and similar ventures, they jokingly proposed that, as a fitting tribute, rocket pioneers should be placed in glass spheres and launched into permanent orbit about the earth.[51] This idea has even been incorporated into the opera *Aniara,* which had its premiere in June 1959 at the Royal Opera House in Stockholm: in the play, passengers on an abortive flight to Mars used this method of "burial."[52]

For relatively brief excursions into outer space—such as orbital flight about the earth or short hauls to the moon—the problems of food, water and waste are not really critical. Project Mercury space pilots will simply carry their full requirements of water and concentrated food; the waste-disposal problem will be partly solved by using low-residue foods, and their urine will be stored in a compartment of their space suit for discharge after landing.[53] For the long-duration flights of the future to destinations beyond the central portion of our solar system, a completely closed ecological system, such as that proposed by Dr. Clark, will be an absolute requirement. Indeed, every atom of atmospheric gases, food, and water will have to be salvaged and re-used indefinitely, unless some form of suspended animation is employed.

PART THREE

G-Forces and Weightlessness

5

Experiments on the Centrifuge

THE first physiological hazard encountered during a trip into space is the sharp acceleration imparted by rocket take-off. One of the last is the deceleration caused by air friction as the space vehicle re-enters the earth's atmosphere on its return. And still other accelerations and decelerations may occur during the trip —either routine or accidental. Fortunately, both acceleration and deceleration have been extensively studied in aviation medicine, and much of the physiological data gathered in connection with problems of aircraft flight will be applicable to the problems of manned space travel. Nevertheless, the range of forces anticipated in space flight is not quite the same as in aviation, so that this research has branched out in several new directions.

In a strict sense, acceleration refers to increase in velocity; deceleration, to decrease in velocity. In physiological research, however, this distinction is not very important. Any change in speed has the effect of multiplying a body's weight. The effect is conventionally expressed in terms of *g*: one *g* is equivalent to the constant force of gravity on the earth. Thus a two-*g* force, whether due to an increase or a decrease in velocity, is one that effectively doubles the body's normal weight. But not every two-*g* force has the same physiological impact. Much depends on such factors as duration of the force, the position of the body, and the use of protective devices and techniques.

We do not yet have a complete picture of the kinds and amounts of acceleration and deceleration that will be encountered in manned space flight. But we know pretty accurately what total acceleration will be needed at takeoff for various trips. For an interplanetary voyage, say, the space vehicle will have to be accelerated to about 25,000 miles an hour to escape from the earth's gravitational field. To reach this speed in one second, the required acceleration would by 1,152 *g*. Of course it can be spread over a longer time. Thus if the acceleration time is extended to two minutes, the acceleration required to reach 25,000 miles per hour is reduced to 9.6 *g*.[1] And the *g*-force goes down correspondingly with further increase in the time allowed for the acceleration.

Obviously there are practical limits to the feasible accelerations —imposed at one end by human tolerance and at the other by the state of our engineering. A prolonged low acceleration would be most comfortable for travelers, but it is out of the question with present-day rocket fuels, which are most efficient at high acceleration rates. (This may change, of course, when nuclear rocket engines become available.) On the other hand, extremely high acceleration would be physiologically intolerable. The dilemma can be solved only by some sort of compromise. Current expectations are for a multistage takeoff, with the peak force probably in the neighborhood of eight *g*. Within this order of magnitude many different patterns for reaching either an earth-orbiting or an escape velocity seem acceptable from the standpoint of both engineering and physiology.

Another set of alternatives exists for deceleration of the space vehicle as it re-enters the earth's atmosphere, but again the final choice of *g*-patterns is dictated by physiological and other considerations, just as in takeoff. With sufficient aerodynamic lift, a vehicle could make a staged re-entry, skipping in and out of the atmosphere. However, the first manned space vehicles are expected to follow a ballistic-type re-entry trajectory, decelerating in a single stage. A steep re-entry path would produce high values for both deceleration and aerodynamic heating; a gradually descending path would reduce peak forces by extending the duration. A few of the hazards were pointed out by Louis G. Dunn, of Space Technology Laboratories, who observed that if a flier dives in too steeply, his vehicle will burn up, whereas if he "comes in too shallow, he is likely to miss the atmosphere and go right on by."[2] There is litle doubt that re-entry will always be a more difficult maneuver than takeoff. But there is broad agreement that gradual descent (at an angle of perhaps three degrees) is best. In this way the maximum deceleration can probably be kept to about eight to ten *g*, and as much as possible of the deceleration will take place at the higher altitudes, where the atmospheric density and therefore the heating are lowest. Re-entry heating, in any case, should prove manageable with present materials and techniques in any trajectory that keeps the *g*-forces within tolerable limits.[3]

Landing on and taking off from other heavenly bodies will involve other sets of *g*-forces, which will depend on the gravitational fields of those bodies, their atmospheric density, and so forth. If there is little or no atmosphere, air friction cannot supply the deceleration required before landing; presumably reverse rocket thrust will be necessary in that case. (This technique could also be used, of course, to help slow down the vehicle on its return to the earth.) Generally speaking, there is little likelihood of extreme forces save in an emergency situation, but the possible range is so great that almost any research data on the physiological effects of acceleration or deceleration may conceivably have some bearing on manned space flight.

LESSONS FROM AVIATION

Physiological research on *g*-forces antedates even the birth of aviation medicine, although aviation first gave these studies their critical importance. In aircraft, *g*-forces are not a real problem, physiologically speaking, in straight and level flight, but they do cause trouble in high-speed turning maneuvers. These expose fliers to what are technically known as "radial" or "centrifugal" accelerations, which produce physiological effects basically the same as in very rapid linear acceleration. Moreover, as aircraft speeds have increased, so has the range of *g*-forces experienced by fliers. Specialists in aviation medicine therefore have increasingly turned their attention to the problems involved. Such problems have been investigated in all major countries, both through study of in-flight experiences and through laboratory experimentation, especially on the human centrifuge.

The centrifuge was used for medical treatment long before it assumed a key role in aeromedical research. The therapeutic value of such an instrument apparently was first suggested in the late eighteenth century by the English poet-physician Erasmus Darwin. He thought that spinning a patient on a wheel with his head outward would produce sleep, and with head inward, would reduce heart activity and tend to suppress fever. Early in the following century, doctors at the Charité Hospital in Berlin set up a centrifuge which exposed patients to as much as five *g*. Besides using it for treatment of mental illness, they conducted some basic research on acceleration (including themselves as test subjects). Their experiments first established some of the circulatory and respiratory effects of centrifugal force.[4]

The use of the centrifuge specifically for research in aviation medicine dates from 1917, when a French scientist, working under the auspices of the Ministry of War, strapped dogs to a wheel and subjected them to forces of 20 to 98 *g*. Only the animals exposed to 98 *g* died, but of course this did not mean that even 20 *g* would be comfortable for humans. Over the following years, centrifuge experiments were carried out at various research institutions with goats, rabbits, apes, and other animals. In June 1932, the Experimental Committee of the American Interplanetary Society (which in a burst of practicality later changed its name to the American Rocket Society) centrifuged two guinea pigs at an estimated 30 *g* for two minutes—and found them dead at the end of the test. This was an unusual example of early centrifuge work in that the spaceflight application was clearly uppermost in the minds of the researchers. But, as in all such animal experimentation, there was no sure way of correlating observed results with the likely effects of comparable forces on humans, especially with regard to purely subjective tolerance limits.[5]

Systematic laboratory experimentation with human subjects began in the mid-1930's, when a large centrifuge (2.7 meters in radius), especially designed for human use, was put in operation by the German Air Ministry at Berlin. Shortly afterward, in 1936, the United States Army Air Corps began studies on a human centrifuge at Wright Field in Ohio. Similar instruments were soon put in operation by the Australian and Canadian air forces, as well as by other aeromedical research centers both in the United States and abroad. Wright Field obtained a new and better centrifuge in 1943, at the same time that air raids were causing the Germans to give up their attempts to install an improved model at Berlin.[6] At present the biggest and best human centrifuge is one belonging to the United States Navy's Aviation Medical Acceleration Laboratory at Johnsville, Pa., just outside Philadelphia. Its radius is 50 feet, and it can be accelerated to 40 *g* in seven seconds. Its gimbal-mounted gondola is equipped with a television camera, an X-ray apparatus, and instruments for registering everything from respiration to brain waves.[7]

The first aeromedical experiments carried out with human centrifuges were mostly concerned with the effects of headward, or positive,* acceleration. A force applied in this direction hinders the circulation of blood to the head, reduces blood pressure at eye level, and at a certain point—usually somewhere around four to five *g*—will cause visual "blackout." At a little higher *g*, actual unconsciousness results; at a little lower, the individual merely experiences "grayout"—an over-all dimming of vision and failure of peripheral vision. Investigation has likewise shown that a sufficient amount of negative (footward) or transverse (forward or backward) acceleration will

* As stated by Neville P. Clarke and Stuart Bondurant in *Human Tolerance to Prolonged Forward and Backward Acceleration* (WADC Technical Report 58-267): "There has been an unwarranted confusion of the terminology of acceleration physiology arising because of the use of either direction of acceleration, [the opposite] direction of inertial force caused by acceleration, or the position of the subject during acceleration to describe the experimental conditions." They recommend that acceleration be always expressed "in terms of the direction in which the body is being accelerated"—with "headward" acceleration to indicate "a change in velocity of the body in a direction from feet to head"; "footward" acceleration to indicate the exact opposite; and "forward" and "backward" acceleration to indicate, respectively, a change in velocity "in the general direction in which the subject is facing" and a change in velocity in the "direction opposite to that in which the subject is facing." Each of these terms will be used, in the sense specified, in the present volume. However, usage has also consecrated the terms "positive," "negative," and "transverse" acceleration, even though Clarke and Bondurant try to avoid them. Hence they will sometimes be used, too, with "positive" equivalent to "headward" in the above definition; "negative" to "footward"; and "transverse" —a very useful catch-all—to either "forward" or "backward."

impair visual acuity one way or another.[8] There is even a tendency for acceleration to produce "oculogravic illusions," which involve the apparent displacement of fixed visual references. This last effect has been observed both in actual flight and in centrifuge experiments. It first received intensive study in the 1940's from investigators at the United States Naval School of Aviation Medicine in Pensacola. They attributed it to increased *g*-forces acting on the vestibular balance organs of the inner ear.[9]

Acceleration impairs muscle performance, because limbs naturally are harder to lift and move when their weight is increased by a multi-*g* force. Research has indicated, for instance, that a prone subject exposed to backward acceleration cannot lift his arms or legs at a force level greater than eight *g*, nor his head at more than nine *g*, although hand and finger movements are only slightly impaired at 12 *g*. In another typical experiment, it was shown that the average time needed to don a parachute rose from 17 seconds at one *g* to 75 seconds at three *g*.[10]

Many investigators have sought to determine the limits of tolerance to acceleration by placing subjects on a centrifuge and applying increasing magnitudes and/or duration of force until a predetermined "end point" is reached. The "end point" can be defined in many different ways, so results are not always comparable, but it is usually taken to be the loss of some critical faculty—*e.g.*, blackout or major visual impairment, inability to breathe, or pain which seriously hampers judgment and performance. Ludwig Bührlen, using the German Air Ministry centrifuge in the 1930's, exposed subjects to as much as 12 *g* (transverse) for three minutes and to 17 *g* for five seconds. These forces were the greatest that any subject managed to endure. Although they produced no permanent ill effect, they were interpreted as upper limits for human tolerance.[11] In more than 20 years of experiments on centrifuges in various laboratories, no subject was able to take a peak force of more than 17 *g*. During World War II two men in Germany did manage to tolerate 17 *g*, applied transversely, for a whole minute. They were ill afterward, but supposedly suffered no permanent injuries.[12] This duration at 17 *g* has not been equalled since. However, the record for the maximum number of *g*'s sustained in a centrifuge has since crossed the Atlantic, thanks to work accomplished on the Navy centrifuge at Johnsville. The German record was first definitely broken in the summer of 1958, when two Navy test subjects, Lieutenant Commander Carter Collins and R. Flanagan Gray, each successfully withstood a peak force slightly in excess of 20 *g* (transverse) for a very brief time. Later Gray passed the 30-*g* mark on the same centrifuge with the help of a special protective device which will be discussed in a later chapter.[13]

Human tolerance to headward (positive) acceleration is roughly one third to one half the tolerance to transverse *g*; and the tolerance to footward (negative) acceleration is lower still. This reflects the fact that in tranverse acceleration the force is applied relatively evenly through the body, and the heart does not have the formidable task of pumping blood up to the head against a multi-*g* force, as it does during positive acceleration. Nor is blood crowded into the head, resulting in "seeing red" or "redout," as occurs under negative *g*. Transverse acceleration presents certain problems, such as respiratory difficulties, but in general they occur at a somewhat higher *g*-level and are more easily tolerated.

For pilots of fast aircraft, the high radial accelerations encountered are typically positive or negative rather than transverse. Seeking to take advantage of the higher tolerance to transverse *g*, German scientists before World War II made flight tests with subjects lying in a prone position during exposure to acceleration. The switch from positive to transverse acceleration definitely raised blackout thresholds. The Germans also experimented with a flop-back seat which could shift a pilot rapidly from the seated to the supine position, thus applying the principal accelerations transversely. These studies were continued during the war, when they were matched by similar investigations in England and the United States. The physiological advantages of recumbent flying seemed to be outweighed by the complications in operating the aircraft. Nevertheless, specialists in aviation medicine continued to study the possible use of prone beds, supine hammocks, and other means of fitting body position to the direction of force and thereby increasing *g*-tolerance.[14] Fortunately, in space flight the accelerations and decelerations will be chiefly in a straight line, and it will usually be easy to arrange matters so that they are sustained transversely.

To the magnitude of the *g*-force, its direction, and its duration, we must add a fourth factor that affects human tolerance: namely, the "rate of onset," or rate of buildup to a given level. For example, a slow buildup of positive *g* may allow certain reflex processes of cardiovascular compensation (constriction of blood vessels, increase in the heart rate) to keep pace and thus actually raise the threshold for visual dimming.[15]

Aviation experience has produced various countermeasures against *g*-forces. Aircraft pilots have learned that they can raise their tolerance levels by crouching, straining, and so forth. Then there are items of equipment that help. It was discovered fairly early that a tight abdominal belt could increase tolerance to headward acceleration by one-half *g* or more, simply by limiting the tendency toward pooling of blood in the lower part of the body. Attempts were made in the 1930's to develop complete anti-*g* suits, but such garments really came into their own only in World War II, when operational models were produced in the United States, Australia, and other Allied countries. By and large, they functioned by applying counter-pressure to the body surface through a system of pneumatic bladders, usually activated automatically by exposure to a given multi-*g* force. Such suits worked especially well against the effects of headward acceleration: they raised blackout thresholds on the order of 1.5 to three *g*. However, the suits were uncomfortable, and many fliers resisted their adoption, citing the ability of pilots to "ride the gray-out," *i.e.*, to sense what was coming and adjust their actions just in time to avoid loss of vision.[16]

It should be remembered that different individuals, or the same individual on different days, may well demonstrate different degrees of tolerance to exactly the same accelerative force. Centrifuge-test subjects generally possess higher than average tolerance levels. They are selected, healthy young males, and have a high degree of what is known in military jargon as "motivation." A young airman who had logged many hours on the Wright Field centrifuge even spoke of the friendly rivalry among centrifuge riders as a sort of game; each man sought not only to advance the cause of science and the United States Air Force but also to outdo his fellows.[17] Needless to say, centrifuge riding makes a rather uncomfortable and even potentially hazardous game, requiring considerable courage. It must further be emphasized that even forces which are technically tolerable can produce some impairment of performance, not to mention such temporary side-effects and after-effects as miscellaneous pains, cardiac irregularities, petechiae (burst capillaries), headaches, fatigue, and irritability. Habitual centrifuge subjects have sometimes noted a premature onset of varicose veins.[18]

TAKEOFF INTO SPACE

Notwithstanding such effects and all reservations about the special circumstances surrounding the tests, it seems safe to conclude that the accelerations necessary for space flight are within human tolerance limits. Indeed, many students of the problem reached this conclusion long ago, on the basis of data accumulated in aviation medicine and in basic research such as Bührlen's pioneer studies of high transverse *g*. In 1939 the enthusiasts of the British Interplanetary Society who published plans for a "B.I.S. Lunar Spaceship" calculated that the maximum acceleration would be four *g* and correctly observed that for the necessary acceleration time this was well within established tolerance limits. One difficulty they foresaw was that even this relatively low level of force might "restrict physical movement and . . . temporarily impair mental activity, so that swift reaction to unforeseen crises might be more or less seriously curtailed." Hence they called for automatic controls during the "thrusting periods."[19] Actually, a four-*g* exit would be almost too good to be true, at least in the immediate future, but the suggestion was typical of an early tendency to underestimate the required peak force of takeoff thrust.

Later the German aeromedical scientists Otto Gauer and Heinz Haber took a more general approach to the problem. In a paper contributed to the United States Air Force publication *German Aviation Medicine, World War II* (Washington, 1950), they included a list of alternative escape patterns ranging from three *g* with a duration of nine minutes and 31 seconds to ten *g* lasting for about two minutes. And they unhesitatingly proclaimed that all these accelerations were tolerable, citing Bührlen's work and some 11-*g* centrifuge experiments directed by Gauer in collaboration with Siegfried Ruff, which confirmed the existence of a safety margin with respect to both the magnitude and the duration of force.[20]

A qualified assent to this view was given by Paul A. Campbell, Director of Aeromedical Research at the United States Air Force School of Aviation Medicine at Randolph Field, in a paper delivered to an aeromedical symposium in November 1951. Campbell observed, however, that there were "no experimental data applicable to sustained acceleration" for the time required to attain escape velocity.[21] Apparently he either had not yet heard of the German experiments or else was hesitant to draw firm conclusions from the reported test data, which showed what a few select subjects had endured, not necessarily what would be acceptable for an operational flight situation. In any case, to examine the problem more closely, scientists in recent years have staged an increasing number of experiments exposing subjects to specific exit accelerations. Alternative *g*-time patterns have been compared from the standpoint of physiological effects, and attention has been given to the advantages and drawbacks of different body positions and restraints. This is a type of work in which the Aerospace Medical Laboratory at Wright Field—though handicapped by a wartime centrifuge which is slightly outmoded in comparison with the Navy's pride at Johnsville—has made possibly its greatest single contribution to the development of space medicine.

As far back as 1952, E. R. Ballinger, reporting on a series of tests he and his Wright Field colleagues had conducted, confirmed that from the standpoint of physiological effects an ideal takeoff pattern would stay in the neighborhood of three *g* (transverse). This was tolerated easily by his subjects for 15 minutes, or about twice as long as needed for escape velocity. In fact, the chief complaint of the test subjects was the monotony of riding the centrifuge for so long a period. The Wright Field scientists recognized that a steeper acceleration would be preferable from the standpoint of rocket-engine efficiency and fuel consumption. Accordingly, subjects were exposed to increasing *g*-loads with decreasing duration. At eight *g*, for a period sufficient to achieve escape velocity, subjects began to experience severe pains and shortness of breath, but they managed better when their position on the centrifuge was changed from supine to semi-supine. Two subjects went two minutes and six seconds at ten *g* in the semi-supine position, but a third did not, and Ballinger concluded by recommending a thrust somewhere below eight *g*.[22]

Later investigations on the Wright Field centrifuge, jointly reported in 1955 by H. Preston-Thomas and a group of researchers representing both the Aerospace Medical Laboratory and Canada's

National Research Council, explored the reaction of test subjects to three-stage acceleration with successive peaks of 8, 5.8, and 5.8 *g*. This was apparently the first series of centrifuge tests to simulate takeoff of a multistage rocket vehicle, and the total acceleration, applied transversely, was sufficient to place the vehicle into orbit. All the subjects completed the experiment. They showed a "slight" decrement in ability to manipulate controls during the acceleration, with experienced centrifuge riders predictably coming out best. Preston-Thomas and his associates concluded from these experiments that "select crewmen" could help to control a space vehicle during the takeoff phase,[23] but this last conclusion was not universally accepted. Rufus R. Hessberg, Jr., who later headed the Aerospace Medical Laboratory's Biophysics Branch, observed that logically the safety factor in human performance should be the same as that required in construction of the vehicle itself, and that no performance decrement could really be considered safe.[24]

Testing of three-stage rocket acceleration patterns has continued on the Wright Field centrifuge. One airman, subjected in a later experiment to the same three stages used by Preston-Thomas, observed:

> During transverse *g* runs, such as this, you feel a weight pressing on your chest. It is almost impossible to breathe, especially at the high *g*'s. I managed to get a few quick breaths during the slowdowns and struggle through the higher *g*'s as best I could. You get a pain in the chest if you try to breathe deeply at the higher *g*'s.[25]

Nevertheless, he made it.

Early in 1958 Neville P. Clarke, Stuart Bondurant, and others were conducting experiments with "successive accelerations to three instantaneous peaks of either 8, 10, or 12 *g*. After each peak, deceleration was effected as rapidly as possible (20 to 35 seconds) to 1.5 *g*, and the next acceleration begun immediately." In each case the acceleration was programmed to simulate a rocket pattern yielding final orbital velocity of more than 18,000 miles per hour. However, a published report emphasized that the centrifuge could not be stopped abruptly after reaching a given peak, whereas the same peak in actual rocket flight would be followed by burnout and abrupt cessation of acceleration until the start of the next stage; as a result, centrifuge subjects actually sustained 15 to 25 per cent more acceleration than required with an equivalent rocket pattern. Yet all these test configurations were found tolerable by "selected" test subjects.[26]

Studies of three-stage acceleration have been carried out elsewhere; for instance, on the centrifuge of the University of Southern California. There a typical pattern of acceleration to orbital velocity in mid-1959 featured successive peaks of 6.5, 4.6, and 2 *g*, which proved readily tolerable even though deliberately run at the end of a long, hard day.[27] However, researchers have not abandoned the study of "plateau" acceleration patterns—building up and then maintaining a predetermined *g*-level. Plateau data can be applied, within certain limits, to the analysis of multistage patterns.[28]

Part of the experimentation at Wright Field in recent years has been concerned with prolonged plateau-type accelerations in various body positions. Some of the most interesting results have to do with headward or positive acceleration. The test data do not necessarily alter previous findings with regard to blackout thresholds and the like, but they do indicate that men can tolerate considerably longer durations of positive *g* than formerly imagined. Experiments show that orbital velocity could be attained even with "headward acceleration of the seated subject," provided the force does not exceed five *g*. With a rate of onset slow enough so that cardiovascular compensation was fully effective, subjects tolerated this acceleration without the aid of an anti-*g* suit. Moreover, two unprotected subjects withstood three *g* (positive) on the Wright Field centrifuge until it was arbitrarily stopped at the end of an hour. A similar *g*-time pattern in actual rocket flight would not be very practical, but it is interesting to note that this acceleration would be sufficient to achieve 235,000 miles per hour—almost ten times escape velocity.[29]

The crowning experiment in prolonged acceleration was conducted at Johnsville on the Navy centrifuge. According to an account published early in 1959, Carl C. Clark rode the centrifuge continuously at two *g* (transverse) for 24 hours:

> He cooked, ate, slept, stood up, made medical observations on himself, wrote and typed, and generally carried out living activities. However, he lost interest in these activities while under stress and passed most of the time listening to the radio and napping.

The acceleration was sufficient to go 45 million miles and to reach an ultimate velocity of 3,800,000 miles per hour! Or, if the subject had "accelerated at two *g* half way and decelerated the other half, he would have reached Mars in 42 hours, made the moon in 3.5 hours, and gone across the country in 15 minutes."[30]

A subsidiary question that received close attention from Clarke, Bondurant and their co-workers at Wright Field was the body position best suited for sustaining transverse acceleration at rocket takeoff. After studying various alternatives, they recommended a seated position with a slight forward tilt of the trunk. Though involving a small headward component which can produce blackout above a certain level, the tilt was found to reduce chest pains and breathing difficulties associated with forward acceleration. In this position there appeared to be no need for special anti-*g* equipment in any likely exit pattern. More recently the Aerospace Medical Laboratory has found by experiment that a nylon-net, form-fitting contour seat, maintaining the forward tilt, further increases the tolerance to *g*-forces. The forward tilt has also been incorporated in the form-fitting "Mercury couch" adopted by the National Aeronautics and Space Administration for use by the astronauts in Project Mercury.[31]

RE-ENTRY

Research on takeoff patterns has thrown considerable light on the problem of re-entry deceleration. As noted before, there is no basic difference between acceleration and deceleration so far as physiological effects are concerned. Furthermore, the total *g*-force required for attaining a certain speed will be the same as that required for coming to a stop from the same speed. This does not mean, however, that the force will be applied in just the same manner.

Until the first Soviet and United States satellites showed the upper regions of the atmosphere to be denser than previously thought —thus facilitating more gradual re-entry decelerations—it was often believed that the *g*-forces might come to a distinctly higher peak in re-entry than in takeoff. One group of centrifuge experiments carried out at Johnsville in the winter and spring of 1957 exposed chimpanzees to a hypothetical re-entry pattern of 40 *g* (transverse) for 60 seconds. This was a true interservice project: the Aeromedical Field Laboratory at Holloman Air Force Base supplied chimpanzees, the Navy spun them at high *g*, and the Armed Forces Institute of Pathology performed post-run examinations. Chimpanzees were used as subjects because the test configuration was expected to exceed human tolerance limits. No one really believed that space crews would have to face such extreme deceleration, but it was felt that whatever happened to a chimpanzee at 40 *g* for 60 seconds might give some clues as to the very worst that a man could expect if exposed to, say, something of the order of 15 *g* for the same period.

All five chimpanzees used in these tests survived the centrifugaation, but electrocardiograph abnormalities were recorded during the tests, and internal injuries were found when the animals were sacrificed afterward. In all but one case these injuries approached irreversible and lethal limits. Just what this proved with regard to the re-entry of a manned space vehicle was not wholly clear, in view of the still uncertain correlation between chimpanzee and human tolerances. However, the test results did confirm the danger involved in exposure to prolonged high *g*. By contrast, chimpanzees at Johnsville some years earlier had taken 40 transverse *g* for 15 seconds with no untoward effects.[32]

After the satellites began to circle the earth, the information they gave about the upper atmosphere indicated that re-entry decelerations might be kept as low as 8 to 10 *g*.[33] On the basis of centrifuge work already conducted, principally in connection with the problem of takeoff, there seemed little doubt that the peak forces involved would be tolerable, both in magnitude and in duration. Probably the greatest single uncertainty is the effect of weightlessness—which will be the normal condition of flight through space—in reducing tolerance to *g*-forces sustained after the weightlessness. Experiments which we shall discuss later have shown that such an effect exists,[34] but the data so far are insufficient for estimating exactly how severe it will be.

Another problem in re-entry is the intricate task of controlling the vehicle to maintain the planned *g*-pattern as it plows back into the atmosphere. There are also questions of body position and restraints, because, even assuming that the *g*-force of re-entry is applied transversely, it makes some difference whether crew members are facing forward or backward. If, for instance, a flier is in the same forward-facing position at re-entry that he would normally assume for takeoff, he will be thrown forward by the deceleration, instead of being pressed back firmly and snugly into his seat. At the very least he will require harnessing to avoid collision with objects in the cabin. Moreover, the slight forward tilt recommended for takeoff would introduce an undesirable component of negative *g* at re-entry.[35]

In fact, it has been realized for some time that human tolerance to "backward acceleration," or "forward deceleration," is slightly lower than tolerance to the same level of *g*-force with the position reversed. Some of the first studies of prolonged backward acceleration on the Wright Field centrifuge showed pains occurring even at levels as low as 2.5 to 5 *g*, with the peak force lasting only five or ten seconds and total test durations under one minute.[36] Among other things, in this test configuration the blood is driven into the feet and hands of a seated subject, causing tiny blood vessels to rupture and producing a rash and a general tingling or "burning" sensation. However, as more tests were conducted, and as Wright Field scientists obtained more understanding of possible variations in body positioning and restraints, higher tolerance levels for backward acceleration were established. An occasional test subject even decided that he liked this better than forward acceleration. As Airman Gordon A. Jones expressed it, "At least you can breathe." Breathing actually is somewhat easier during backward acceleration, although still difficult above eight *g*. Jones' attitude was not universal, and the tolerance limits still were lower in backward than in forward acceleration. However, results of Wright Field experiments published in 1958 indicated fairly high tolerance times for backward acceleration—averaging four seconds at 12 *g*, 41 seconds at eight *g*, and two minutes at five *g*. Individual subjects, of course, might significantly exceed these figures, and an "average" tolerance to backward acceleration of four seconds at a 12-*g* peak would not preclude tolerance for considerably longer periods at lower *g*-levels as part of the same re-entry configuration.[37]

These results were achieved by seated subjects using a full-restraint suit especially designed by Albert Bernardini of the Wright Field Aerospace Medical Laboratory. Standard Air Force straps and harnessing had been found inadequate for re-entry stress of five *g* or more; something better was needed, not merely to restrain the flier adequately, but to make sure that force was distributed as evenly as possible over the entire body. A regular anti-*g* suit gave some help, but not enough. The answer, as worked out by Bernardini, was a suit of

> . . . interwoven nylon and cotton material reinforced with one and three-quarter inch type web nylon belting and arranged so that it absorbed tension from the pressure points and applied it over larger areas of the body through use of reschel nylon netting. . . . The suit was attached to the

seat at six points on either side [and] was snugly fitted to the arms and legs of the subject to offer counterpressure and thus help to prevent petechiae formation and leg pain. The legs were sharply flexed in this system with the feet in the stirrups of the ejection seat. This also aids in prevention of leg pain encountered in other restraint systems.[38]

A special helmet with padded chin rest was included as part of the "integrated" costume. Finally, the forward tilt recommended for takeoff was replaced by a position in which head and trunk were essentially erect.

An alternative that has received consideration is to turn the flier completely around between exit and re-entry, so that he can face rearward during the latter phase. In this way re-entry deceleration would be experienced as equivalent to forward acceleration, and no full-restraint system would be needed, unless for possible emergency use. Such a procedure would increase *g*-tolerance somewhat. It will be used in Project Mercury; the attitude of the Mercury capsule will be reversed before it starts its re-entry.[39] It was also simulated in recent re-entry studies conducted at Wright Field with the Aerospace Medical Laboratory's nylon-net contour seat. Clarke reported in June 1959 on one such experiment in which the force was gradually built up to an instantaneous peak of 16.5 *g* as part of a total exposure lasting not quite three minutes. The test configuration represented a velocity change of roughly 24,500 miles per hour and was "designed to encompass [and exceed] several of the possible re-entry patterns of the Mercury capsule." With the help of net support, five out of seven subjects were able to complete the 16.5-*g* profile, and the others almost succeeded.[40]

Despite the added tolerance obtainable by reversing the direction of the flier before the re-entry phase, this approach will not necessarily be followed in all future space operations. Especially for a pilot-controlled landing, the forward-facing position has obvious advantages. Consequently the Wright Field scientists have pointed out that it may often be desirable to keep the subject facing the same way at both takeoff and re-entry and to equip him with a Bernardini full-restraint suit or something similar, plus an adjustable seatback which can be tilted forward at takeoff and readjusted later for re-entry (as well as for comfort and convenience during the flight proper).[41]

Centrifuge work at Wright Field has demonstrated that with adequate restraint, re-entry at low *g* could be tolerated in any standard position except head-forward, *i.e.*, negative-*g*. Foot-forward re-entry would be equivalent to the *headward* acceleration that was found tolerable at the three-*g* level for a whole hour. However, it would not be wise to count on maintaining such a low level, especially in the early days of manned space flight. Thus it will clearly be best to take the re-entry deceleration transversely, in which case a variety of patterns can be tolerated, in both forward-facing and backward-facing positions.

The Aerospace Medical Laboratory at Wright Field has not been alone in studying the problem of re-entry. The Navy laboratory at Johnsville, to cite only one example, has also made contributions, and not only by the chimpanzee experiments already discussed. The Johnsville centrifuge is uniquely fitted for re-entry work. Unlike the Wright Field instrument, it has a gimballed system allowing reproduction of various buffetings and oscillations which are likely to occur during re-entry. It even has a system of "closed-loop" simulation, whereby a subject riding in the centrifuge gondola can make flight-control motions and experience the same accelerative forces from those motions that he would in a true flight situation.[42]

Beginning in March 1957, the Johnsville centrifuge was used for hundreds of simulated "flights" of the rocket-powered X-15. The test pilot, Scott Crossfield, took part as a subject in preparation for flying the X-15.[43] Although the plane was not to go all the way into orbit, it would have some re-entry problems. The Johnsville centrifuge also tested a wide variety of specific exit and re-entry patterns which may be encountered by other advanced vehicles, including the Mercury capsule. These tests led to modifications and improvements in seats, restraints, and vehicle design.[44] One interesting result was that "highly skilled test pilots" actually did better at operating controls under moderate acceleration loads (four to six *g* transverse) than under static conditions. Apparently a certain amount of challenge can serve to improve performance. But the challenge must not be too great: the pilots did not do as well at the higher *g*-levels.[45]

At Johnsville, and at Wright Field as well, the centrifuge has been used to try out a new approach to cushioning astronauts against *g*-forces: immersing them in water. But that is another story, which we shall reserve for a later chapter. Meanwhile we must review the work in another basic area of *g*-force research: the study of short-duration forces of the impact type.

6

Impact Forces and Colonel Stapp's Sled

THE centrifuge is made to order for the study of low and medium *g*-forces with durations of a few seconds or longer, but it is poorly adapted to experimentation with very abrupt forces, of the impact or crash type. Such forces (whose principal effects on the body are mechanical damage to the tissues rather than circulatory or respiratory disturbance) have to be considered as a major problem of space flight, for instance, at re-entry. They have been studied for some time, of course, in connection with automobile and air crashes and aircraft escape devices, and an impressive array of techniques has been developed for this research.

As a matter of fact, a certain amount of physiological research on impact-type forces has been carried out with no test facilities at all, simply by analyzing the results of free falls and transportation mishaps. There are various ways of calculating the *g*-forces involved in falls, and some interesting data have resulted. Human beings have been known to survive, with little injury, falls in which the estimated impact amounted to something of the order of 150 *g*.[1] Similarly, a great deal has been learned from studies of automobile and aircraft accidents.

Research programs on accidents, together with crash experiments under controlled conditions, have been conducted by the National Advisory Committee for Aeronautics (now incorporated in the National Aeronautics and Space Administration) and the Institute of Transportation and Traffic Engineering of the University of California at Los Angeles, which is interested primarily in automotive crash forces.[2] Other agencies and institutions have also been active in this line of work. Volunteer human subjects have occasionally participated in low-impact experimental crashes, and animals have served too. But the standard "passenger" in artificially staged crashes has been the anthropomorphic dummy. The investigations have produced better understanding of impact forces, advances in vehicle design, and a number of safety devices, such as lap or seat belts and aircraft crash harness. This progress will be of benefit to astronautics. Parachute landing of the Project Mercury capsule, to cite just one pertinent analogy, has been graphically compared to a small car hitting a brick wall at 20 miles per hour[3]—although the effect naturally depends to a certain extent on just where the capsule lands.

Crash problems, including means of protection, can also be studied on laboratory test facilities capable of simulating impact situations. One such facility is the "deceleration tower," in which a test platform slides down vertical guide rails to an abrupt landing. Devices of this type were used in crash research on animal subjects by aeromedical scientists in Germany and the United States during World War II. The Germans applied impact forces up to 600 *g*. Experimenters at the School of Aviation Medicine at Randolph Field exposed cats to impacts ranging as high as 1,045 *g* on their deceleration tower. A surprisingly high percentage of the subjects lived through this ordeal, thanks to a plaster of Paris cast in which they were embedded during the test.[4]

Another rudimentary instrument is a swing-mounted seat which can be stopped abruptly by an attached cable, exposing test subjects to decelerative forces lasting one-tenth of a second or less. Such a device, developed by Siegfried Ruff, was used by German scientists during the war to study human tolerance to *g*-forces with only a lap belt for protection. The results showed that a force of 15 *g* could be tolerated by forward-facing subjects wearing a nonstandard, 16-inch-wide lap belt; about 30 *g* was easily tolerated in the backward-facing position. In neither case was there an attempt to establish an actual tolerance limit. Tests conducted on a similar swing-seat in the period 1955-1958 by the Aeromedical Field Laboratory at Holloman Air Force Base indicated a tolerance level of at least 23 to 26 *g* in the forward-facing position with only a lap belt for protection. But some subjects reached their critical pain threshold. With seated hogs as subjects, the Holloman swing was further used to explore the range from serious to lethal injury caused by practically instantaneous deceleration (forward-facing) with lap belt only. In these tests it was found that about 40 *g* was needed to produce "definite injuries to lungs, heart, abdominal organs," and "something in the order of 50 *g*" for lethal effects.[5]

While studies of this kind, even with hog subjects, were useful for demonstrating the value of lap belts in crashes, aviation presented another problem which called for basic physiological research on brief-duration *g*-forces. This was the problem of bailing out of an aircraft. Originally, bailout meant climbing out of the cockpit and jumping off, and a substantial *g*-force was sustained at the opening of the parachute. Usually the shock of a parachute opening is not too severe, but it can deliver 30 to 40 *g*. One of the highlights of United States aviation medicine during World War II was the record parachute jump of W. Randolph Lovelace II, then head of the aeromedical laboratory at Wright Field. He jumped from 40,200 feet, seeking to explore, among other things, the effect of parachute opening at high altitudes. It had been calculated that the opening shock in his jump would be under eight *g;* actually it was 32 *g*. The impact knocked him out. This test showed that a flier bailing out at high altitude should delay opening the chute until he reaches the denser air at a lower level.[6]

As aircraft speeds increased, it became more and more difficult to crawl out of a disabled plane and jump with safety. The ultimate solution was the powered ejection seat, pioneered during the war by Germany and later adopted for high-performance aircraft in all countries. With this device a new physiological problem was added; namely, the impact thrust required to propel the seat upward (or downward) with sufficient speed to clear all surfaces of the moving plane. Human tolerance to the applied *g*-load was a limiting factor in ejection-seat development, especially as the force was applied in a relatively unfavorable direction—parallel to the long axis of the body. The force was too brief to produce the circulatory disturbances typical of headward and footward centrifugal acceleration, but it did raise the possibility of serious spinal injury.

To obtain needed data on human tolerance to ejection thrust, special test facilities were devised, including ejection-seat towers or vertical accelerators—aircraft-type seats which were attached to vertical rails and shot straight up or down to simulate possible ejection patterns. Contraptions of this sort were used after the war at Wright Field, at the Navy's Air Materiel Center in Philadelphia, and elsewhere. The results generally indicated that fliers would tolerate momentary exposures of about 10 to 15 *g* (negative) for downward ejection and about 20 *g* (positive) for upward ejection.[7]

Another escape problem, which became increasingly severe as aircraft reached the speed of sound, was the abrupt deceleration imparted by the "wall of air" immediately after a pilot was ejected from his fast-moving plane and before the opening of his parachute. This force was applied chiefly in the favorable transverse direction, but it could exceed the ejection thrust in both magnitude and duration. Its effects were compounded by the sudden onslaught of windblast *per se* on the human body, not to mention possible tumbling and spinning. Some of the most dramatic research in recent years has been related to this problem of air-drag deceleration, using another type of test facility—the high-speed track.

THE STAPP SLED

Test tracks of one sort or another have been used for a wide variety of research on deceleration and impact, including much that is of direct interest to space medicine. Even before World War II, German aeromedical scientists had conceived a "large testing catapult" for physiological research. Its purpose was to expose subjects to *g*-forces with durations of several tenths of a second—shorter than those obtainable on a centrifuge but longer than those obtained later in swing-seat experiments. The catapult was to consist of a light cabin propelled by means of a falling weight and connecting pulleys along horizontal guide rails; the cabin was to be braked mechanically in a variety of deceleration patterns. However, while under construction, during the war, the apparatus was twice severely damaged by Allied air raids, and on the second occasion the Germans simply gave up.[8]

At the end of the war the initiative passed to the United States. A number of research tracks have been built in recent years and have played important roles in the testing of military hardware. Track testing has also been used for human-factor research. And in this use it is associated primarily with the name of United States Air Force

Colonel John Paul Stapp. The Brazilian-born son of a Baptist missionary, a Doctor of Medicine and Doctor of Philosophy—and on the lighter side, a punster and phrase-maker—Stapp is certainly one of the most colorful characters in the whole field of aviation and space medicine.

Stapp first attracted the attention of his colleagues with a series of experiments in the period of 1947-1951 (when he was a major). He started his work on a 2,000-foot track at Edwards Air Force Base in California, which had been built (but never used) as a test launch facility for a United States version of the German V-1 buzz bomb. Stapp converted it to a deceleration track on which human, animal, and dummy subjects rode a rocket-propelled sled that was stopped abruptly by mechanical friction brakes. The force was applied transversely in most cases, with position either front- or aft-facing.

The first tests on living subjects were scheduled to be performed with chimpanzees. The animals were late in arriving however, so Stapp climbed aboard the sled himself. (For his eagerness to use himself as a test subject, Stapp was "grounded" more than once by his superiors, but he always returned to the test sled sooner or later.) In due course he exposed himself and other human subjects to forces as high as 45 *g*, at 500 *g* per second rate of onset. Stapp did not emerge unscathed from this experiment, suffering among other things a retinal hemorrhage in his right eye. A co-worker, Sergeant Raymond Leach, lapsed into unconsciousness as a result of an experiment which produced 38 *g* at a sharper rate of onset (1,370 *g* per second). While no test resulted in lasting ill effects, any exposure that might cause unconsciousness would not be considered tolerable in an operational situation.[9]

Stapp also exposed anesthetized chimpanzees on the Edwards track to deceleration plateaus of 65 *g*, rates of onset up to 3,400 *g* per second, and peaks of about 150 *g*, without finding the lethal point or even the point of irreversible injury.[10] He staged other experiments with hogs, using a separate monorail decelerator.[11] Indeed, Stapp has always had a special fondness for chimps and hogs as fellow test subjects. As he once explained to a Congressional subcommittee, a type of forum at which some military researchers would be hesitant even to broach the subject of animal experimentation:

> You wonder why I use hogs—hogs and chimpanzees? Well, man is somewhere between the hog and the chimpanzee. Some people are more like hogs; others are more like chimpanzees.[12]

In all the work at Edwards the duration of decelerative force was short, ranging in the human experiments from 0.15 to 0.42 second. These tests, held mainly for purposes of crash research, suggested that the human body, if properly positioned and secured, could actually tolerate more *g* than an aircraft structure and so could endure any crash forces in which the plane itself stood up.[13] Useful information was obtained on strap and harness designs and on the possible advantages of a backward-facing passenger seat. The test results could also be applied to the problem of human tolerance to abrupt rocket thrust, and Stapp himself later observed that they established "an ample margin for drogue recovery of a manned [space] capsule."[14] But such applications were still rather remote at the time.

Another problem that engaged Stapp's attention was wind-drag deceleration and windblast in escape from high-speed aircraft. This research, too, was immediately oriented toward atmospheric flight, although not without application to the whole question of *g*-forces in space travel and to the escape situations that may occur in the early part of an ascent or during re-entry.

Stapp's new project involved *g*-forces with a slightly wider range of duration. In addition, the inclusion of windblast testing called for much higher sled velocities than his previous experiments, which had not gone beyond a peak velocity (for the human runs) of 226 feet per second. For these and other reasons, Stapp looked around for something better than the 2,000-foot Edwards track and finally found what he wanted at Holloman—a track built originally as a rail launcher for tests of the Snark intercontinental missile. It was 3,550 feet long—before a series of track extensions made it longer—and well instrumented. It had a water-brake system, operating by means of a scoop attached to the sled which reached down into a series of water dams between the rails. This system permitted a wide, but carefully controlled, range of peak *g*, onset, and duration.[15]

To his delight, Stapp (by now a lieutenant colonel) was assigned to Holloman in April 1953 as Chief of the Air Force Missile Development Center Aeromedical Field Laboratory. To be sure, he had to wait almost a year before he could take a ride on the Holloman track. A special rocket sled had to be constructed and tested for his program. This vehicle, known as Sonic Wind Number 1, was built by the Northrop Corporation. The sled and other equipment were put through a series of practice runs, and on January 28, 1954, the first run was made with a live subject—a chimpanzee.[16]

In due course, Headquarters of the Air Research and Development Command gave its authorization to conduct human runs, and on March 19, 1954, Colonel Stapp was strapped in for his first Holloman rocket-sled ride. The objective of Colonel Stapp's first ride was to "evaluate human reactions to exposure to about 15 *g* of linear deceleration for about 0.6 seconds duration, approximately double the duration possible for the same magnitude of force on the crash decelerator previously used at Edwards . . ."[17] The run was essentially successful, with a top speed of 615 feet per second, a peak deceleration of 22 *g*, and only momentary ill effects.[18]

After a number of animal experiments principally to evaluate the test equipment, a second human run took place on August 20, 1954, with Stapp again as subject. The test was designed to explore windblast effects, from which he had been shielded in the March test by a solid panel windshield. This time the windshield consisted of two swinging doors which opened suddenly during the run to provide abrupt wind pressure. The run reached a velocity of 736 feet per second, but the peak deceleration was kept to 12 *g*. Stapp's head was covered with a special helmet, and he suffered no ill effects save temporary and quite minor blood blisters, apparently caused by windblown grains of sand that penetrated his clothing. The ride, he claimed, was the "easiest" of the 28 he had made at Edwards and Holloman.[19]

For the next few weeks chimpanzees monopolized the aeromedical test sled. One run made use of a movable seat designed to evaluate the effect of tumbling, at a rate of 105 revolutions per minute, in combination with deceleration and windblast. Other chimpanzee runs tested a new device for producing abrupt exposure to windblast. It was a windshield which could be jettisoned explosively at a given point during the run. Unfortunately, the jettisonable windshield proved something of a hazard to the chimpanzees, causing the death of more than one in the course of the experiments.[20]

THE RECORD RUN

Much of the activity of the Aeromedical Field Laboratory in the fall of 1954 consisted of preparations, including chimpanzee control runs at 600 miles per hour and faster,[21] for Colonel Stapp's most memorable rocket-sled ride: the run of December 10, 1954. This test aimed to explore both deceleration and windblast. The jettisonable windshield was still unreliable, and the swinging-door system weighed too much for the sled to attain the desired velocity, so Colonel Stapp took his seat with no windshield at all; he merely wore the helmet he had already used in August. As on that run, his arms and legs were well secured against flailing, a windblast hazard already well known from aircraft bailout incidents.

The run attained a peak velocity of 937 feet per second, or Mach 0.9. This was fast enough for the sled to overtake and pass a T-33 aircraft flying overhead. The maximum windblast was 7.7 pounds per square inch, or better than 1,100 pounds per square foot, and the water brake brought the sled to a complete stop from the maximum velocity in just 1.4 seconds. The rate of onset of the deceleration was approximately 600 *g* per second, reaching a plateau that averaged over 25 *g* for roughly a second, with peaks of 35 and 40 *g*. The jolt Colonel Stapp received has been compared with that which "an auto driver would experience were he to crash into a solid brick wall at 120 miles per hour."[22]

As was to be expected, this time Stapp showed much more obvious effects of his ride. There were some strap bruises, and blood blisters from grains of sand. In addition, he suffered extremely painful effects on the eyes, not from windblast but from deceleration. In Stapp's own words, when he entered the water brake his vision became a "shimmering salmon," followed by "a sensation in the eyes . . . somewhat like the extraction of a molar without an anesthetic."[23] This sensation overshadowed all his other physical sensations and minor injuries during and after the run. Yet, even his eyes did not suffer long-range or irreversible damage. Colonel Stapp's vision returned in about eight and one-half minutes, although his experience left him with two black eyes which lasted the usual interval. To use his own words:

> There was no fuzziness of vision or sensations of retinal spasms as had been experienced in 1951 following a run [at Edwards] in which a retinal hemorrhage occurred. Aside from congestion of the nasal passages and blocking of paranasal sinuses, hoarseness and occasional coughing from congestion of the larynx, and the usual burning sensation from strap abrasions, there was only a feeling of relief and elation in completing the run and in knowing that vision was unimpaired.[24]

As soon as possible after admission to the base hospital, where he went for further examination, Stapp "ate heartily and spent two hours accommodating demands of motion picture photographers making documentary coverage of the run."[25]

What the run proved, essentially, was that windblast on a properly secured and protected body at over 600 miles per hour at 4,100 feet above sea level—equivalent to mach 1.6 at 40,000 feet[26]—was quite negligible in comparison with 25-*g* deceleration for approximately one second. This duration was the longest yet attained experimentally for such high *g*-forces, and the effects were at least temporarily debilitating. Yet the deceleration, sustained with the help of fairly elaborate harnessing, was shown to be humanly tolerable.

One other result of the December 10 experiment—and to a lesser extent of Colonel Stapp's two previous rides on the Holloman track —was to give the Air Force doctor a large measure of popular renown as "the fastest man on earth." Stapp's emergence as a national hero led to a spate of television appearances, including one on Ralph Edwards' "This is Your Life" which required him to be mysteriously called to Los Angeles from a conference he was attending in the East, and his portrait appeared on the cover of *Time*. For obvious reasons it was news throughout the nation and even overseas when the "fastest man" was charged by the Alamogordo, N.M., police with speeding at 40 miles per hour (unspecified rate of onset) in a 25-mile-per-hour zone. The Justice of the Peace before whom he appeared dismissed the charge, issued a new citation against a fictitious "Captain Ray Darr," and paid the fine from his own pocket.[27]

Colonel Stapp's famous ride was reproduced in a fictional and somewhat romanticized version in the Twentieth Century-Fox motion picture "On the Threshold of Space." This picture was partly filmed at Holloman, where a number of special sled runs were staged in the fall of 1955 in cooperation with the film company. An advance showing of the picture took place at the Holloman base theater in March 1956, with a collection of Hollywood stars on hand.[28]

On a more serious level, Stapp received additions to his already substantial collection of honors and awards. Among them was the Air Force's annual Cheney Award "for an act of valor, extreme fortitude, or self-sacrifice in an humanitarian interest performed in the preceding year," given to Stapp in August 1955 personally by General Nathan F. Twining, Chief of Staff. He received an honorary Doctor of Science degree from Baylor University, his alma mater, in

May 1956, when an honorary degree was also given to President Eisenhower.[29] Naturally the awards and citations to Stapp often cited not only his achievements on the sled but also his other pioneering work at Holloman and elsewhere.

In some respects his national renown was almost a disadvantage. The Air Research and Development Command at one point raised a military objection to Colonel Stapp's participation in a scientific gathering, on the ground that public appearances, both professional and otherwise, were already demanding too much of his time. Command headquarters had counted 62 "known" appearances in roughly the first eight months of 1956.[30] Despite all distractions, however, Stapp never lost sight of his main objectives. In fact, he had scarcely recovered from his ride of December 10, 1954, before he was speaking of his desire to take another ride at supersonic speed. What he had in mind was a rocket-sled experiment at about 1,000 miles per hour, designed primarily to explore human tolerance to windblast *per se* rather than windblast combined with deceleration.[31]

But Stapp's supersonic ride was not to be. Indeed, in June 1956 Stapp was startled to read in the newspapers that he had been "grounded" from all future high-speed runs, on the basis that he was too valuable for the Air Force to risk.[32] But animal experiments on the Holloman high-speed track continued. Within a week after Stapp's most famous ride, a chimpanzee ran through another track test of the jettisonable windshield, which this time failed to jettison at all. Early in 1955 Stapp conducted a series of sled runs at Holloman to explore the effect on chimpanzees of abrupt windblast in combination with 40-*g* deceleration for durations under one second. The speeds were comparable to that attained by Stapp in December 1954, and the windblast effects were again negligible. With regard to *g*-forces, the results were somewhat inconclusive.[33]

Later deceleration and windblast studies on the Holloman high-speed track explored steadily higher values. They also followed increasingly separate lines of development. A program of windblast studies began in May 1955 with a new sled, Sonic Wind Number 2, which was lighter and therefore capable of substantially greater speeds. The *g*-forces were carefully controlled so as not to overshadow the physiological effects of supersonic wind pressure *per se*. This experimentation not only produced significant "pure" research data on windblast but indicated some possible improvements in protective equipment for fliers.[34] However, these studies have little or no specific application to problems of space travel, with the possible exception of emergency escape during exit or re-entry, and this is rather remote. The X-15 rocket aircraft is equipped with an open ejection seat,[35] but escape from true space vehicles probably will be executed in an enclosed escape capsule, where the occupant will experience no direct wind pressure.

The primary studies on deceleration, conducted with the sled Sonic Wind Number 1, went on to *g*-forces far beyond anything likely to be encountered in escapes from aircraft. Colonel Stapp and his co-workers were interested, of course, not only in aviation problems but also in basic research and in possible applications to space flight.

TESTS AT HIGHER G'S

By November 1955 chimpanzee tests were being programmed for 80-*g* deceleration at nearly 5,000 *g* per second rate of onset. In March 1956 the experiments were suspended for about a half year for reconstruction of the deceleration sled, after an accident in which it became airborne. At the same time the Holloman track was extended to slightly over 5,000 feet. This made possible significantly higher sled performance. Deceleration runs were resumed on the 5,000-foot track in October 1956, and 15 were conducted from then through March 1957. This new series was programmed for deceleration plateaus ranging up to 120 *g*, but actual peak forces went considerably higher. A force of 247 *g* lasting just one millisecond was experienced by a chimpanzee on February 2, 1957. The rate of onset for that test was over 16,000 *g* a second, also a record; the total duration of the decelerative phase was 0.34 second.[36]

The effect on anesthetized chimpanzee subjects varied with the number of *g*'s, the duration, and the body position. The run that attained a 247-*g* peak caused only "moderately severe" injuries to the test subject; this was the one run in the series during which the chimpanzee was seated facing backward. A run of January 12, 1957, with the subject facing forward, proved fatal within four hours, even though the peak force was 233 *g* (lasting one millisecond). This, of course, again confirmed the superiority of the aft-facing position for deceleration. One other fatality occurred at a considerably lower deceleration level, but in that case the subject's death apparently was due in large part to an ailment unrelated to *g*-forces. Speaking of the entire series of high-*g* runs on the 5,000-foot track, Stapp observed that significant injuries, particularly to the heart and lungs, began in the neighborhood of the 135 *g* (with forces of extremely short duration and with subjects "optimally restrained by nylon webbing"). He also hypothesized that in the two seated positions, backward-facing and forward-facing, chimpanzee tolerance to transverse *g* was at least comparable to that of human beings; this point was admittedly uncertain, and, when it came to probing the range of severe to lethal injury, no human test subject would attempt to verify the assumption.[37]

These specialized deceleration experiments were undertaken essentially as a form of basic physiological research on *g*-forces. The test results were then related by Stapp to problems of space flight such as manned re-entry.[38] The experiments took place at a time when estimates of the peak forces to be encountered in re-entry deceleration were still highly uncertain. Hence scientists concerned with the re-entry problem needed as much data as possible on tolerance to deceleration, including information on the forces that could be expected to produce serious injury, and the work on the Holloman high-speed track helped to meet this requirement. To be sure, no one expected that re-entry patterns would include anything like the extreme decelerations applied in these tests. However, in reaching conclusions about human capability from chimpanzee test results, it was desirable to have a wide margin for possible error. And it was comforting to know that fellow primates had experienced forces above 100 *g* with only minor injury and, in one case, had actually lived through a deceleration peak of almost 250 *g*.

Peak deceleration at re-entry was not the only space-flight problem to which the test results might be applied. Stapp cited the case of the parachute landing of a space capsule with "partial failure" of the parachute and "violent impact terminating a rapid descent." Referring specifically to the 247-*g* backward-facing experiment, he drew the lesson that

> . . . a properly restrained subject suspended within a capsule in the aft-facing, semisupine, transverse orientation should survive an 80-knot impact of the capsule in a hard landing on average soil, provided the capsule did not fail, crushing in on him. Forces would be in the order of half the injurious exposure for animals.[39]

At first glance this particular application may seem to involve a great many contingencies, but it is just one of the many things that *could* happen in manned space flight.

The high-*g* chimpanzee runs on the Holloman track ended in March 1957. In fact, biological tests were suspended for more than a year. The entire track was taken up and replaced with a structure 35,000 feet long—the longest research track in the world. By the time this work was substantially finished, Colonel Stapp had left Holloman for Wright Field to take command of the Aerospace Medical Laboratory there. Subsequently the 35,000-foot track was used for a continuation of windblast studies,[40] as well as for evaluation of special means of protection against *g*-forces which will be discussed in the following chapter.

There are, of course, other tracks, besides this one and the 2,000-foot track at Edwards Air Force Base, that have been used for research. Stapp himself directed some specialized windblast runs with chimpanzee subjects on a 10,000-foot track at Edwards (later extended to 20,000 feet) and on the Supersonic Naval Ordnance Research Track (SNORT) at China Lake. New aircraft ejection systems have been tested with anthropomorphic dummies or chimpanzees on the Edwards long track and on still another Air Force track at Hurricane Mesa in Utah.[41] The British aeromedical research unit at Farnborough, England, maintains a relatively low-performance 2,000-foot track to study such problems as catapult launching stress in aircraft-carrier operations.[42]

Holloman also has a short track, called the Daisy Track, designed expressly for use by the Aeromedical Field Laboratory. It consists of two rails five feet apart and 120 feet long. Stapp's original proposal for this track called for a compressed-air catapult as the propulsion system, so it was named after the Daisy air rifle. The compressed-air system was not actually installed until 1959, but the track began operation in September 1955 with a cartridge system instead. Precisely controlled decelerative force is supplied by means of a metal piston on the front of the sled which thrusts into a water-filled brake cylinder at the end of the track.

The Daisy Track cannot compete with the Holloman long track in sled velocity or exposure to windblast. In deceleration it is capable of producing *g*-forces as high as those tried on the long track but not of as long duration. On the other hand, it is superior to the long track in simplicity, in economy of operation, and in the ease with which sleds can be adjusted to carry a subject facing in almost any direction (and either sitting or lying on his side). Thus the track is admirably fitted to compile basic data on as broad as possible a range of short-duration *g*-forces, in all phases of body orientation.[43]

The first living subject on the Daisy Track was a chimpanzee. Tests have been made with Stapp's other favorite among animal subjects, the hog, as well as with rats and even bears. But most of the participants in Daisy tests have been people. Human tests started in February 1956 with a series of low-*g* experiments intended mainly for subject indoctrination. Since then several dozen officers and enlisted men assigned to the Aeromedical Field Laboratory have taken part, naturally including Stapp himself (his so-called "grounding" from high-speed experiments did not, of course, apply to the Daisy Track).

The maximum *g*-forces sustained in Daisy tests by human subjects have varied greatly, according to the position of the subject and other factors. Men have tolerated more than 30 *g* lying on their side with *g*-forces parallel to the spine, in a test configuration simulating upward ejection from aircraft. This exceeds what was originally accepted as the tolerance limit for ejection thrust. In other positions the forces successfully tolerated have exceeded both this level and the highest peak sustained in human experimentation on the long track. But the total duration of these stresses has seldom been much more than one tenth of a second.[44]

The record on the Daisy Track was a run by Captain Eli L. Beeding in which the deceleration, measured on Beeding's chest, reached a peak of 83 *g*—the highest any human volunteer has ever experienced, at Holloman or elsewhere. The total duration of the decelerative force was one tenth of a second, and the rate of onset was calculated at 5,000 *g* per second. Beeding was seated upright and facing backward. After the run he gradually went into a state of shock, but he recovered in less than ten minutes. He entered the base hospital for treatment of sore vertebrae and detailed observation, but he suffered no lasting ill effects. However, he concluded that 83 *g* was about the most the human body could stand in the test configuration that was used, and that he might never have fully recovered from the ordeal if he had been facing forward. On his historic ride, which took place May 16, 1958, Captain Beeding did not ride alone: the sled also carried two rats as fellow passengers.[45]

Experiments such as Beeding's record run have their practical side. The basic information they develop on human tolerance to high-*g* deceleration is potentially applicable to the physiology of both aviation and space flight. Even when specific applications are not instantly apparent, the test results reduce the area of uncertainty about the problems that may arise in manned space operations. Moreover, the Daisy Track, like the Holloman high-speed track, has figured in the testing of novel techniques of *g*-protection which are primarily of interest for space flight. The presence of the rats on Beeding's sled is related to one such technique and is among the topics discussed in the next chapter.

7

Anti-G Devices

DEVICES for protection against *g*-forces range from the standard seat belt to the complex harnesses used in military aircraft and in high-*g* deceleration tests. They include the anti-*g* suit and the Project Mercury form-fitting "couch." The theoretical principles and actual equipment worked out in connection with problems of aviation and automotive transportation have provided a useful basis for protection in space flight. Even when the protective techniques are not directly applicable, ideas and components can often be adapted to meet the requirements of manned space travel.

And yet the possibility remains that *g*-protection in space flight will demand radically new solutions—quite unlike anything ever adopted in aviation on a regular operational basis. Among the novel approaches, one of the most intriguing is the technique of fluid immersion, which in recent years has been the subject of widespread laboratory experimentation.

Fluid protection is a rather familiar device of Mother Nature. The brain is protected by virtue of floating in the cerebrospinal fluid, of very similar density, and so is an egg yolk by floating in albumen.[1] Journalists and public relations officers seldom miss an opportunity to trace current concepts of fluid protection back to Archimedes, the Greek scientist of the third century B.C. There is nothing to indicate that Archimedes conducted research on the physiological effects of multi-*g* acceleration, but supposedly he was the first man to observe that when a body is immersed in fluid it loses a portion of its weight equal to the weight of the fluid it displaces. According to the familiar story, this principle occurred to him as he was taking a bath one day, whereupon he jumped from his tub shouting "Eureka!" and ran naked down the street.[2] It is sometimes assumed from Archimedes' principle that a space traveler in a water-filled capsule would be essentially weightless and, therefore, immune to any number of *g*'s, because he would have no weight to be multiplied by the acceleration force.

In reality, of course, things are more complicated; indeed, some of the theoretical and practical aspects of fluid protection are still imperfectly understood. Nevertheless, this general approach does raise interesting possibilities. A technical report issued by the Aerospace Medical Laboratory at Wright Field points out that

> . . . the immersed subject, rather than being exposed only to the inertial force caused by acceleration, is suspended, as it were, between this force and an opposite and almost equal force due to buoyancy. Acceleration causes a proportional increase in the magnitude of both of these forces. Thus, even at large accelerations, there is little net force acting to displace the subject.[3]

With certain exceptions which will be mentioned later, acceleration of the immersed body produces no significant circulatory disturbance or displacement of internal organs or tissues in relation to one another. Martin G. Webb, Jr., and R. Flanagan Gray, two United States Navy investigators, expressed the matter in these terms:

> If we assume a specific gravity of the arms and legs of about 1.07, then at an acceleration of 15 *g* the extremities should feel as heavy as they do at one *g* in air. If a solute were added to the water, the specific gravity of the water solution could be adjusted to that of the arms and legs and the result would be a sensation of weightlessness of the extremities at very high accelerations. Tissue deformation would be prevented and fractures and other injuries would not occur.[4]

WATER-FILLED SPACE SUITS

For more than 2,000 years after Archimedes, no one attempted to use the principle of buoyancy either for simple weight reduction (as an alternative to going on a diet) or for protection against acceleration. The first concrete efforts to use water as an anti-*g* device date from 1934, when German scientists pioneered a water-lined anti-*g* suit, extending from neck to feet. It consisted of two layers of material: an inelastic but flexible outer layer, and an inner layer which was elastic and waterproof, with water between the two layers. The expectation was that during exposure to multi-*g* force the weight of the water would be increased and pressure from the water would minimize circulatory disturbances (as the later pneumatic-type anti-*g* suits were designed to do). More specifically, the external pressure applied to the body would balance the acceleration-induced hydrostatic pressures in the circulatory system. Thus the blood would not tend so strongly to pool in the lower part of the body under headward (positive) acceleration, and there would be no blacking out or unconsciousness at the usual levels. The Germans' water suit worked, but it was rather heavy and bulky, seriously interfered with freedom of movement, and was discarded as impractical.[5]

During World War II the idea of a water-lined anti-*g* suit was revived by the Canadians. The so-called Franks flying suit, developed by the Royal Canadian Air Force in the early part of the war, was based on the same general principles and was the first anti-*g* suit actually put to use in combat.[6] Yet the Canadians, too, ultimately abandoned the water suit as impractical, or at least as inferior to the pneumatic anti-*g* suits being developed at that time.

Canada's wartime research on water protection included centrifuge tests with a monkey riding in a special tank filled with water to chest level.[7] Other centrifuge experiments, using human subjects in a "specially constructed bathtub," were carried out in the United States during the war at the Mayo Aero Medical Unit in Rochester, Minn. The investigators found that, with submersion to the level of the third rib, there was an average increase in tolerance to headward acceleration of about 1.7 *g*.[8] However, the United States never went as far as the Canadians in actually applying the protective technique.

Work on fluid protection was allowed to languish by the end of the war, but it picked up again gradually and in the post-Sputnik era became a veritable scientific fad. So many agencies and individuals took up studies in this field that it would be difficult, if not impossible, to indicate in every case precisely who did what and when. Probably the agency that has conducted the most varied experimentation on water immersion and *g*-forces is the United States Navy. The Navy's role is quite appropriate, in view of the protective medium involved, but its interest is chiefly in learning basic facts about *g*-protection and in applications to space navigation rather than to oceanic navigation, or even to aircraft flight.

During the late 1940's some centrifuge experiments with immersed animal subjects, notably rabbits, were conducted at the Navy's School of Aviation Medicine at Pensacola.[9] Later the Navy's Aviation Medical Acceleration Laboratory at Johnsville launched what was to prove a more significant program on the theme of water protection. The Johnsville program began modestly in 1952, using one of its smaller centrifuges and mice as test subjects. Under the direction of James Ziegler and R. Flanagan Gray, mice were exposed to transverse accelerations of 100 to 1,500 *g* both in and out of water, with exposure times varying from 26 to 38 seconds. For some reason the tests failed to demonstrate any "significant difference in the survival ratios of mice out of water and in water." In 1953-1954 two other Johnsville scientists exposed submerged rats to headward acceleration. Balloons in the water were used as a source of pressurized air, and many rats were killed by overexpansion of the lungs.[10]

THE WATER CAPSULE

Gray continued studying the theoretical aspects of water protection and developed models of protective equipment. In 1956, as a result of this work, he requested a patent for his design of a man-sized, water-filled metal capsule. Construction of the capsule began in January 1957, using the joint services of the David Clark Company of Worcester (a firm which also makes pressure suits and similar equipment) and another engineering company. The general appearance of the capsule is well depicted by the nickname it has received: the "Iron Maiden." It is designed to be entirely filled with water, covering the subject seated inside to the very top of his head. Special eyeglasses allow hydraulic pressure to act even on the subject's eyes without seriously interfering with his vision, and a breathing mask is provided. The subject maintains constant pressure on a "dead man's switch"; if he releases the switch at any point, the centrifuge automatically stops and an emergency dump valve opens. Preliminary studies of the Iron Maiden's effectiveness against transverse acceleration on the large Johnsville centrifuge were conducted in May 1958. The tests were soon suspended because of equipment difficulties, but those that were made showed that up to a level of nine *g* enclosed subjects "experienced no evidence of any physiologic or psychologic disturbance."[11]

The "Iron Maiden" was not the first man-carrying water tank to be spun on the Johnsville centrifuge. A month earlier tests had been staged at Johnsville with the "bathtub" used in the wartime centrifuge experiments at the Mayo laboratory. Sitting in this tank, subjects were exposed to headward acceleration levels ranging up to 16 *g*. They were submerged to eye level, holding their breath and using a mask to keep water out of the mouth and nose. Electrocardiographic data were recorded, and the subject's "vision and state of consciousness were checked by his response to lights in the periphery of his visual field." Gray and two other subjects took part, but only Gray was exposed to the 16-*g* maximum (with four seconds of the complete run above 15 *g*). Without the help of immersion in the bathtub, he had lost peripheral vision under headward acceleration at 3.25 *g*; with the protection in this experiment he did not lose it at all. Each of the subjects remarked on "the lack of a feeling of increased weight with increased acceleration" and on the ease of arm and leg movements at all *g*-levels. What caused Gray to desist at 16 *g* was "slight trauma" of the soft palate and upper pharynx, apparently due to the passage of air. Certain other minor pains were noted during the tests. However, the 16-*g* force successfully tolerated was a world centrifuge record for headward (positive) acceleration. Except for impact-type exposures of very brief duration, as on the Daisy Track at Holloman Air Force Base, this was more positive *g* than any human being had ever sustained without unconsciousness, regardless of means of protection.[12]

Subsequently the Iron Maiden was put back in service at Johnsville for studies of transverse acceleration (back to chest) at gradually increasing *g*-levels. Gray successfully withstood 31 *g*, in a pattern with a total duration of 25 seconds including five seconds at the 31-*g* peak. Another subject stopped at 26 *g* because of difficulty in breathing between runs, attributed to apprehension. Still another stopped at 28 *g*, because of a sinusitis due to irritation of his nose by the breathing mask; Gray and the other subject had simply held their breath during the run. In no case was there indication of visual dimming, or of any serious discomfort other than the case of sinusitis. Limb movements seemed relatively unhindered by acceleration (though subjects in the Iron Maiden do not have much room for movement in any case because it closely matches the contours of the body). A limiting factor at 31 *g* was the capability of the centrifuge, with the 700-pound combined weight of man, water, and capsule.[13] Even so, this was a record for acceleration of any sort sustained by a human subject on a centrifuge. It surpassed the 25-*g* average sustained for roughly one second by John Paul Stapp in his rocket-sled ride of December 1954, although it did not surpass the peak forces registered in that or other track experiments.

Before the Johnsville laboratory began water experiments with human subjects, the Navy's School of Aviation Medicine at Pensacola had resumed work with immersed animal subjects. These tests were inspired in large part by the work of Italy's Rodolfo Margaria, discussed later. According to detailed results published in the first half of 1958, in the Pensacola experiments mice under water proved capable of surviving 1,300 *g* for 90 seconds, provided they were breathing pure oxygen. This apparently helped to overcome the effect of the extreme hydraulic pressure due to the increased weight of the water during acceleration. The pressure tends to compress the confined volumes of gas within the body. Fish, however, are inherently better able to withstand the hydraulic pressure. Hence guppies, spun on a small centrifuge at Pensacola at rates varying from 50 to 10,000 *g*, did better than the mice. Even guppies experienced brief disorientation when exposed to 50 *g* for one minute, but for them the lethal range started at the high level of about 7,500 *g* (for a similar length of exposure), and some guppies could live for a half minute at 10,000 *g*.[14]

An animal-world record for resistance to centrifugation was set at Pensacola by the one-celled organism *Euglena gracilis*. About 50 per cent of the *Euglena* "subjects" managed to withstand—under water, of course—a force of 212,000 *g* for four hours! This probably did not prove much about human space travel, but it was suggested hopefully that such results might throw some light on the "absolute limits of life-supporting environment." Not that the "absolute limits" in terms of *g*-forces had necessarily been reached even yet. Pensacola scientists were said to be aiming for one million *g*, although they needed new equipment to reach such levels.[15]

From *g*'s measured in the hundreds of thousands, it is rather anticlimactic to turn to water-tank experiments at the 12-*g* to 16-*g* level at Wright Field's Aerospace Medical Laboratory, with mere humans as test subjects. This Air Force program has been conducted by William Blanchard, Stuart Bondurant, Neville Clarke, and associates, with strong support from Colonel Stapp (who firmly denies that his interest in water immersion has anything to do with the fact that his parents were Baptist missionaries).

The Wright Field experiments have employed a coffin-like container mounted on the centrifuge. In it a test subject can be completely covered with water; he uses a skin-diver's equipment for breathing. Transverse acceleration was studied in three body positions—prone, supine, and semi-supine. In each case the subjects found it easy to move their limbs during acceleration. However, in the prone and supine positions chest pain and breathing difficulty were serious limiting factors. The semi-supine position, with the torso and head propped up at an angle of 35 degrees to the hips, was more successful. It corresponded roughly to the forward tilted position recommended by Wright Field scientists for forward acceleration of a seated subject out of water. In this position, of course, there was less water pressing down on the chest.

Thus all the Wright Field records for underwater *g*-tolerance have been achieved in the semi-supine position. When these experiments were first publicized in the spring of 1958, the highest force tolerated was given as 12 or 13 *g* for about four minutes. At or near this level, chest pains and difficulty in breathing were again limiting factors, and there was even occasional blackout with one type of face mask. At lower *g*-levels much longer exposures were possible: at six *g* a subject could apparently go almost indefinitely; for any given acceleration level above six *g*, the tolerance time appeared to be more than twice what had usually been reported in experiments out of water. By 1959 the record peak force sustained in the Wright Field water box had been raised to slightly more than 16 *g*. This did not approach the 31-*g* peak attained with the Iron Maiden at Johnsville, principally because of the greater limitations of the Wright Field centrifuge. But at Wright Field the durations studied were generally longer.[16]

The Aeromedical Field Laboratory at Holloman Air Force Base also initiated a program of water-immersion research. Holloman has no human centrifuge, but the possibility of using its research tracks for the study of fluid protection could scarcely be overlooked. Accordingly, Holloman engineers designed a tank capable of carrying large primates, including people, down the 35,000-foot, high-speed track. The tank was delivered to Holloman in the fall of 1959, and a series of dummy runs was promptly started to check it in preparation for experiments with living subjects.

In the meantime, some exploratory studies involving water immersion were conducted on Holloman's other track facilities by Albert Zaborowski. These began in the first half of 1958 on the "Bopper," a short, portable track, with shock-cord propulsion, whose primary purpose is best described by its official title, Crash Restraint Demonstrator. The test "subjects" were small blocks of wood immersed in a sugar solution; the purpose of these first runs was to work out test procedures and to study the behavior of objects exposed to deceleration in fluids of slightly varying density. Later Zaborowski progressed from blocks of wood to frogs—which appeared to interpret the increased hydraulic pressure from the multi-*g* force as a sign of deep water and tried to swim away from it! Zaborowski has worked with doll-size anthropomorphic dummies and, without abandoning the Bopper, has conducted water experiments on the Holloman Daisy Track, which is capable of much higher performance. These activities have not yet offered a major contribution to basic research, but they have made a definite contribution to test methodology.[17]

Experiments in the use of water for protection against *g*-forces have been conducted in Europe. The German water-lined anti-*g* suit has already been mentioned. The Russians (who managed to find a reference to the principle of water protection in the works of their pioneer space theorist Tsiolkovsky) have reported an experiment in which a frog immersed in liquid was subjected to 1,000 *g*.[18] Little detailed information is available, however, about the Soviet studies along these lines.

Europe's foremost authority on *g*-forces and water immersion is Rodolfo Margaria of the Laboratorie di Fisiologia at Milan University. Margaria proposed the use of water protection at least as far back as 1953. With his Italian colleagues, he has carried out experiments on a variety of test subjects. Small fish (*Gambusia Hoolbrocki*) and frogs were exposed in water on a centrifuge to as much as 3,000 *g* for ten minutes. Most survived but suffered injury to the otolith organs, which help to provide balance and orientation.* As a result,

* The role of the otoliths will be discussed more fully in Chapter 8 in connection with the problem of weightlessness.

the fish could not pick up the food in their tank and eventually starved to death. The frogs did better, apparently learning to compensate for the otolith damage by relying more fully on their eyes for orientation.

Margaria carried out other tests with rats, not on a centrifuge but by dropping them in a special container from a height sufficient to produce a desired multi-*g* impact. Without water in the container, lethal injuries began at about 100 *g*; in shallow water rats could survive ten times as much force, but increasing the depth of the water was bad for the rats, because it also increased the weight that pressed upon them. The rats experienced no injury to their otolith apparatus, apparently because the exposure in this case was so brief, but they did suffer pulmonary injury with increasing *g*-force.

Margaria's rat tests provide an unusually good illustration of one limitation of the fluid-immersion technique which was evident in other experiments, but seldom in such clear-cut form. This is that protection is effective only to the extent that the organs and tissues of the body have roughly the same density as the fluid used for immersion. Even if the fluid has the same density as the body as a whole—and water almost meets this requirement—a particular internal organ may be displaced during acceleration because its density differs from that of surrounding tissues. Usually the difference is not great enough to matter, but Margaria observed in his rat experiments that the air in the air-filled lungs tended to be forced upward by a high-*g* impact, so that the lungs were severely damaged. He emphasized the point with another experiment in which unborn rats, having no air yet in their lungs, survived an impact of 10,000 *g* while their mother (which had been about ready to deliver) was killed immediately despite the benefit of water immersion.[19]

Nor is it only the lungs that are vulnerable. The experimenters at Wright Field emphasized that the heart and mediastinum are, basically, "immersed in the air-filled lungs and never in water," so that fluid protection cannot annul "the forces acting on them during acceleration."[20] There seemed to be a definite connection between the chest pains reported by subjects in the Wright Field water-filled "coffin" and the fact that the heart is exposed to pressure both from acceleration and from the weight of water (multiplied by several *g*) resting on the chest.[21]

Despite these and other limitations, water immersion clearly does help, even though it must be emphasized that a great amount of research on this technique is still necessary and that it may pose complications from the standpoint of vehicle design and weight. Numerous potential applications of the fluid-immersion principle have been suggested. Margaria noted one very interesting possibility when he suggested that an individual in a water-filled capsule "presumably" might make a landing on the earth without the aid of a parachute. He called to mind, in this connection, that one theoretical *g*-pattern for achieving orbital velocity is 1,000 *g* lasting for approximately four-fifths of a second. Margaria seemed to imply that even a force of this order of magnitude might be endured with fluid protection (by unborn rats, especially!)[22]

The Wright Field experts also have given thought to the possible uses of water in space flight. They have pointed out that on a short trip—for instance, a few orbits around the earth—a space flier might well remain submerged to eye level; he would have vision unimpaired to watch the dials, while his hands could manipulate controls easily under water.[23] An ingenious variation, suitable for longer trips, was suggested by Hugh R. Wahlin, design engineer for the Aerojet-General Corporation, who proposed

> . . . putting crew members in suitable protective clothing and immersing them in [the] fuel tank of spacecraft. When fuel is exhausted, tank can be turned into pressurized cabin simply by venting it to vacuum to get rid of remaining fuel vapor and repressurizing with air.[24]

This suggestion would neatly solve the weight problem posed by the addition of water, because the rocket fuel itself would serve as the protective fluid. But it would work only with liquid-fuel rocket engines and on the outward journey.

There have, of course, been many other concrete proposals, serious and otherwise, for adapting fluid protection to the needs of manned space travel. Significantly, the Aerospace Medical Laboratory recently expressed interest in a possible revival and improvement of the water-lined suit, specifically for purposes of space flight.[25]

A writer in the English magazine *Aeronautics* shrewdly observed that something like Wahlin's rocket-fuel solution would do away with the need for a fuel gauge: the space pilot could simply look around to see how much fuel he was standing in. Referring to the slightly more conventional notion of immersing space travelers in water to eye level, the same Englishman commented on the "fascinating sight" of "serried rows of eyeballs, 12 abreast, down the long sweep of the cabin," not to mention stewardesses with "the stamina of Olympic swimmers, crawling the length of the gangway in fulfillment of their duties."[26]

Obviously the water-protection idea has its skeptics. And the scientists who have studied human tolerance both in and out of water have generally been careful to emphasize that, according to the available test results, selected astronauts could safely withstand the expected forces of takeoff and re-entry without the help of water.[27] Fluid protection is, however, worth investigating further, both to gain a fuller understanding of its physiological effects and to determine how it could best be applied operationally. It is something to fall back on when and if needed—perhaps to increase rocket-engine efficiency by permitting the use of a sharper takeoff acceleration than could be safely tolerated with ordinary means of protection, or to meet some eventual requirement for exposure to prolonged high *g*. But it is not likely to be used on the first space trips.

THE RIGID ENVELOPE

Among various other unconventional forms of protection that have received scientific attention is one which encloses the individual in a "rigid envelope," rather than water. An example of this technique was mentioned in the preceding chapter: namely, the cats that were put in a plaster cast. In these experiments, at the School of Aviation Medicine at Randolph Field, the cats dropped 19.25 feet in a cart sliding down the rails of a "deceleration tower," and at impact they experienced peak decelerative forces as high as 1,045 *g*. Many survived, thanks to the plaster of Paris cast in which they were embedded. The experimenters had put them in casts to control their body position rigorously.

In a study published more than ten years later, in 1958, James Roman of the Aerospace Medical Laboratory at Wright Field pointed out that the cast, acting as a "rigid envelope," afforded protection by preventing internal displacement of tissues, as fluid immersion does.[28] Roman reported some studies of his own, expressly testing the plaster-cast technique as a means of protection against whole-body vibration in various situations, including space flight.* He assumed that a technique which prevented injury from vibration should be about equally effective against injury from impact force. He found that a mouse in a plaster cast suffered no sign of damage even after three hours of severe vibration on an electrodynamic shake platform. Tests with human subjects, in a 35-pound cast which covered all the body except the arms, legs, and face, showed that this was also remarkably effective in preventing pains from vibration which they suffered when they wore only strap-type restraints.

No one has proposed covering the entire body with plaster of Paris (as some enthusiasts for fluid submersion have proposed to do with water), but Roman believes that rigid-envelope protection is a practical possibility for at least some parts of the body. He has also observed that it could be used in combination with partial fluid immersion. Another possibility is a semi-rigid envelope—a "close fitting inelastic garment designed to keep different body segments at constant volume" (for instance, a modified partial-pressure suit). Roman tested the semi-rigid technique, using devices such as a miniature partial-pressure suit for rabbits in impact tests and a special harness simulating a "flexible envelope" in human vibration experiments. These devices gave a significant degree of protection.[29]

"MULTI-DIRECTIONAL" POSITIONING

A rather different approach involves automatically positioning the body so that it always receives the *g*-forces in the most favorable orientation. A space traveler will normally want to take his *g*'s transversely rather than parallel to the spine (headward or footward); this is true no matter what additional protection may be used. And as long as the direction of acceleration or deceleration remains more or less regular and predictable, proper positioning can be achieved without too great difficulty. If, however, the flight trajectory becomes

* J. C. Guignard of the Royal Air Force Institute of Aviation Medicine, Farnborough, has pointed out that even during coasting flight a space vehicle may have a vibration problem in its auxiliary equipment, "transferring vibratory energy to a structure which, in free fall and *in vacuo,* is devoid of external damping." This might "impair human comfort and efficiency" even if it did not cause biological injury. (Paper presented to Space Medicine Symposium of the British Interplanetary Society, October 1958).

irregular or uneven—as may happen especially during re-entry or in some emergency situation—the problem is more complex. Exposure to transverse *g* may then be combined with appreciable and rapidly varying components of positive and negative *g*, as the vehicle moves on an erratic course. Just how serious a danger this is remains to be seen, but a possible solution has been proposed by Harald J. von Beckh, an Austrian-born scientist who in January 1958 joined the Aeromedical Field Laboratory at Holloman.

Dr. von Beckh's proposal, on which he was working even before he came to Holloman, is rather grandly entitled "multi-directional *g*-protection." It takes the form of a special compartment ("anti-*g* capsule") which turns automatically and, if necessary, continuously during flight so that the net resultant of *g*-force is always applied transversely to the occupant. Von Beckh first proposed this system for use in atmospheric flight, including the development of an enclosed device for escape from aircraft. It calls to mind the experimental aircraft seats, sometimes referred to as "barber chairs," designed to lower a pilot into a semi-supine position whenever a certain level of headward acceleration is reached. But von Beckh's system is based on a much more sophisticated design concept, and it is also applicable for use in manned space vehicles or animal-carrying research rockets.[30]

Von Beckh tested the basic features of his idea in animal experiments soon after his arrival at Holloman. Early in 1958, in collaboration with Grover J. D. Schock, he exposed mice to high *g*-forces on two small materiel centrifuges. They were positioned in swings which successfully ensured that all forces "acted transversely to the spines of the test animals." The mice, although dizzy from spinning at the end of the run, were otherwise unharmed by exposures up to 400 *g* for almost 15 seconds. Von Beckh also tested rats on a swinging anti-*g* platform, at somewhat lower *g*-levels, on Holloman's Daisy Track. Regardless of its starting position, the platform turned automatically in such a way that longitudinal *g*-forces were kept to insignificant values during the run.

The most famous Daisy Track test in which Von Beckh's rats participated was the record run on May 16, 1958, when Eli L. Beeding took a deceleration of 83 *g* (see the preceding chapter). Two rats were fellow passengers with Beeding—one on an anti-*g* platform, the other fastened head-first on the sled. The latter (the "control" rat) had a bad time, despite the generally higher *g*-tolerance enjoyed by rodents, but its specially mounted companion emerged unscathed.[31]

A rat on an anti-*g* platform even traveled the Holloman long track, on no less an occasion than the official dedication of the rebuilt, 35,000-foot facility on February 25, 1959. Before a crowd of 1,000 persons, including New Mexico's senior Senator Dennis Chavez and other dignitaries, the protected rat took a 1,050-mile-per-hour ride and about 10 *g* without suffering any ill effects. On the same ride a "control rat" which lacked the benefit of "multi-directional *g*-protection" and which to make matters worse, rode lengthwise on the sled, was slightly the worse for wear.[32]

These experiments, using an incomplete version of Von Beckh's anti-*g* device, were conducted only to demonstrate the principle involved. Later a capsule of the type he proposed was tested in actual rocket-flight experiments with animal subjects. Von Beckh had observed that his system was well suited for such tests, not only because for animal experiments a simplified form of capsule would suffice but also because "during the re-entry phase, during ejection from the nose cone and especially during uncontrolled parts of the trajectory, which might be caused by imperfections of the automatic guidance system, the subject would be exposed to severe accelerations with continuously varying direction, intensity, and rate of onset."[33] He further pointed out that in a spin-stabilized nose cone the subject could be positioned to take the resultant of the centrifugal acceleration from spinning and the linear *g*-forces arising from the trajectory as a single transverse acceleration.[34]

In any case, during 1958 scientists of Space Technology Laboratories, firing Thor-Able missiles from Cape Canaveral, sent three ill-fated mice aloft in swiveling animal containers patterned at least in part on von Beckh's concept of an anti-*g* capsule. Alas, all the mice were lost at sea, so that it was impossible to get a complete account of how well the system functioned. But two of the mice were instrumented, and data radioed back from the missiles in flight indicate that the animals apparently stood up well under the launching stress and also under the later deceleration, exceeding 60 *g*, as they re-entered the atmosphere.[35]

Like fluid immersion and rigid-envelope protection, multi-directional *g*-protection is only an idea under trial, and no one can say definitely how valuable it might be in manned space travel. It may well be used some day in one form or another, presumably in combination with other protective equipment.

"ANTIGRAVITY"

Finally, perhaps we ought to make some brief mention of the most radical approach of all: the search for "antigravity," or just doing away with gravitational attraction altogether. If the secret of the nature of gravity were solved by science, and if the gravitational force could be overcome at will, space travel would be immeasurably simplified. A takeoff for Mars would be essentially no different, technologically or physiologically, from taking off for any point on earth.

"Antigravity" magic, in forms such as a gravity-resisting material for the hull of a spacecraft, has been a favorite theme of the more fantastic science-fiction writers. An early reference appeared in the book *Voyage to the Moon,* published in 1827 by Professor George Tucker of the University of Virginia under the pen name of J. Atterley. He described a metal having a natural tendency to fly away from the earth; just one of the troubles with this idea is that if you really had such a substance for your space vehicle, you would need as much energy to *return* to earth as normally it would take to get away![36]

Not only fiction-writers but also some pseudo-scientists have dabbled in antigravity. An interesting example is the work of the Gravity Research Foundation at New Boston, N.H., founded by the stock market analyst Roger Babson. The Foundation has sought, among other things, to discover an "insulator" against gravity.[37]

To be sure, there are serious studies of the phenomenon of gravitation from the standpoint of pure research. Gravity is worth considering for its own sake, and if we ever understand its operation, just conceivably some useful applications of our knowledge may result. Among the institutions that have conducted or encouraged such studies over the past few years are the University of Detroit, various aviation companies, the Institute of Aeronautical Sciences, and the United States Air Force. There is also considerable interest in these matters in the Soviet Union, as shown by garbled references to United States efforts in *Komsomolskaya Pravda,* the Communist youth organ, and by reports that a member of the Soviet Academy of Sciences predicted that an important breakthrough in gravity research was just around the corner.[38]

It must be added that even if all the secrets of gravity were unlocked, building a spaceship immune to gravity's pull would be something else again—something which most scientists are prepared to label in advance as intrinsically implausible. What is not at all impossible is to counterbalance the ever-present pull of gravity by opposite forces of inertia, thereby realizing effective weightlessness even within a gravity field. Indeed, this promises to be a routine condition of both orbital and interplanetary flight.

8

The Problem of Weightlessness

RESEARCH on the problem of weightlessness is space physiology in one of its purest forms: it has no substantial roots in aviation medicine or in any other specialty preceding the space age. To be sure, weightlessness itself is not a completely strange phenomenon: brief exposures to it can and do arise in fairly normal circumstances—for instance, in a dive off a diving board, or in a plane suddenly caught in a downdraft. Weightlessness attracted some attention in aviation medicine as far back as the first World War; one French text published in 1918 observed that it produced insecure control movements in fliers who encountered it in dives or other maneuvers.[1] But most exposures to weightlessness in conventional atmospheric flight are extremely brief and relatively unimportant. Weightlessness never became a subject of comprehensive study in its own right until after World War II, when its significance for the coming space age was realized.

According to an old misconception which used to be put forward in works of space fantasy and still turns up at times in surprising places, the phenomenon of weightlessness will occur in space travel because the space vehicle will get entirely away from the earth's gravity. In reality, of course, this is impossible. The earth's gravitational pull weakens steadily with increasing distance, but it never vanishes entirely. In vastly attenuated form it reaches all the way to Mars, which has a gravitational pull of its own. And both the earth and Mars, as well as anything traveling between them, are in the gravitational field of the sun. Indeed, one cannot really "get away from" gravity anywhere. As Sir Isaac Newton pointed out, every particle of matter in the universe attracts every other particle.

In everyday usage, a body's weight is conventionally defined as *m* (mass) times *g* (the gravitational pull of the earth). But complications enter the picture when a body undergoes a change in velocity. As noted in connection with problems of acceleration and deceleration, an increase in velocity will tend to increase the body's weight, and a sudden stop or decrease in velocity will have a similar effect. Moreover, a body on the earth or in the earth's atmosphere is normally subject to external supports, such as the floor underneath one's feet or the aerodynamic lift that permits an airplane to fly. The role of these external supports is particularly important in understanding the phenomenon of weightlessness. Whenever a body is suddenly deprived of all support and begins to fall freely, it is for all practical purposes weightless. It is subject to the downward pull of gravity, amounting to an acceleration of one *g*, and to a counterbalancing force of inertia, which in this case also amounts to one *g*. One minus one is zero; thus zero-*g*, or the weightless state, has been attained.[2]

The problem of human weightlessness has really existed since the first time a prehistoric man fell out of a tree. If it was a rather low tree and if the subject's fall was unchecked by branches, he was essentially weightless all the way down. Strictly speaking, of course, friction with the surrounding air, or air drag, would give him some degree of support, so that he was not 100 per cent weightless. Ultimately the air drag on an object falling through the atmosphere may actually restore its original weight, although this would never happen in falling from a tree or off a diving board. The example of a diving aircraft is more complex, but a plane can approximate free-fall weightlessness for several seconds, if its motor provides the exact amount of propulsion needed to balance the air friction.

It is the absence of aerodynamic drag in space, or of any kind of external support or force save Newtonian universal attraction, that will make weightlessness the normal condition in space flight. A space vehicle and its inhabitants can be expected to have weight only while the engine is accelerating (or during later deceleration). Once the engine is turned off and the vehicle merely coasts—which will be most of the time, for fuel economy if for no other reason—the inertial effects of the vehicle's motion will just cancel the gravitational pull of the earth and other heavenly bodies. The spaceship, together with every person and thing inside it, will then be weightless, as in an unhindered free fall.

POSSIBLE EFFECTS

Much early speculation on the problem of weightlessness centered on the possibility of a falling sensation leading to "space sickness," so named by analogy to seasickness (or airsickness). Actually seasickness is associated with lurching, rolling, uneven motion, whereas the motion of a rocket ship coasting through space will be just the opposite. But weightlessness does affect the human balance and orientation mechanisms.

Whether at sea, in the air, or in space, the body obtains information on its position, direction, and external support from the eyes and from four key mechanoreceptors:

(1) the pressure or tactile sense of the skin;
(2) the muscle spindles, which are nerve endings sensitive to changes in muscle tension;
(3) the posture sense, which is attributed to the so-called Vater-Pacini corpuscles;
(4) the vestibular or labyrinthine function of the inner ear.[3]

The pressure sense records the support given by the floor to the soles of the feet in a normal gravity field; in flying it provides the "seat-of-the-pants" sensation, whereby changes in pressure between the pilot's skin and the aircraft seat give information on accelerative forces. Its importance was emphasized by a famous 1928 experiment of Hubertus Strughold, who anesthetized his buttocks before going up in a small airplane and found the effect in the air rather unpleasant, even disorienting: "I often had the feeling that the aircraft had slipped away under my body. . . ."[4]

The muscle spindles also respond to gravity and other accelerative forces, because the tension they record is affected by the amount of resistance that the muscles have to overcome. The posture sense is less well understood. It seems to operate through the Vater-Pacini corpuscles in the subcutaneous tissues of the hands and feet and also near the joints and tendons. Apparently these corpuscles are stimulated when the muscles change form in movement, and so can give information on the relative position of the limbs independent of outside forces.[5]

The most important of the mechanoreceptors is the vestibular function, which involves two groups of balance organs: (1) small semicircular canals which are responsive to angular acceleration, and (2) the otoliths. The otoliths are tiny particles, literally "ear stones," supported on sensitive hairs by a jelly-like substance. They are responsive to the linear accelerations and decelerations imparted by velocity change and by gravity. The importance of the vestibular apparatus in flying has long been realized; during World War I it was sometimes looked upon as *the* organ of equilibration, and sensitive vestibular reactions were thought essential for a pilot. Yet in certain circumstances such reactions can be a handicap. In the late nineteenth century, scientists established a relation between seasickness and the inner ear; they observed that deaf-mutes, with damaged vestibular function, were almost never seasick.[6] By the same token, deaf-mutes might well prove at least partly immune to "space sickness."

During exposure to weightlessness the vestibular apparatus and the other organs of balance and orientation may easily produce misleading or disturbing sensations. These problems were analyzed in some detail for the first time in the years just after World War II by aeromedical scientists in Europe and the United States. Systematic discussion began even before any significant amount of experimentation had been performed on human or animal responses to weightlessness, and on the basis of general physiological and psychological knowledge, scientists compiled a long list of difficulties that *might* arise. Otto Gauer and Heinz Haber, in their contribution to the United States Air Force's massive and to some extent misnamed study, *German Aviation Medicine, World War II* (1950), even raised the possibility of an "absolute incapacity to act" resulting from weightlessness. They also speculated that small stimuli such as the accelerations imparted by personal movements—which normally might lie beneath the threshold of perception—could well produce disproportionate sensations, in accord with the Weber-Fechner law that response is proportional not to the stimulus itself but to the relative amount of change (as when the dark-adapted eye is dazed by sudden exposure to ordinary light).[7] Siegfried J. Gerathewohl, another German scientist who after the war went to the United States Air Force School of Aviation Medicine at Randolph Field, wrote a little later that the impact of zero-gravity might be "befuddlement and uneasiness, if not . . . actual terror."[8]

Such statements were admittedly speculative, and everyone hoped that the worst would not materialize. Nevertheless, it appeared likely that during weightlessness the impressions received from visual perception and from the mechanoreceptors would often be startlingly different from what a human being is accustomed to, and furthermore that these impressions would sometimes be in apparent conflict with one another. The eye might well perceive objects (even persons) to be hovering in mid-air or upside down. The pressure sense of the skin would be stimulated by impact with other objects but would not record any support given by the floor to the soles of the feet—assuming that the feet were actually on the floor and not hovering in mid-air—much less any "seat-of-the-pants" sensation. An article of 1951, written by Dr. Gerathewohl and Heinz Haber, while the latter was working at Randolph Field, suggested that to move across the cabin a space traveler would have to push off against one wall and brake himself with his hands when he reached the other, and that at this point the stimulation to the pressure sense and other mechanoreceptors would be about the same as if he were doing a handstand on the wall.[9]

Muscle sensations would still be activated by voluntary movements, such as wall handstands, but not by gravity. The normal feeling of tension in the leg muscles when standing would be absent; even for voluntary movements, the muscle force required and the muscle sensations felt would not be the same as when the limbs are subject to a constant gravitational pull. The posture sense, on the other hand, would presumably be little affected by the absence of gravity. And for this reason, Gerathewohl and Haber predicted that weightlessness would "produce a dissociation of the normally concerting sensations of the muscle sense and the posture sense."[10]

Perhaps the greatest amount of speculation focused on the operation of the vestibular apparatus. It was generally accepted that during the weightless state the semicircular canals, responsive to angular acceleration, should function more or less normally, but the otoliths were a different matter. They would continue to record linear accelerations and decelerations arising from voluntary movement—especially if, as Gauer and Haber suggested, the gravity-receptive organs developed a heightened sensitivity after exposure to weightlessness. But it was far from clear how the otoliths would react in the absence of gravity or any other linear acceleration. Louis Gougerot of France predicted in 1946 that the result would be "a sort of very abnormal excitation, because of the absence of customary impressions."[11] Treating the question in more detail, the English scientist A. E. Slater suggested in an analysis published in 1950, and slightly revised two years later, that the otoliths might (1) transmit no signals at all to the brain; (2) send impulses at a constant minimum or "basic" rate; or (3) send impulses at a special "frequency which is characteristic of weightlessness." In the first of these possibilities, there would be no question of disagreeable or misleading sensations: there would be no sensations at all from the otoliths. If they sent forth a constant "basic" signal, Slater pointed out that a rather weird condition might arise: Since the otoliths are arranged in different planes, if *all* sent the same signal simultaneously they might inform the brain that the head was upright and also lying on both sides! This was a very ingenious argument, but Slater went on to suggest that the most likely possibility was that the otoliths would convey no signals at all.[12]

Besides the possibility of confusing sense impressions, weightlessness appeared to pose problems in coordination. Obviously when one raised his arms he would tend to overreach in the absence of gravity, until he learned to compensate for the new condition. And he would have to push his limbs down as well as up, since he could no longer let them merely drop with the aid of gravity. Gauer and Haber pointed out that in the gravity-free state one could turn a hand crank only if shackled or held down in some way, for otherwise the muscular effort exerted would cause rotation of the body around the axis of the crank; any movement in the extremities would produce a counter-movement of the body.[13]

These and similar difficulties in muscular activity could be predicted with a fair degree of certainty on the basis of known physiological and mechanical principles. No one doubted that they could be overcome by a combination of cabin engineering, common sense, and gradual adaptation. But there were other problems to be solved. A whimsical British writer of letters-to-the-editor discussed the jet effect of breathing in a spaceship. He reasoned that exhaling would have a stronger effect than inhaling on the ground that waste products would make the mass of air exhaled greater than that inhaled. Thus a sleeping space traveler, he concluded, would "slide gently to and fro, powered by his twin orifice pulse jet, with suction intake air, and efflux mass flow increased by fuel injection and heating, until rudely awakened by his head striking some part of the cabin."[14] The solution to this problem, obviously, is to tie the sleeper firmly into bed, which would be necessary in any case just to keep him from floating off at any random twist or movement. For that matter, the bed and all other items of furniture would have to be securely bolted to the floor—or to the "walls" or "ceiling," for there would really be no difference unless they were painted contrasting colors just to tell them apart.

The discussion of breathing suggests a further problem—the need for fans to keep the air in motion so that exhaled air will not remain suspended in front of one's nose. Normally it rises, because it is warmer and therefore lighter than the air around it, but in a gravity-free state all air would be equally weightless.[15] Dust poses another minor problem, because it would remain suspended in the air in the absence of any gravitational force to pull it floorward.[16]

A later chapter will discuss certain long-term disabilities which may develop gradually from exposure to weightlessness. A great many complications, both short-term and long-term, can be imagined, although some authors have minimized the importance of even the most ingenious complications that they themselves have thought up. A case in point is Slater's discussion of the otoliths, in which he observed that, if they did send mutually contradictory signals to the brain, the effect would probably be no worse than the sensory confusion often faced by a pilot flying blind within the atmosphere. Slater also dismissed most of the other predictions of serious difficulties.[17] Indeed, one can imagine various potential *advantages* of weightlessness. As far back as 1638, the moon-traveling hero in Francis Godwin's *Man in the Moone* found that hunger, thirst, and fatigue were all left behind in making the transition from gravity to weightlessness.[18] In practice, hunger and thirst may not be quite so easy to overcome even in space flight, but certainly escape from the pull of gravity will bring a great reduction in the required expenditure of human effort.

PROPOSED COUNTERMEASURES

The possible complications of weightlessness have been great enough for many scientists and writers on space travel to consider artificial means of simulating the familiar effects of the earth's gravitational pull. Their suggestions include the use of shoes with suction cups, metallic-cloth spacesuits with electromagnetic seats, and other devices along the same line, some of which have actually been tested.[19] A more radical solution, which is notably simple in its conception but would be less so in execution, is to endow space travelers with weight by a slight, constant acceleration by means of the rocket engines. This possibility was considered by such pioneer modern theorists of space flight as Robert Esnault-Pelterie, co-founder of the Société Française d'Astronautique, who regarded it as something to be tried only if weightlessness should prove intolerable.[20] The idea has its recent advocates, including H.F. Michielsen of the Lockheed Aircraft Corporation, who suggests that a constant low acceleration not only would eliminate the physiological problem of weightlessness, but might also permit the use of lighter structure in space vehicles.[21] Still, sustained acceleration would pose difficulties with regard to the fuel load. And constant acceleration is out of the question for a vehicle that has to stay in orbit—e.g., a space station or satellite.

Another alternative would be to rotate the ship: the centrifugal force thus generated would endow both people and things with weight to hold them in place. This idea, too, can be traced back to some of the pioneer modern theorists, including Tsiolkovsky.[22] The proposed British Interplanetary Society Lunar Space-Ship of the late 1930's was designed for rotation, on the ground that the physiological effects of prolonged weightlessness were unknown and it was best to play safe.[23] Two English enthusiasts, H.E. Ross and R.A. Smith, in 1948 described a design for a man-carrying rocket (somewhat similar to the German V-2) which called for rotation, but with special controls so that the rotation of the cabin could be annulled for experiments in weightlessness.[24] And when Wernher von Braun made his classic proposal for an orbital space station—a wheel 250 feet across, rotating around its axis—he had a built-in centrifugal force amounting to one-third *g*.[25]

Apart from engineering difficulties, this last approach offers complications with regard to human factors. As listed by the Dutch aeromedical scientist M.P. Lansberg,[26] they include possible vestibular disturbances, repeated changes in weight as one walks with or against the direction of rotation, and the fact that objects dropped, fluids poured, or limbs moved would be deflected slightly to one side.* All these and several other effects of rotation might well be annoying to crew members, in some cases even disorienting, although they could generally be made less appreciable by lengthening the radius of rotation. Von Braun sought to accomplish this by putting the crew at the rim of his wheel; another suggestion, going back at least to Tsiolkovsky, is to split the space vehicle at a given moment into two parts, connected by a long cable, and start them rotating about their common center of gravity.[27]

As suggested by Von Braun's proposal, the rotation would not have to give space travelers the same weight they have on earth: a fraction of one *g* would suffice. For trips to the Moon or to Mars it would be better *not* to have one *g* all the way, so that crew members might begin accustoming themselves to the weaker gravitational field at their destination.[28] Actually there is still no firm information as to how much *g* is desirable on a space flight or the best means of obtaining it. It has not even been established that any *g* is absolutely necessary. Such questions can be answered with confidence only on the basis of more and more experimental data. Scientists have, therefore, been seeking the answers through a growing number of subgravity† research programs.

* The earth's rotation also produces this last effect. The top of a high building moves faster in the direction of the rotation than does the ground below; a dropped object, preserving its forward speed as it falls, will tend to land not directly beneath the point where it started but slightly east. However, because of the size of the earth such effects normally are not noticeable.

† The terms subgravity and zero-gravity are often used loosely. "Subgravity" means something less than one *g*. But should it include zero-gravity, as the extreme case of subgravity, or should zero-gravity and subgravity be regarded as mutually exclusive terms—complete weightlessness being contrasted with any *g*, however small? Current usage is not always clear on this

Apparently the first man to expose test subjects to subgravity conditions for scientific research was the German scientist Heinz von Diringshofen, a pioneer in aeromedical research on acceleration forces. Just before and during the second World War, while exposing subjects to multi-*g* acceleration, von Diringshofen put some of them through about eight seconds of subgravity, attained by means of vertical dives. The experiments were too brief to produce much information; he made them almost as a matter of curiosity. Nonetheless, von Diringshofen seems to have the best claim to being called the originator of this type of human experiment.[29]

A less clear-cut German precedent in subgravity research was set by Hubertus Strughold in the experiment mentioned earlier in this chapter, in which he anesthetized his buttocks before going up in a plane. He was not primarily interested in investigating weightlessness, but in effect he simulated the weightless condition as far as the pressure sense of the skin is concerned.

The work of von Diringshofen and Strughold did not lead to any concerted or continuing program of subgravity research in Germany. German scientists did contribute some valuable theoretical studies shortly after the war, as did scientists in other European countries. But the first major landmark in research on weightlessness was a series of rocket experiments with animal subjects conducted by United States Air Force investigators in 1948-1952. These and other rocket-borne animal experiments will be reviewed in the following chapter.

question of terminology. Moreover, many of the experiments on "weightlessness" have been conducted not strictly at zero-gravity but at some very small fraction of one *g*. So for convenience in dealing with the tests, we shall include in the term subgravity all small values of *g* down to and including zero-*g* (except where otherwise specified).

PLATE I—Launching of a Thor-Able rocket. This rocket has played an important role in biological experiments. The capsule in the nose is similar to the one used to carry a mouse to the highest altitude ever attained by a living creature.

PLATE II—The first primate successfully recovered after a rocket flight. This monkey was shot into the upper atmosphere in an Air Force Aerobee rocket in 1951.

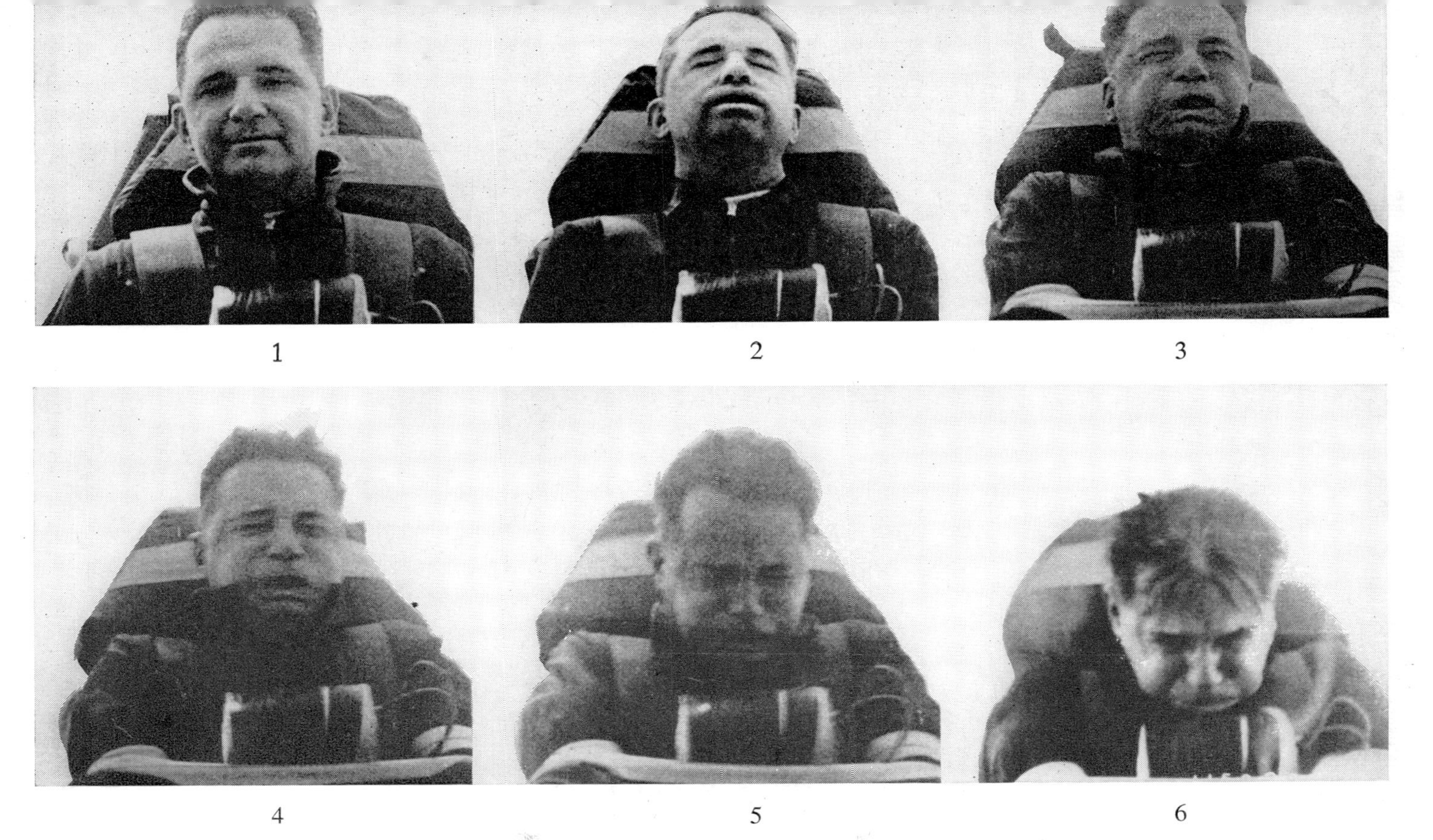

PLATE III—Reactions of John Paul Stapp to his first ride on the Holloman high-speed sled. The first four pictures show him during acceleration. In deceleration (5 and 6) a peak of 22 *g* was applied transversely.

Plate IV—Record ride of Eli L. Beeding on the Holloman Daisy-track sled. He rode backwards to minimize the effects of an 83-*g* deceleration force. The braking mechanism that stopped the sled consisted of a cylinder entering a water chamber, part of which can be seen at the extreme left.

PLATE V—John Paul Stapp during his record sled ride of December 10, 1954. At the instant this photograph was taken, the sled was moving at 632 miles per hour —faster than the jet plane flying overhead.

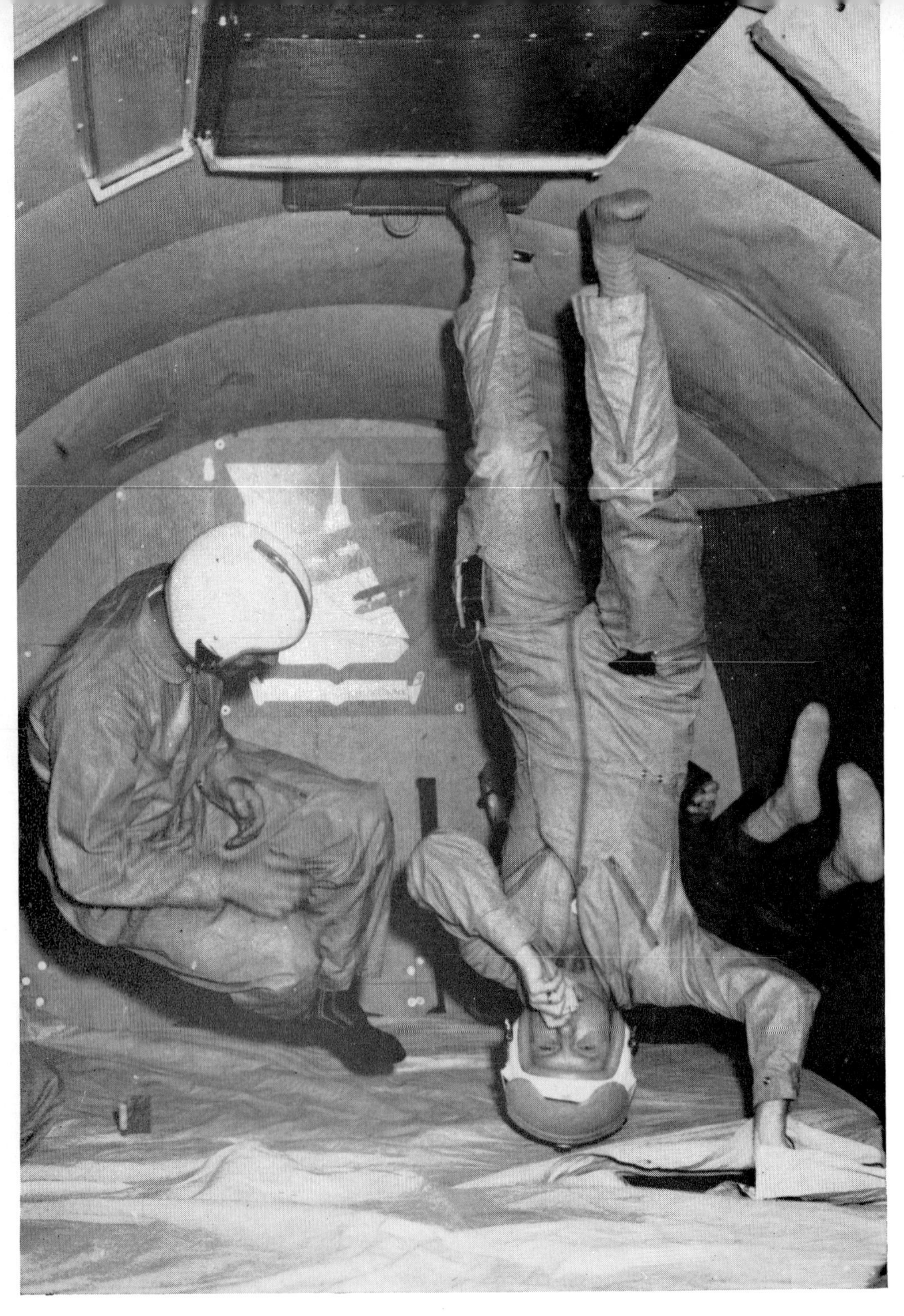

PLATE VI—Air Force experimenters experience weightlessness induced by parabolic flight in a specially modified C-131 transport.

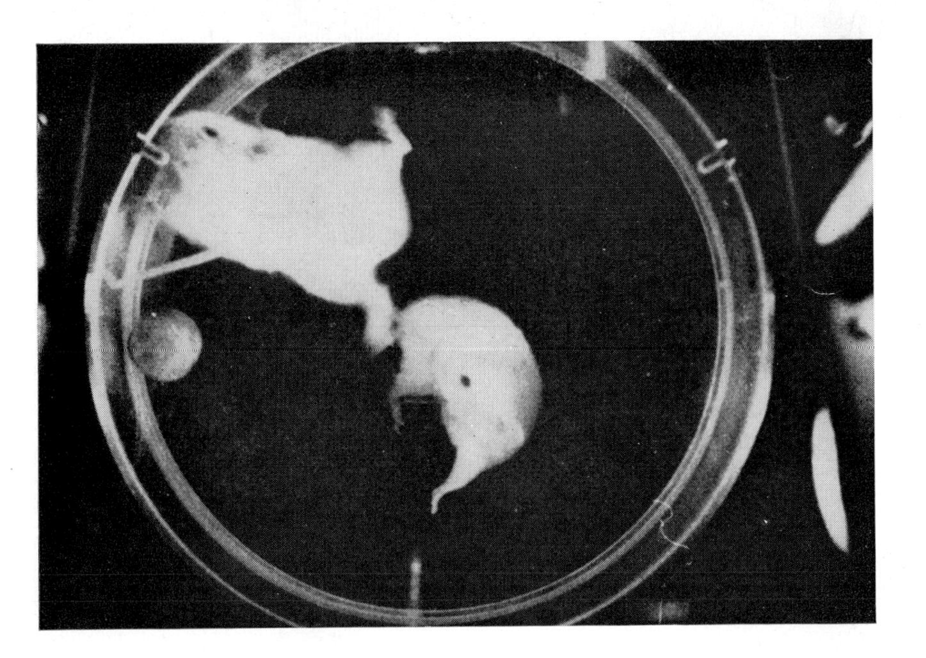

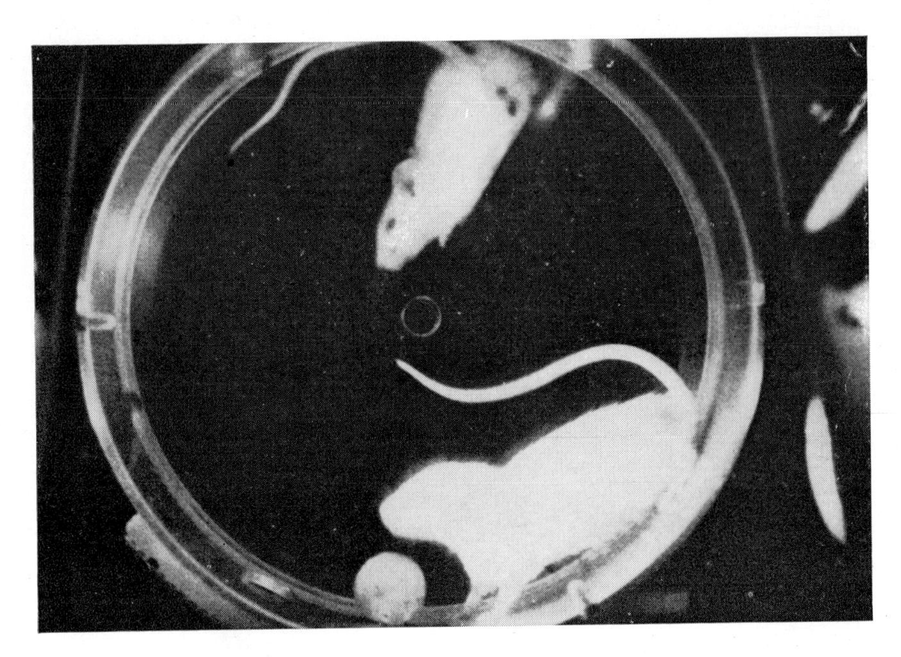

PLATE VII—An early weightlessness study. At top, mice experience weightlessness induced by rocket flight; the mouse floating in the middle shows obvious signs of disorientation, while the other mouse, having a paddle to cling to, remains quiet and relatively oriented. Bottom photo shows the mice after normal conditions have been restored.

PLATE VIII—This balloon, seen as it was launched from a mine pit on August 19, 1957, reached 102,000 feet, setting a new record for manned balloons. Its passenger was David G. Simons.

PLATE IX—David G. Simons, seated in the capsule in which he made his record ascent. Part of the complex equipment is shown.

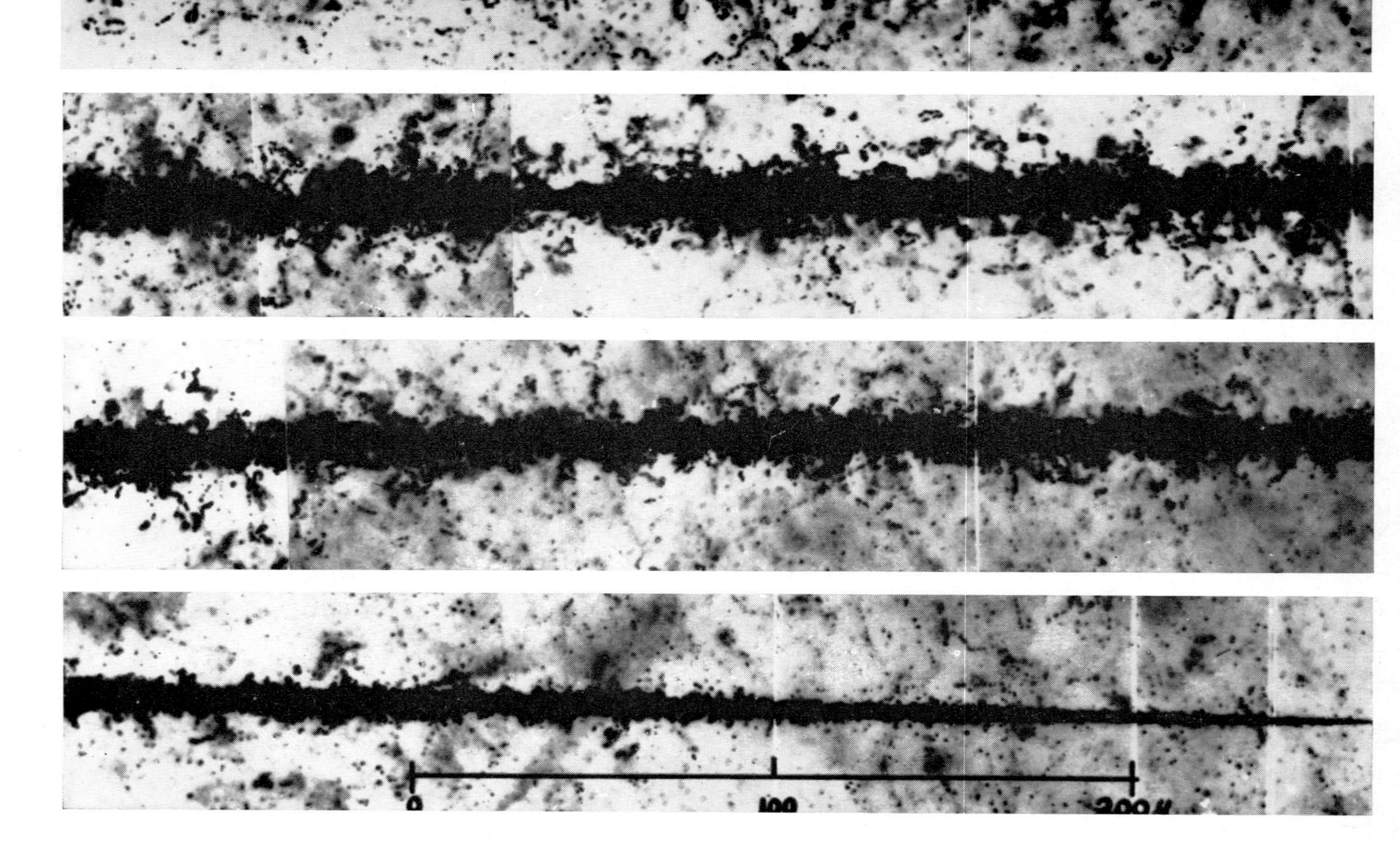

PLATE X—A cosmic-ray particle thindown. The track is to be read from left to right and top to bottom. The emulsion track illustrates the gradual expenditure of energy in ordinary ionization, shown by the tapering off of the track.

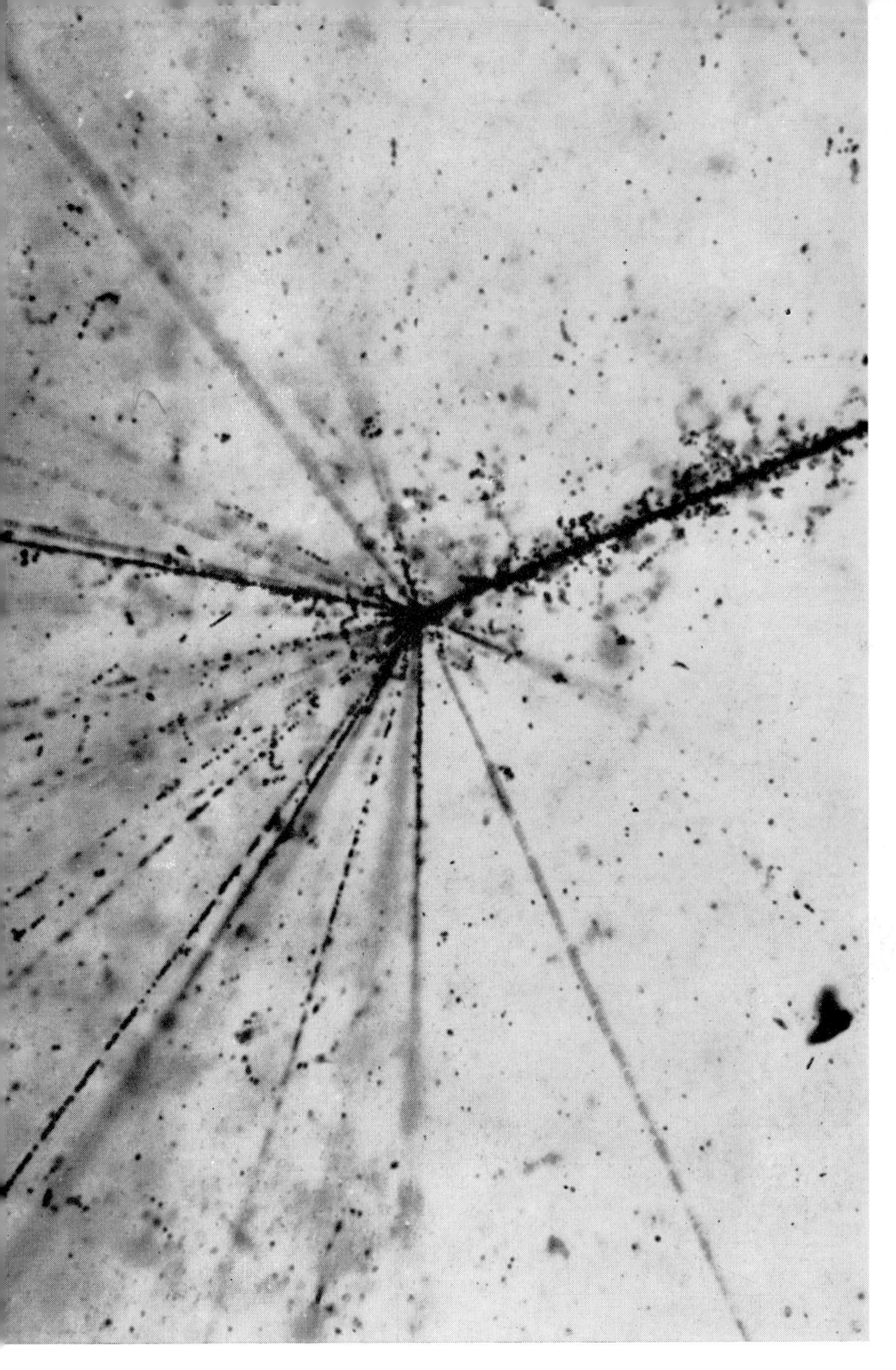

PLATE XI—A star in a nuclear emulsion, produced by the collision of a cosmic-ray particle with another atomic nucleus. Secondary particles, which are fragments from the collision, can be seen streaming in all directions.

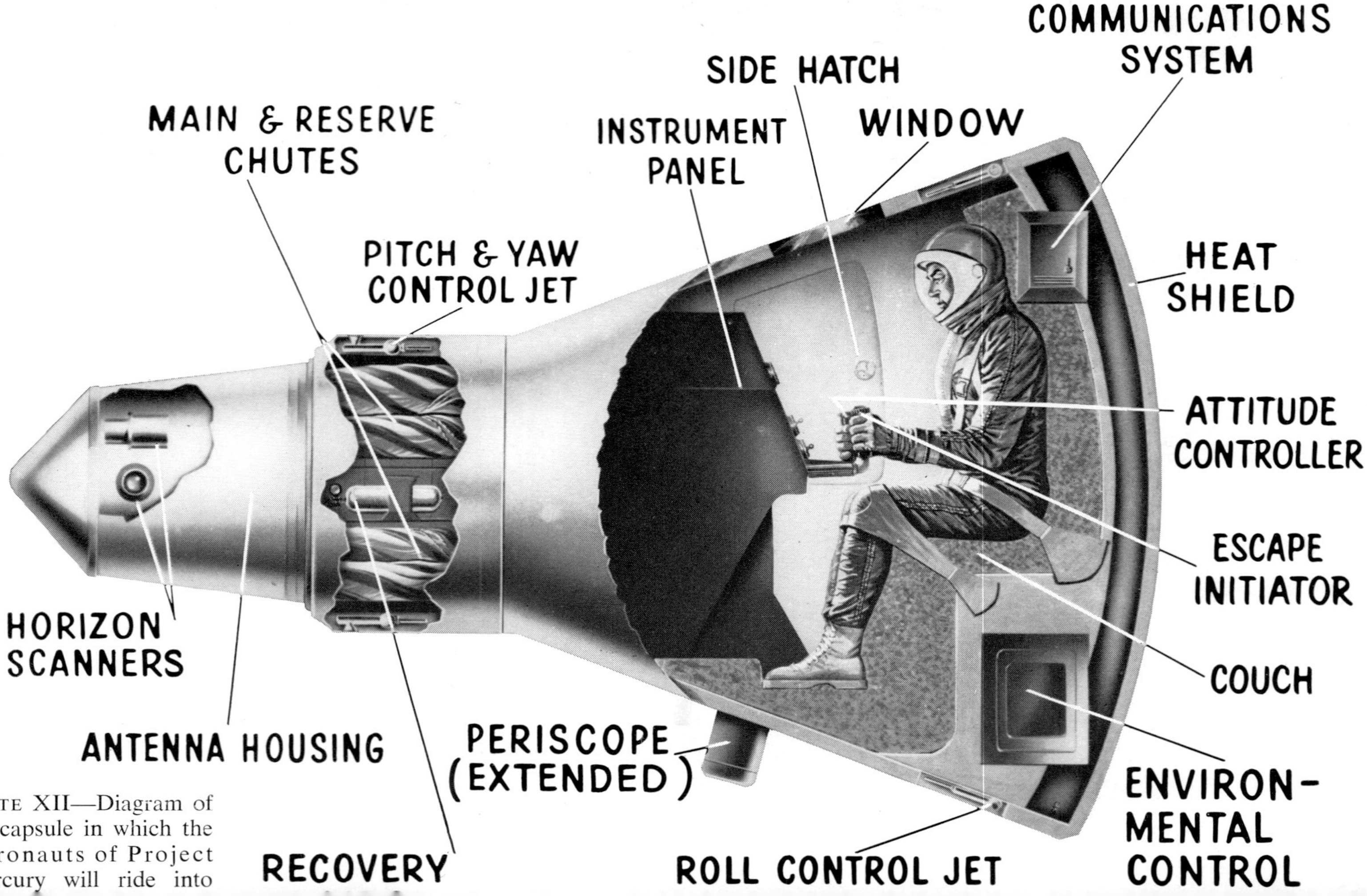

PLATE XII—Diagram of the capsule in which the astronauts of Project Mercury will ride into

9

Rocket Experiments

AMONG the many research preparations for man's entry into space, the one activity that has received perhaps the greatest and possibly a disproportionate share of public attention is the sending of animals aloft in rockets and satellites. The "human interest" appeal of animals for newspaper readers naturally is multiplied when they do something so exotic as riding in a rocket. And the experiments have evoked the inevitable protests from some readers. Of course, the protests raised from time to time over alleged cruelty to animals in scientific experimentation overlook the safeguards which any good scientist adopts to avoid needless suffering for the animals. Furthermore, in this case animal flights are an indispensable prelude to man's venture into space. Their journeys have in fact helped to clarify several of the major problems of manned space operations, notably the problem of weightlessness.

The first biological rocket flights, made in 1946-1947, carried seeds, fruit flies, and fungus spores to explore the effects of cosmic radiation (discussed in later chapters). But the first really important flights began in June 1948, when the Aero Medical Laboratory at Wright Field (later renamed the Aerospace Medical Laboratory) sent off a primate in a research rocket. The guiding spirit of these tests was James P. Henry, head of the laboratory's Acceleration Unit, and among his principal collaborators was David G. Simons, a young physician just out of medical school who was serving his first tour of duty with the Armed Forces.

As explained by Captain Simons, the objective of these tests was to establish the over-all feasibility of human space flight:

Today there is no place on the earth's surface more than 40 hours' travel from any other place, so the question of feasibility of travel beyond the reaches of the atmosphere inevitably arises. But what are the problems of space flight in a rocket? By theorizing, the various possible dangers and limiting factors can be appraised and appropriate means of protection against each surmised. However, only by actually performing the experiments can one prove or disprove the validity of the hypothesis, learn better ways of protecting against known hazards, and realize for the first time the existence of unsuspected dangers. Only the recovery of a live animal showing no demonstrable ill effects will permit the claim that no major difficulty has been overlooked.[1]

Live recovery was not effected until the seventh try. Yet even the failures made an important contribution toward developing the techniques that led to successful recoveries later, and all but two of the tests produced valuable physiological data.

Never did the Aero Medical Laboratory have the luxury of a research rocket all to itself. However, the Air Force's Cambridge Field Station (which later became the Air Force Cambridge Research Center) offered space for biological experimentation in the "Blossom" series of shots made with captured German V-2 rockets to explore the upper atmosphere. Informed that animal passengers could be sent along, Dr. Henry leaped at the chance. With Simons and other Wright Field scientists he set to work devising methods for conveying a small monkey in a rocket. Some sort of pressurized capsule to go inside the nose cone was needed. The space available was extremely limited, and there were no exact precedents to go by, but the capsule was made. The scene then shifted to White Sands Proving Ground in southern New Mexico for the final pre-flight preparations. Early in the morning of June 11, 1948, a nine-pound anesthetized Rhesus monkey was sealed inside the capsule, which in turn was placed in the nose of a V-2 rocket. The monkey was carefully instrumented to record its heart and respiratory action. Because its name was Albert, the entire operation became known as the Albert Project.[2]

Unfortunately, that project was plagued by a series of operational failures. The apparatus for transmitting respiratory movements is known to have failed before the time of launch. This probably made no real difference, because there are indications that Albert died as a result of breathing difficulties in the cramped capsule, even before his rocket left the ground and climbed to an altitude of 37 miles. The parachute recovery system devised to lower the nose cone with its animal capsule back to earth also failed to function properly; Albert would have been killed upon impact in any case. The recorder placed within the capsule was successfully recovered, and it showed no evidence of physiological activity at any time during the flight. This could mean either that the animal was dead from the outset or that the electrocardiographic apparatus and the instrument for recording respiration had failed.

The net result of the first Albert experiment, then, was experience for the scientists who had taken part in it and the incentive to do better the next time. This they succeeded in doing. For the second experiment, which took place on June 14, 1949, the capsule was redesigned to let the subject (Albert II) assume a less cramped position. The instrumentation also was improved. So was the parachute recovery system, but not enough, for Albert II died at impact. However, the respiratory and cardiological records established that he lived throughout the flight, which reached approximately 83 miles above the earth.

The third V-2 animal experiment was marred by unsatisfactory rocket performance—a mid-air explosion, to be exact. But the fourth again did better. It followed a pattern identical with that of the second experiment: successful recording of data from the living primate throughout the flight and, in the end, parachute failure causing death at impact. Again, the heart and respiratory record gave no sign of serious disturbance of the animal's functions. Of course, it had not been expected that subjects would receive any major damage from the few minutes' exposure to cosmic radiation attainable in a V-2. Even if harmful cosmic-ray effects did occur, they would presumably have been detected only through careful post-flight observation, which was impossible because of the failure to recover the animals safely. Nor were the acceleration and deceleration forces during the flight of an order likely to cause injury. On the second flight, for instance, the peak forces were about 5.5 *g* (applied transversely) during acceleration and 12 or 13 *g* at the shock of the parachute opening. These were well within the tolerance limits of a properly secured subject.

EFFECTS OF WEIGHTLESSNESS

There remained principally the question whether exposure to weightlessness during the period of the rocket's coasting and free fall in the thin upper atmosphere had caused the animals any harm. The exposure lasted only two to three minutes, but it was substantially longer than had previously been attainable by other means. The results were encouraging, for the animals came through the experience without any apparent ill effects.

To be sure, only the functioning of the heart and respiratory system was specifically recorded by the instruments, and *a priori* there was little reason to assume that either would be seriously affected by a subgravity state. The heart and the lungs are not primarily dependent on gravity for their operation. The weight of the blood does play some part in regulating circulation, but not an indispensable part. Indeed, because the heart normally has to pump blood *against* gravity, it is even conceivable that a person with a weak heart might be benefited by a reduction in gravitational force. (John Paul Stapp has pointed out, however, that treating heart patients to a trip in a spaceship would be a "very expensive form of therapy,"[3] not to mention the difficulty of keeping the takeoff thrust within limits that the patients could tolerate.)

In order to explore subgravity effects more fully, the fifth and final V-2 experiment of the Wright Field laboratory, carried out in the summer of 1950, introduced a new procedure. This time a mouse was used as the subject instead of a monkey, and no attempt was made to record its heart action or breathing. Unlike the monkeys, the mouse was not strapped in or anesthetized, because the purpose of the experiment was to record the conscious reactions of an animal to changing gravity conditions. For this purpose, the mouse capsule was equipped with a camera system to photograph the animal at fixed intervals. The recovery system again failed, and the mouse did not survive impact. But the photographs came through successfully. They indicated that the mouse retained normal muscular coordination after the onset of the weightless condition. Interestingly enough, the pictures showed that the animal "no longer had a preference for any particular direction, and was as much at ease when inverted as when upright relative to the control starting position."[4]

Even before this last V-2 blasted off toward space, project scientists were making plans to continue their experiments using the newly developed Aerobee high-altitude rocket, which was specifically designed for research purposes. The test program was still directed from laboratory headquarters at Wright Field, but launch operations now shifted from the White Sands Proving Ground to Holloman Air Force Base, located 40 miles northeast on the other side of New Mexico's Tularosa Basin.

The first biological Aerobee streaked skyward from Holloman on April 18, 1951. It carried an experiment basically similar to the first four V-2 tests—a monkey fully instrumented to record the breathing and heart rates. And the result was the same as before: physiological data successfully recorded, no sign of gross disturbance in the subject—and the parachute failed again.[5]

When the second Aerobee in this series was fired on September 20, 1951, the long-awaited breakthrough in parachute recovery was successfully accomplished. This vehicle carried an arkful of animals to an altitude of 236,000 feet and brought them all back alive. Included in the menagerie were: a monkey instrumented to record heart beat, respiration, and blood pressure; nine mice that went along chiefly to be exposed to cosmic radiation; and two other mice in separate compartments of a slowly rotating drum, for photographic observation of their reactions to subgravity.

As in the previous experiments, the monkey showed no obvious disturbance of its heart or breathing, although there was a slight, possibly not significant, decrease in its arterial blood pressure during the subgravity period on this flight (the only one in which blood pressure was successfully measured). The monkey died two hours after landing, but there was no indication in the recorded data, or in an autopsy later, that this resulted from effects of the flight *per se*. Apparently its death was due to landing shock or heat prostration or both. There had been a slight delay in retrieving and opening the capsule after it was successfully parachuted down, and the monkey's small compartment became too hot in the midday sun of southern New Mexico. Two mice also died following recovery, but none of the mice suffered any apparent ill effects from cosmic radiation.

In the subgravity mouse experiment, one of the two mice in the rotating drum had undergone a prior operation depriving it of the orienting vestibular function that is responsive to gravitational forces.

Because of the operation, this mouse was already accustomed to orienting itself primarily by vision and touch, and it did not seem affected by loss of gravity during the flight. It had no trouble holding onto a slight projection in the side of the compartment. But the normal mouse in the other compartment clawed at the air and appeared definitely disturbed during the weightless phase of the trajectory.[6]

A third and final biological Aerobee, fired at Holloman on May 21, 1952, was an even more successful experiment. Not only were all its passengers—two mice and two monkeys—brought back alive from the upper atmosphere, but they were rescued in time from the New Mexico sun.

The mice in this experiment were both normal and again were both placed in a rotating drum. One was given a paddle to cling to, while the other was not. The former remained "oriented and quiet" throughout its exposure to subgravity.[7] During most of the subgravity phase, the mouse with nothing to cling to also rode quietly. The natural rolling motion (about one rotation per second) of the rocket while it was coasting, combined with some pitching and yawing, produced transverse acceleration of about 0.05 *g*; as Dr. Simons later observed, the experiment "suggests that a little *g* can go a long way in supplying helpful orientation." But after the nose cone separated from the rocket and began to fall, it attained pure weightlessness for about 15 seconds before it encountered atmospheric drag. During this interval the mouse that lacked a perch "hopped disconcertedly back and forth."[8]

As for the two monkeys—one of which rode seated upright, the other supine—the recorded physiological data indicated that neither was harmed by any phase of the experiment. Simons concluded from this and the previous flights

> . . . that the weightless state itself produces no disturbance of circulation in terms of heart rate or arterial and venous blood pressures. This does not mean that the circulation might not be involved secondarily, due to emotional and autonomic reactions to weightlessness. Such secondary reactions are essentially the same whether caused by weightlessness, a rough sea, or an obnoxious mother-in-law.[9]

The monkeys' trip was distinguished chiefly by the fact that they were the first primates to survive a journey so far into the upper atmosphere—36 miles. Both were presented to the National Zoological Park in Washington, D. C. One later died from wounds inflicted by the other, but the victor in this unseemly quarrel was still alive and healthy at last report.[10]

It is interesting to note that, while these flights aroused a certain number of complaints from animal lovers in the United States and abroad, including the British Royal Society for Prevention of Cruelty to Animals, they also inspired a surprising number of human volunteers to write and offer themselves as passengers in the next rocket. Such offers arrived at Holloman from as far away as the Philippines. Sometimes they were made by persons hoping to pay some debt to society by gathering scientific data at considerable risk and inconvenience to themselves; one offer, in fact, came from a resident in Washington State Penitentiary.[11] So far, all the offers have been declined with thanks.

The Air Force staged its next animal rocket experiment on April 23, 1958. A luckless mouse was sealed inside a Thor-Able intermediate range ballistic missile, was fired aloft from the Air Force Missile Test Center at Cape Canaveral, and was never seen again. This mouse represented the first installment of Project MIA (for Mouse-In-Able), directed by the Space Technology Laboratories of Los Angeles working with the Air Force Ballistic Missile Division. The scientist in charge was Miss Franki Van der Wal, who wangled permission to include a mouse as hitchhiker on each of three Thor-Able missile re-entry test flights.

The second and third flights took place in July 1958. Their passengers, like the first mouse, presumably ended up on the bottom of the Atlantic Ocean; the recovery ships (outfitted with mouse-care manuals) never located the nose cones. These two mice, however, had been instrumented to record their heart beats, and the physiological data were successfully telemetered during flight. They went higher (1,400 miles) and farther than any of the animals on the earlier rocket trips, and they experienced about 45 minutes of weightlessness, as well as a re-entry deceleration force of 60 *g* (applied transversely with the aid of the automatic positioning technique described in Chapter 7). The re-entry *g*-loading was far beyond anything in the earlier Air Force animal flights. The exposure to weightlessness, of course, was also much longer than in the previous flights. But so far as the records of their heart beats showed, the two mice suffered no serious effects from the deceleration, the weightlessness, the rocket noise or the 17-*g* peak acceleration at takeoff.[12]

The 1,400-mile altitude reached by these mice still stood as a record at the time this book was written. But other shots that followed the MIA experiments produced more physiological data. The next one was launched at Cape Canaveral in December 1958. It was an interservice effort: the Navy's School of Aviation Medicine at Pensacola led in preparing the experiment; other Navy and Army scientists assisted; the Army Ballistic Missile Agency at Huntsville provided a Jupiter rocket; and the United States Air Force supplied the launch site at Cape Canaveral.

The subject this time was a one-pound squirrel monkey named Gordo. Placed in a capsule specially heated to resemble his native tropical environment, Gordo traveled to a height of 300 miles. He was lost at sea, through a failure of the nose-cone recovery gear, but his reactions in flight were well recorded by instruments. The period of weightlessness was about nine minutes, and the peak *g*-forces (which he took in a supine position) were roughly 10 *g* at takeoff and 40 *g* for a brief instant at re-entry. These figures were more modest than those attained in Project MIA, but they were not inconsiderable. Furthermore, the test gave more detailed information, by virtue of much more elaborate instrumentation recording the heart beat, blood pressure, respiration, and even "voice response," as well as the functioning of controls of the environment. As far as could be ascertained from the telemetered data, no phase of the test produced any significant physiological impairment of the passenger.[13]

The military services again collaborated in the next animal launching, a Jupiter shot from Cape Canaveral on May 28, 1959. This time they recovered the passengers—two female monkeys named Able and Baker. The subjects successfully withstood flight conditions comparable to those on Gordo's trip. As an added feature, of special interest for the study of coordination and psychological reactions during weightlessness, Able was supposed to press a telegraph key every time a light blinked. This plan unfortunately did not pan out: the first announcements said that electronic difficulties intervened, but according to later rumors the reason was a last-minute change in selection of monkeys using one that was not properly trained to perform the act. Another misfortune was that Able died a few days after her space flight during an operation to remove an electrode implanted under her skin, which had started a slight infection.[14]

The two monkeys were only part of the biological payload on this particular Jupiter flight. Also on board was a miscellaneous assortment of molds, tissues, seeds, and other "test subjects." These items were selected primarily for purposes of radiation research (which will be discussed in later chapters). However, the sponsoring scientists even included sea-urchin eggs and sperm, triggered to produce fertilization *during* the flight. This last experiment was supposed to throw some light on the problem of human reproduction in multigeneration space voyages. Unfortunately, these eggs disintegrated somewhere along the way, but sea-urchin eggs that had been fertilized shortly before the flight apparently continued to develop during it.[15]

In September 1959 a somewhat similar Jupiter-load of test specimens was launched from Cape Canaveral, only to be cut down for range safety reasons before it really got underway.[16] And in early December an escape procedure designed for the Mercury man-in-space capsule was tested with a monkey named Sam, supplied by the Air Force School of Aviation Medicine. The capsule was fired from the National Aeronautics and Space Administration test center at Wallops Island off the coast of Virginia; 19 miles up, the escape mechanism was triggered, and the capsule separated from the booster rocket. The capsule climbed to an altitude of 55 miles before starting down again, and it was successfully recovered by parachute. Sam was unharmed. The following month a female monkey, "Miss Sam," rode in a similar device during an experiment in which the capsule was separated from the booster at an altitude of about seven miles and continued to rise for another two miles. She, too, was unharmed. However, these two flights did not give very long exposure to weightlessness or other space-equivalent conditions, being important chiefly in helping to establish the biological adequacy of the Mercury system.[17]

RUSSIAN EXPERIMENTS

The Soviet Union's program of biological rocket experiments has been, in some ways, even more impressive than that in this country. During the period 1953-1957, when the United States temporarily abandoned the field of animal rockets, the Russian scientists were the only ones working in this field. Although their work was not widely publicized until 1956-1957, it seems that they launched their first animal flight about 1951, and they have carried out a larger number of such experiments than we have.

Despite a widespread impression to the contrary, the Russians have not used only dogs as test subjects. But they have certainly favored dogs: their tradition of canine experimentation, of course, goes back to Pavlov. In all the earliest tests, the dogs were sealed into pressurized capsules. In a later test series, dogs had their own space suits made to order and got along without a full-fledged environment-controlled compartment. The peak altitudes were around 100 kilometers at first, and by 1958 had reached 473 kilometers, about 294 miles. To get the animals back, Russian scientists performed such spectacular feats as catapulting them in "ejector chassis" from falling nose cones at an altitude of 75 to 85 kilometers (47 to 53 miles), with the parachute recovery system going into operation just three seconds later. When this procedure was used, the total descent took about an hour.[18]

In the course of their program, the Russians have recorded blood pressure, pulse, breathing, body temperature, etc. They have also photographed the reactions of test animals in flight. They state that none of the animals appeared to be harmed by weightlessness, lasting on the order of three to six minutes, or by rocket acceleration and vibrations, re-entry or recovery procedures. A Russian scientist also claimed, as of 1956, that no dog had ever been lost through failure of its breathing equipment or "effects of external factors connected with flight in the upper atmospheric layers."[19] He did not specify how many may have been lost for other reasons. The skill developed by Soviet scientists and engineers in parachute recovery of animal test subjects has allowed them to use the same dog on three or more different flights, but it is difficult to believe that the Russians wholly avoided the deaths-at-impact that marred the earliest United States animal rocket flights.

Be this as it may, the Russian procedures and test results substantially paralleled United States experiments—until they put the dog Laika in orbit aboard Sputnik II in November 1957. Laika, a female, was one of ten small dogs that had undergone a rigorous course of training. Her orbital flight did not take her as high as the record altitude of 1,400 miles reached by the Project MIA flights conducted by the United States the following year, but Laika set an unmatched record for the length of her sojourn in space, which lasted roughly a week before she died, apparently from lack of oxygen.[20]

In addition to a controlled environment, Laika had an automatic food-dispensing unit, even a sanitary waste-disposal apparatus. The one great limitation of the Sputnik II biological experiment was simply the failure to bring the dog back, either dead or alive. Instrumentation measured Laika's heart beat, blood pressure, respiration, and motor activity and transmitted the data to earth. According to published results, Laika fared well throughout, although the combination of acceleration (transverse), noise, and vibration during the takeoff phase led to a pronounced quickening of the heart beat. The effect was within tolerable limits, but it persisted after the acceleration about three times longer than would have been expected from centrifuge experiments with the same animal. Russian scientists attributed this at least partly to the fact that the animal's recovery had to take place under a condition of weightlessness rather than in a normal one-*g* field. The United States animal experiments have not established the same effect of post-acceleration weightlessness, but they do not offer very clear-cut evidence in this matter. Laika's experience did suggest an interesting parallel with the results of certain human subgravity experiments which will be described in the next chapter.

Laika's heart beat and breathing ultimately returned to normal, and for the remainder of the experiment they showed no deviations that could be attributed to weightlessness. Russian reports stated further that the animal was pressed against the floor of the cabin during acceleration but easily pushed away from it after acceleration ceased. The dog's coordination and movements are said to have presented no difficulty during the weightless phase; but actually Laika had very little room to move about and very little to do except eat the food mechanically doled out at set intervals. The Russians reasoned that eyesight "compensated to a certain degree the disturbance of locomotive power"[21] due to weightlessness. They also admitted, perhaps overmeticulously, that because of the satellite's "slow revolution" the passenger's weightlessness was not total but only "practically" complete; actually, any *g*-force present during the orbital flight was insignificant. From every standpoint the test was a major landmark, and in particular it confirmed the hope that the problem of weightlessness could be mastered.

Moreover, Sputnik II set a precedent which will surely be followed by further biosatellite experimentation. In June 1959 the United States Air Force tried to put a biological payload in orbit and to improve on the Russian achievement by recovering the animals. Four black mice were sealed in a Discoverer satellite and launched from Vandenberg Air Force Base, at the gateway to the Pacific Missile Range. Recovery crews and Air Force mouse doctors were deployed to welcome the precious cargo as it came back from orbit. Alas, it never got into orbit, and presumably was destroyed as it plunged back prematurely into the atmosphere. The whole effort, in fact, was slightly premature, in that satellite-recovery techniques were still in a highly experimental stage; there was admittedly only an off-chance of everything working out as planned, even if the satellite entered orbit.[22] Nevertheless, the challenge to do better the next time was even more pressing than at the unsuccessful conclusion of the pioneering Albert I rocket flight in 1948. No other known method can rival the biosatellite for long-duration exposure to such conditions of space flight as weightlessness and cosmic radiation.

10

Experiments in Aircraft

THE airplane, of course, has played its part in research on the biological effects of weightlessness. It cannot equal the length of exposure obtained in research rockets, much less that obtainable with satellites, but it has had one major compensating advantage: it can carry human subjects safely and reliably.

We have already noted that Heinz von Diringshofen in Germany conducted some early subgravity experiments with aircraft in vertical dives. The brief exposures obtainable in a dive were not very satisfactory for research, but fortunately a means of lengthening the duration was not long in coming. In May 1950 the brothers Fritz and Heinz Haber outlined it in a memorable paper at the Chicago meeting of the Aero Medical Association on "Possible Means of Producing the Gravity-Free State for Medical Research."[1] Both men, former German scientists, were working at the time in the Air Force School of Aviation Medicine at Randolph Field. In introducing their topic, they were careful to justify it primarily in terms of "operational" subgravity situations which were already arising in flight within the atmosphere and were bound to become ever more important as flight altitudes and performance increased. They pointed out, for example, that a rocket plane coasting at an altitude of 100,000 feet with its engines throttled would be close to zero-gravity, because of the slightness of the air drag. But the pertinence of their remarks to the problems of space flight was certainly not lost on their audience.

The Habers considered several means of creating a weightless state for human experiments. Free fall was the most obvious, but because of air friction true weightlessness could not be achieved for an appreciable period by this method. In a skyscraper elevator, they pointed out, it was possible to have a subgravity force of 0.9 to 0.7 *g* for as long as 25 seconds. However, actual weightlessness could not be properly simulated in any kind of ground laboratory (as many other conditions of space flight can). The solution they recommended, therefore, was to fly an airplane in a parabolic arc, or Keplerian trajectory. With aircraft then available, this maneuver was capable of producing 10 to 35 seconds of zero-gravity and an even longer total exposure to subgravity conditions.

Such a parabola could be regarded as a segment of an elliptical orbit around the center of the earth. The moon, in its elliptical orbit, develops just enough centrifugal force to counterbalance the earth's gravitational attraction; in the words of another author, it is really "falling freely through space, but in a curving path that never brings it downward toward the center of the mass that attracts it."[2] The test aircraft that the Habers had in mind was intended, at least briefly, to do the same thing. Within the atmosphere there was one complication, air friction, not present in the case of the moon, but this could also be counterbalanced by applying just the right additional amount of engine acceleration.

The full mathematical demonstration of this procedure for any given starting speed and angle is a rather complex affair. Flying the prescribed trajectory is harder still. But in broad outline it resembles an attack maneuver developed by German fighter pilots in World War II for coming up underneath Allied bomber formations and then diving again to get away.[3] The length of subgravity exposure is, in large measure, a function of aircraft speed. In executing the maneuver, a pilot first builds up speed by putting the plane into a dive and then pulls out of the dive and enters the parabola at a steep climb. This subjects the plane and its occupants to increased *g*-force (the exact amount depending on the type of parabola flown), and so does the later pullout from the parabola in returning to normal flight. Between these two peaks the *g*-force falls off to a fractional value and then, if all goes well, to actual zero-gravity. But it is always hard to achieve the full potential, because of small irregularities due to such factors as pilot error and atmospheric turbulence.[4]

The first concerted efforts to apply the Habers' principles occurred in 1951. That summer the noted test pilot Scott Crossfield flew a number of Keplerian trajectories at Edwards Air Force Base in California on behalf of the National Advisory Committee for Aeronautics. He attained virtual weightlessness for periods of 15 seconds or longer. Crossfield reported some "befuddlement" during the transition into this condition on his first few flights, and occasional vertigo at pull-out, but he had no loss of muscle coordination except a tendency to overreach with his arm.[5]

During the same year the Air Force also conducted parabolic subgravity flights at Edwards and at Wright Field in Ohio. Major Charles E. Yeager, who served as pilot in the Edwards tests, reported some sensation of falling and one serious instance of disorientation: after 13 seconds of weightlessness on one flight he felt a spinning sensation, and after 15 seconds a feeling of being "lost in space."[6] At Wright Field an F-80 jet fighter, in flights directed by E. R. Ballinger, created the weightless state for 15 to slightly over 20 seconds. Measurements of heart activity made during flight showed no significant changes. Ballinger's test subjects, like Crossfield, showed a "mild tendency to overreach," but they found that this was easily corrected with practice. They had no difficulty in orientation, although they felt this might not have been the case if they had been deprived of visual orientation and of the belts that held them firmly in place.[7]

This burst of subgravity flights in the United States was followed by two years of relative inactivity. In Argentina, however, related experiments were being conducted by the Austrian-born scientist Harald J. von Beckh, who had served in World War II as a Luftwaffe flight surgeon. Now living in Buenos Aires, von Beckh did research on his own and in collaboration with von Diringshofen, who was in Argentina for a five-year period as adviser to the Instituto Nacional de Medicina Aeronáutica, where von Beckh taught. In his first experiments he used vertical dives in aircraft, attaining something close to weightlessness for about seven seconds. Then he turned to the Haber technique of parabolic flight, for longer subgravity exposures. When he asked the Argentine Air Force for a suitable aircraft, to his own and everyone's amazement he found a Fiat fighter practically on his doorstep in just one week. The only explanation von Beckh received for this remarkable victory over government red-tape was that the plane itself was "weightless"—a variety of joke which was funny in the early years of subgravity research but has by now worn a little thin.[8]

Dr. von Beckh introduced the South American water turtle to the menagerie of subgravity test subjects. The animal offered special advantages for this research: it is accustomed to moving in a three-dimensional field; it has a vaguely S-shaped neck which requires close muscular coordination; and it has a voracious appetite. Von Beckh found that when he took these turtles on subgravity flights, they showed definite signs of disturbance. Normally they strike at bits of food with pinpoint accuracy, but they proved unable to do so under the test conditions. (The water in their airborne tank also behaved strangely, sometimes rising straight up, turtles and all, and making it necessary for von Beckh to fit the container back around the water.) However, there was one turtle whose vestibular function had been injured through accidental overheating of the water in the aquarium. This turtle apparently had learned to rely on visual cues and was not disturbed by subgravity unless its eyes were covered. Its experience resembled the case of the vestibular-operated mouse in the second animal Aerobee. For that matter, even the normal turtles gradually improved their performance after a sufficient number of flights. Presumably they, too, learned to compensate by visual orientation, although they never became as proficient as their injured companion.

Von Beckh also worked with human subjects, using a simple test of eye-hand coordination which involved marking crosses in prescribed squares. The test was conducted in normal flight and during subgravity, with eyes open or closed. It was found that weightlessness caused a definite loss of coordination, especially when the subject lacked visual orientation. But von Beckh's human subjects, like the turtles, improved their accuracy on later flights. Pilots who were experienced in instrument flying showed the fastest improvement.[9]

Von Beckh noted with great interest that when the plane entered a subgravity arc after high acceleration (6.5 *g*), it took the subjects appreciably longer than usual to recover from the acceleration-induced visual blackout. This was puzzling, because the annulment of gravity during the weightless period should make it easier for the heart to pump blood upward to eye level. Von Beckh had no ready explanation for the anomaly. He has suggested, with von Diringshofen, that the delay in recovery during weightlessness may be caused by a poor reaction of the haemostatic regulators in the circulatory system, which are normally adjusted to one *g*. Or it may be due to a relaxation of muscle tone, which might lead to a delay in the return flow of blood from the lower part of the body.[10] In any event, von Beckh's observation was important, because the conditions responsible for the prolonged blackout—strong acceleration followed immediately by weightlessness—are exactly what one will encounter in the takeoff of a space vehicle.

During 1954 and 1955 von Beckh spent part of his time studying the problem of motion sickness. He did this in a series of 12 ship crossings of the Atlantic between Argentina and Europe, studying a grand total of 12,500 subjects. While he was at it, he also looked into the occurrence of optical illusions due to constantly changing *g*-forces in the bow of a vessel in a rough sea.[11] As we have already mentioned, von Beckh later moved to the United States, worked with the Human Factors Division of the Martin Company, and in January 1958 joined the Aeromedical Field Laboratory at Holloman, where he resumed his studies of subgravity flight.

AIR FORCE SUBGRAVITY PROGRAMS

The Holloman project that von Beckh joined had been underway for several years. David G. Simons, head of the laboratory's Space Biology Branch from 1953 to 1958, had instituted a series of subgravity experiments with T-33 and F-89 jet aircraft flying parabolic trajectories. One of the first test subjects was John T. Conniff, assigned as task scientist for subgravity studies. Another subject was Dr. Simons himself, who was so enthusiastic about this research that he would insist on continuing a flight even when he became violently ill.[12]

In the fall of 1955, after the assignment of Grover J. D. Schock as task scientist, the program was intensified. Captain Schock began subgravity flights in an F-94C jet fighter, which became the standard vehicle for subgravity studies. Schock devoted himself primarily to this work for more than two years, and his contributions were such that he received from the University of Illinois the first known Ph.D. degree in space physiology. His thesis was entitled, "Some Observations of Orientation and Illusions When Exposed to Sub and Zero-Gravity."[13] After von Beckh arrived in January 1958 to help in the subgravity work, Schock widened his own range of duties and responsibilities. Had he not been grounded by a training accident,[14] he would have been the pilot in the famous Man-High III balloon flight, which took place in October 1958 with Clifton M. McClure as pilot instead.

The Holloman subgravity program has to be considered in connection with a twin program at the School of Aviation Medicine at Randolph Field (relocated in 1959 to the nearby Brooks Air Force Base). By the time Randolph launched its work, the Habers (the exponents of the parabolic flight method) had left that post, but there were other scientists at Randolph keenly interested in this research, notably Siegfried J. Gerathewohl. In 1955 Gerathewohl started subgravity experiments with aircraft.[15]

The Randolph program began with a T-33, flown in vertical dives and in parabolic trajectories. But this aircraft had certain yaw and roll movements which, despite the services of a highly skilled pilot, Herbert D. Stallings, caused certain irregularities in a test parabola; in addition, its fuel flow was by gravity, so that there was danger of flameout during the subgravity phase. Gerathewohl, Stallings, and their co-workers therefore turned to the superior F-94C, already in use at Holloman. The F-94C had pressure fuel flow and gave a smoother and longer parabola. It ultimately provided virtual weightlessness lasting over 40 seconds.[16] To be sure, even the F-94 presented some operating difficulties in test flights, but these were successfully overcome. Aside from more serious problems involving flight safety, it was discovered, for instance, that the standard microphone was unable to transmit clear messages between the pilot and the test subject during subgravity. As a result of research on this problem, a more satisfactory type of microphone was installed, and Captain Schock at Holloman was finally able to conclude that "voice communications in future space vehicles should present no problem."[17]

The scale and intensity of the subgravity work underscored the importance of getting accurate measurements of fractional and zero gravity. The standard aircraft *g*-meter, which had not been designed for this purpose, was quite inadequate. On some early flights the test for zero-gravity was to toss a pencil or similar object into the air: if it stayed suspended in mid-air, weightlessness was confirmed. Another technique, used both at Holloman and at Randolph, involved tapping a golf ball suspended by a string from the roof of the cockpit. But neither the pencil nor the golf ball could indicate all the minor fractions of gravity. And these were worth studying in their own right, apart from the importance of more accurate information to the pilot aiming to get the maximum amount of weightlessness from his trajectory.

Schock, in particular, took pains to improve test instrumentation so that he could accurately record the whole range of gravity and subgravity states obtainable in the parabolic flight pattern. He finally employed a combination of differently placed accelerometers. Information on the varying *g*-forces experienced was relayed constantly to the aircraft pilot by two sensitive microammeters installed in his field of vision, and the same information was carefully synchronized with a film record of the test subject's reactions. There was also progress in the adaptation to subgravity flight tests of standard instruments for recording physiological data. Improvements in the various types of test instrumentation were made at the School of Aviation Medicine as well as at Holloman. Nevertheless, it would be too much to claim that perfection was achieved. Moreover, the array of accelerometers, cameras, and other test paraphernalia tended to clutter up the aircraft, creating further problems of maintenance and flying safety.[18]

Finally, there were the financial problems. When the Air Force was caught up in an austerity drive in the summer of 1957, the hardest hit research program at Holloman's Aeromedical Field Laboratory was the subgravity work. A formal directive ordered its immediate cessation. "Cessation" was soon clarified to refer only to work that cost money—but this included the F-94C flights, the heart of the program, which cost an estimated $63 an hour for aircraft operation, without counting maintenance and overhead. In effect, Captain Schock was grounded. The suspension was lifted after Sputnik, but the time lost could never be wholly regained.[19] This was one of many examples of the difficulty of getting and keeping support for basic scientific research in our space program.

Despite all obstacles, however, subgravity flights at Holloman and Randolph were accumulating a growing mass of research data. By April 1958 Major Stallings at Randolph claimed to have logged more than 37 hours of weightlessness, in more than 4,000 test trajectories.[20] No other pilot became such a specialist in subgravity flight as Stallings, but the number of subgravity parabolas flown both at Holloman and at Randolph was impressive. Moreover, the results obtained at one research center generally confirmed and complemented those obtained at the other. The results also tended in general to confirm the tentative conclusions reached as far back at 1951-1952 from the early rocket and aircraft experiments.

SENSATIONS OF WEIGHTLESSNESS

One fact that seems well established is that participants in subgravity tests vary widely in their subjective reactions. For the Seventh International Astronautical Congress held in 1956, Gerathewohl analyzed the experiences of 16 persons who had made subgravity flights at Randolph. They fell in three broad categories: eight had "sensations of comfort and pleasantness," three had unusual "sensations of motion," and five had "sensations of unpleasantness and psychosomatic symptoms." As the number of subjects increased, with continued experimentation, the relative proportions in the three categories remained much the same.[21]

Some members of the first group commented:

"The 'feeling of well-being' is somewhat analogous to the relief experienced upon removing a heavy burden. . . ."

"There was a total absence of the 'seat of the pants' sensation while in the weightless state. The mental sensation of weightlessness can best be described as one of incredulousness or even slight amusement. The incongruity of seeing objects and one's own feet float free of the floor without any muscle effort can only be described in those terms."

"Actually, I've never been so bloody comfortable in all my life. . . ."[22]

Major Stallings was one of those who reported pleasant sensations, but Dr. Gerathewohl placed himself in the middle group. He reported that he had had a falling sensation at least once, and that in another case "concentrated insight during weightlessness with eyes closed yielded a feeling of backward rotation which started with the sensation that the head gets bigger and flips backward, and then the body follows as if one were in an inverted position."[23] The complexity of this last observation suggests that "concentrated insight" by a specialist in subgravity research may not always be a good thing. Gerathewohl also reported some slight attacks of motion sickness, especially during the pullout from the subgravity parabola, when he was exposed to *more* than one *g*. On the whole, however, he expressed neither strong liking nor violent dislike for the subgravity state.

As for those who had a distinctly unpleasant time, some typical comments were:

"At the height of the parabolic arc it felt like my stomach was in my throat; I began to look forward to the plus *g* maneuver on pullout, at which time my stomach would feel like it were in the proper position again. At the completion of the fifth zero-gravity state I knew it would be only a matter of time before an emesis would occur. . . ."

"I had a sensation of feeling that I was going over (float or fall) the instrument panel."[24]

It is interesting that Gerathewohl and his subjects made numerous references to a "floating" sensation but few mentions of "falling," despite predictions that a continual falling sensation might prove typical of weightlessness. This may, of course, reflect only the fact that all the subjects were held by seat belts, and that they were subject to occasional bumps and nudges caused by unevenness in the subgravity trajectory.

Much the same variety of impressions was recorded in subgravity flights at Holloman, but Schock had a harder time than Gerathewohl. Along with most other participants in his tests, he reported definite spatial disorientation during subgravity runs in which the head was covered to eliminate visual cues. This, of course, was in close accord with theoretical predictions. In addition, Schock was subject on occasion to extreme symptoms of motion sickness; it is not clear, however, to what extent such discomfort is due to subgravity and to what extent it is related to the rapidly changing motions and forces encountered in a complete test flight, including entry to and exit from the subgravity parabola. Symptoms basically due to other causes might be aggravated temporarily by an interval of weightlessness but not continue through a weightless flight of long duration. On the other hand, a person who could easily endure 30 seconds of subgravity might conceivably do less well with a three-minute—or three-month—dose of the same thing.

It is perhaps significant that one of those who professed to enjoy subgravity was Captain Joseph W. Kittinger, Jr., the test pilot for the Man-High I balloon flight of June 1957, who piloted a great many subgravity flights at Holloman. In his case, as in Major Stallings', it is likely that his broad previous flying career had helped prepare him for the experience, although there is no reason to assume that any number of flying hours is a guarantee against feeling ill-at-ease during a gravity-free state. In any event, it seems clear that the tests for selecting crew members for space travel should always include exposure to weightlessness; indeed, subgravity flights have already been conducted as part of the training program of the candidates for Project Mercury.[25]

Following the example set by von Beckh in Argentina, the subgravity flights at Holloman and the School of Aviation Medicine made extensive use of eye-hand coordination tests. Typically, the subject was required to try to mark crosses in a given pattern or to try to hit a paper target with a metal stylus. As von Beckh had found, the subjects sometimes missed during the subgravity state, particularly when their eyes were closed, but they had no major impairment of coordination. At Randolph an experiment compared the subjects' performance during subgravity with that during exposure to a force of three *g*. Whereas subgravity tended to make the subject's aim deviate upward, the accelerated state deflected it toward the bottom half of the target. The subjects usually found it much easier to learn to compensate for the first error (under subgravity) than the second.[26]

Other tests sought to explore the problem of eating and drinking without the help of gravity. It appears that eating will present no major difficulty during weightlessness, if the food is thoroughly masticated and then forced to the back of the mouth, where the swallowing reflex goes into action without regard to gravity. Water also must be forced to the back of the mouth by the tongue, but again the swallowing reflex is unimpaired. Keeping the food or drink down was not always so easy; the stomach contents sometimes came right up again through the "weightless regurgitation phenomenon," to use a term apparently invented at Randolph Field. This "phenomenon" could be triggered even by very slight pressure on the abdomen, and it suggested (among other things) that space travelers will have to take their food a little at a time. Drinking, apparently, will require the use of a squeeze bottle or similar contraption, for cups and glasses are quite useless during weightlessness. Indeed, scientists at the School of Aviation Medicine observed that one might conceivably drown while trying to drink out of an open container.[27]

At the School of Aviation Medicine, subgravity studies were extended to the problem of micturition. The results indicated that most subjects, if plied with water before takeoff, had no serious trouble in performing the function. On the other hand, a majority did notice a "slight to marked decrease in urinary urgency" during subgravity. This effect would be a disadvantage from the health standpoint, but could be offset on space voyages by adequate indoctrination.[28]

The possible occurrence of visual illusions in connection with subgravity flight also was explored. Centrifuge studies, especially some conducted by scientists of the United States Naval School of Aviation Medicine, had established that increased *g*-forces may bring about an "oculogravic illusion"—*e.g.,* apparent motion of a fixed target. These test results were attributed to a vestibular reaction. They suggested that similar illusions might occur during a gravity-free state, or at least during the transition to and from subgravity. Dr. Gerathewohl discussed the theoretical aspects of the problem at some length in a paper published in 1952.[29] Subgravity flights at both Holloman and Randolph Field studied the problem further. At Holloman, the subject's head and the target, a small luminous cross, were placed under a large and ominous-looking black hood. Deprived of normal visual references, the subject stared at the cross throughout a subgravity run, and the target did appear to move. However, the illusion was always most pronounced during the periods of *increased g*-forces, on entering and leaving the subgravity parabola. During the weightless phase itself the target appeared to stabilize—at a higher than normal position—except for certain oscillations which were attributed to failure of the test aircraft to maintain an even trajectory.[30]

At Randolph Field, subgravity test subjects were instructed to stare at a light in front of them, close their eyes, and then concentrate on the after-image. Like the luminous target at Holloman, this image was found to move downward during acceleration and to stabilize at higher than normal position during weightlessness. The latter effect was termed an "oculo-agravic" illusion by Dr. Gerathewohl, who thus related it to the *absence* of gravity and sought to distinguish it from the "oculogravic" illusion.[31] The precise significance of these results for manned space flight is not clear, but it is perhaps doubtful that the "oculo-agravic" illusion will represent a critical problem.

When von Beckh joined the Holloman program in 1958, he brought with him as a carry-over from his work in Argentina a special interest in the relation between subgravity and human tolerance to such acceleration effects as blackout or greyout. At Holloman he initiated flights expressly designed to produce subgravity either just after or just before exposure to a force of roughly four to 6.5 *g*. These values were higher than those produced in flying most subgravity parabolas and were maintained for a longer period, because the purpose of the flights was to duplicate as far as possible the patterns associated with space-vehicle takeoff and re-entry. To simulate these patterns, the *g*-force was built up and sustained by flying the test airplane through a diving spiral either before or after the subgravity parabola. For refined measurement of the subjects' responses to the stresses involved, they were fitted with electrocardiographic apparatus and with equipment to measure galvanic skin resistance. The latter measurements were an innovation in subgravity tests.

The test results confirmed von Beckh's earlier experimental finding—and Laika's experience: namely, that when the subject was exposed to weightlessness immediately after acceleration, recovery from the acceleration effects was delayed. Not only did blackout last longer, but subjects reported a generalized discomfort and even "pronounced disorientation." Similarly, when exposed to multi-*g* acceleration *after* weightlessness, some subjects blacked out below their usual threshold, while those who did not black out reported greater discomfort than in control runs when the same acceleration was produced without previous exposure to weightlessness. Von Beckh pointed out that in these tests the *g*-forces were applied parallel to the long axis of the body, whereas in space voyages care will be taken to apply them in the more tolerable transverse direction. Nevertheless, the tests offered new evidence of a relationship between weightlessness and *g*-tolerance which John Paul Stapp has described as "sinister" in its implications. It need not be a barrier to manned space flight, but it will certainly have to be taken into account.[32]

On the favorable side, von Beckh found that the measurements of heart rate and the skin's electrical resistance did not show any significant signs of distress on the part of the subjects. Unlike Laika, they generally recovered their normal heart rate in spite of post-acceleration weightlessness without any unusual delay, though the rate often continued to fluctuate for a time. As for the skin-resistance measurements, there were some disturbances, but these could be explained as arising from anxiety and the anticipation of possible discomfort rather than from weightlessness *per se*.[33]

In the course of these tests, von Beckh included an experiment designed to explore the problem of awakening from sleep in a weightless condition. Several investigators had theorized that the awakening might occasion major disorientation; Dr. Simons had actually had such an experience, not during weightlessness but when he awoke from a short nap in his record Man-High II balloon flight.[34] Von Beckh selected for his test an experienced pilot, Clifton M. McClure (who later piloted the Man-High III balloon flight). To make sure that he would fall asleep, Lieutenant McClure stayed awake for 48 hours beforehand. Von Beckh's report of the test:

> After a full breakfast, which increased his sleepiness, he entered the rear cockpit of our experimental F-94C. He unhooked his headset at 11,000 feet, so as not to be disturbed by the conversation among the pilot, tower, and experimenter. Twenty-five minutes after take-off the subject fell asleep, leaning against the right side of the cockpit. A string was fixed on his left wrist, which the pilot could pull to awaken him. The pilot avoided any rough maneuvers. The aircraft was then flown in a zero-*g* trajectory and the subject was awakened.
>
> His first impressions upon awakening were that his arms and legs "were floating away from him" so that he felt a desperate need to pull them back toward his body to maintain some sort of normal posture. He tried to hold on to the canopy and some part of the cockpit. He could not orient himself. He is a pilot of over 500 jet hours and never felt such a pronounced disorientation before.[35]

Animals were not entirely neglected as subjects in subgravity experiments in aircraft. The latest pet of subgravity researchers—at least in the United States—appears to be the cat. It is of special interest because of its highly developed vestibular function, upon which it relies for balance and orientation more than human beings do. The cat is also noted for its reflex ability to land on all fours after being dropped upside down.

Tests were conducted at both Randolph and Holloman to determine how this righting reflex and other posture reflexes in cats would operate during subgravity. Judging by the results, they do not work very well. At Randolph it was found that the righting reflex still worked if the cat was dropped near the beginning of a subgravity parabola, but as true weightlessness was approached it worked tardily or not at all. But of course the cat did not have to turn its feet to the floor, because in the weightless state it did not fall. (What is hard to understand is why a cat instantly begins to right itself when dropped under normal circumstances, for in the first moment of release it is in the condition of free-falling weightlessness!)

During the second half of 1957 Captain Schock at Holloman conducted cat tests of a more intricate nature, experimenting in some cases with cats that had been operated upon to impair their vestibular function. If this function was only partly impaired, weightlessness confused the animal, pretty much as it did normal cats; if the function was entirely destroyed and the animal had learned to rely on vision, weightless flight did not affect its righting reflex. But if such a cat was blindfolded, then it "clawed wildly, scrambled" and seemed altogether disoriented. In short, the tests demonstrated the role of the vestibular apparatus and at the same time confirmed that visual orientation can compensate for the lack of gravitational clues in weightless flight.[36]

Scientists at both Holloman and Randolph Field carried out some experiments with simulated subgravity conditions at ground level. In particular, they immersed subjects in water—the technique described in Chapter 7 as a device for protection against high *g*-forces. On the ground, a body immersed in water is under less than normal sensory stimulation (*e.g.*, from muscle tension) and is in a good approximation of the gravity-free state.[37] To learn something about the perception of subjects in this condition, Leon A. Knight of the School of Aviation Medicine began subgravity tests in a swimming pool. He placed submerged subjects on a tilt table, with their eyes covered, and observed how readily they became conscious of changes in position. On the average, they did not become aware of a change until the tilt was at least 17 degrees, and then usually because of some extraneous sign such as a change in water temperature or the movement of bubbles across the skin.[38]

Later Captain Schock at Holloman made somewhat similar experiments, conducting them in the swimming pools of the El Paso YMCA and the New Mexico School for Visually Handicapped in Alamogordo because the Base itself had no indoor pool. Schock and his fellow subjects assumed various positions under water and with a luminous pointer tried to show what they perceived to be the true vertical or horizontal; they were also rotated in the water and then required to indicate in what direction they thought they were facing. In these various tests they suffered an impairment of orientation which Schock considered comparable to that observed in aircraft experiments when the subjects lacked normal visual cues. The swimming-pool method of subgravity research has obvious limitations, but it does provide longer exposures than the 30 or 40 seconds of subgravity in most aircraft tests, and it costs virtually nothing: thus Schock and his fellow swimmers were able to go on with it even during the 1957 austerity drive.[39]

In mid-1958 the Air Research and Development Command decided to discontinue the subgravity research program at Holloman. This was done not merely to avoid duplication with the School of Aviation Medicine but to allow Holloman's Aeromedical Field Laboratory to concentrate chiefly on preparation for biosatellite experiments. Of course, satellites would eventually provide even better vehicles for weightlessness research than aircraft could.

THE WRIGHT FIELD PROGRAM

Holloman's place in Air Force subgravity work was taken by a slightly different program of the Aerospace Medical Laboratory at Wright Field. Scientists at Wright Field dabbled in subgravity before, as when W. J. White conducted some early underwater tests and found no significant impairment of performance in a simple "tracking" exercise.[40] However, the main efforts of the Ohio laboratory began in 1958 under the direction of Edward L. Brown. The tests were conducted in a propeller-driven C-131 cargo aircraft—the military version of the Convair commercial airliner. This plane could give only 10 to 15 seconds of weightlessness, but it offered a spacious cabin to work in. Thus it was possible to test several subjects simultaneously and to carry out a much wider range of experiments than could be made in a cramped fighter cockpit.

The tests have ranged from studies of performance in manipulating switches and levers to a comparison of alternative means of human locomotion under weightless conditions. The switch-lever study showed, rather predictably, that once a person became accustomed to weightlessness his performance was essentially unimpaired. The locomotion studies have been more spectacular. Test subjects have floated the length of the cabin, after pushing off gently from a wall; they have tried to "swim" through the air with motions of the arms and legs; they have tried walking about with magnetic and suction-cup shoes; and they have propelled themselves with a hand-held "reactor gun" which can also be used for stopping.[41]

Experimentation with magnetic shoes and other gadgets of this sort is a unique contribution of the Wright Field program. Theorists had discussed the possible need for such devices, and opinions differed as to their practicability. For instance, Heinz Haber argued in a magazine article in 1951 that any floor capable of holding down magnetic shoes would play havoc with delicate scientific instruments in the spaceship cabin.[42] Now, at last, there is a suitable laboratory in which to test these ideas under weightless conditions—and so far the results have been encouraging. The Wright Field experiments also demonstrated that the use of magnetic or suction shoes tends to make weightlessness slightly less bizarre for the passengers. Test subjects walking along a ceiling gangway in those special shoes felt that the aircraft pilot, not they, had been turned upside down.

The Wright Field C-131 tests were also noteworthy for the fact that women took part—apparently the first in the world to test subgravity. Their response was no different from that of the men at Wright Field, who mostly enjoyed the experience. Brown himself, moreover, has joined the front ranks of weightlessness boosters. He predicts that in this respect, at least, space travel will be a pleasant experience.[43]

Aside from the programs already described, there have been only a few others in the Western world. Some private institutions in the United States—such as the Cornell Aeronautical Laboratory[44]—have shown an interest in theoretical studies and in underwater simulation of weightlessness, but have lacked the means to conduct flight tests. Canada has conducted a series of subgravity research flights in a T-33 jet trainer at the Defence Research Medical Laboratory of Toronto, under the direction of Walter H. Johnson. The Canadian experiments have used human and animal subjects, including vestibular-operated cats.[45] The work in Argentina has already been mentioned, but apparently subgravity research there has languished since the departure of von Diringshofen and von Beckh.

In Europe the obvious leader is the Soviet Union, thanks to its rocket dogs and, above all, to Laika. There have also been unconfirmed news reports of Russian subgravity tests in jet aircraft.[46] Conceivably these accounts may derive from Russian references to non-Russian experiments: misunderstandings of this sort often crop up in Western journalistic reviews of Russian literature—and may even be fostered, at times, by deliberate vagueness on the part of Soviet popular-science writers. No discussions of parabolic flight experiments have appeared in the Russian scientific literature readily available in this country. Nevertheless, it would be very surprising if the Russians have not tried such experiments.

In other European countries there has been much theorizing about weightlessness but comparatively little testing activity. In France, the aviation research center at Brétigny has conducted some parabolic subgravity flights but has not emphasized this type of research.[47] In Italy, Rodolfo Margaria was a pioneer in the study of orientation problems by the water-simulation technique, with results generally comparable to those obtained in the United States.[48] In Rome, three scientists at the Study and Research Center for Aviation Medicine—Tomaso Lomonaco, L. Fabris, and M. Strollo—constructed a 15-meter-high "subgravity tower" in which a subject could be jerked up and down while seated in a simulated cockpit. One test run lasted eight seconds and gave the subject three consecutive bounces up and down. The maximum duration of sustained subgravity was 1.7 seconds, alternating with exposures to a force of three *g*. According to a report presented to the Seventh International Astronautical Congress in September 1956, subjects tried to jab at a paper target during subgravity, as was done in aircraft tests at Randolph Field. They, too, tended to hit above the target. But in general, the test conditions on this tower make it hard to distinguish what effects are clearly attributable to subgravity.[49]

The Italian subgravity tower bears a vague resemblance to a more elaborate contraption proposed in the United States by the late Howard Walton of Argonne National Laboratory. Walton envisaged a test compartment riding up and down in a vacuum tube 1,148 feet high, which supposedly would offer 41-second periods of zero-gravity alternating with brief exposures to four *g*.[50] Quite apart from all questions of practicability, this scheme had little to recommend it over the aircraft experiments already in progress. Hermann J. Muller of the Indiana University Zoology Department has made another intriguing suggestion: place a human subject in the horizontal position (to nullify most of the gravity drag on his blood flow); immerse him in brine with the same specific gravity as his body; then spin him at a speed sufficient to "disengage the vestibular apparatus from effective gravity pull in any direction."[51] Essentially the same method has long been used to nullify gravity effects in studies of plants. Muller's idea would allow prolonged exposure, but not much leeway for performance testing!

C.L. Barker, Jr., chief of an astronautical engineering section at the former Army Ballistic Missile Agency in Huntsville, proposed a ground-level space-flight simulator which would combine exposure to weightlessness and realistic *g*-forces. As explained in an Army technical report of March 1959, the vehicle he has in mind

> . . . travels around a circular track of large radius at increasing velocities simulating, by centrifugal force, the acceleration due to boost stage. After several circuits of the circular track during which desired performance is matched, the car is shunted into an upward directed vertical track on which true weightlessness is obtained. Following loss of velocity the vehicle returns down the vertical track and reverses its direction around the circular track where re-entry forces are simulated.[52]

Barker carried out a "preliminary study of site locations" for his test facility; he found the 3,000-foot-high El Capitan peak in Yosemite National Park the most promising.[53] Again leaving out the question of practicability, this would be a rather expensive device, to say the least. The mere fact that such procedures as these are suggested (and under perfectly respectable auspices) is the best possible indication that no completely satisfactory method of producing the weightless state for research purposes yet exists—nor will it exist until the first manned satellite is launched and recovered.

Nevertheless, a substantial amount of information has been collected, and so far none of it suggests that weightlessness will be a major obstacle to flight through space. Some test subjects have shown symptoms of disorientation, motion sickness or other discomfort, but severe disorders have been the exception. Nor is there any indication of really serious coordination problems. Although aiming tests and similar exercises generally confirm the assumption that it may take a little time to learn exactly what force to exert in limb movements when gravity is lacking, the same tests show that a capability for adaptation definitely exists. Finally, the experiments of von Beckh have shown that certain functions may be adversely affected by weightlessness in conjunction with exposure to high *g*-forces, but the effects seem likely to be tolerable, if uncomfortable, and presumably would not be present throughout an extended flight at zero-gravity.

The basic question still to be answered is whether prolonged weightlessness may have disabling effects not yet detected in the brief exposures. Normal activities such as eating and drinking can impose some unusual stresses under gravity-free conditions, and General Don Flickinger, Special Assistant for Bioastronautics to the Commander of the Air Research and Development Command, has pointed out that these stresses might take their toll over a long period. He adds that over the long run "reduction or impairment of circulatory and excretory functions" may result.[54] In addition, many scientists have expressed the fear that muscle tone and fiber will tend to degenerate. A special exercise machine may be needed to keep space crews physically fit; one possible solution, jointly suggested by von Beckh and von Diringshofen, would be a centrifuge bed to which space fliers could retire from time to time as a means of combating muscular and circulatory relaxation.[55] It has further been argued that basic changes in metabolism might materialize. To cap the matter, a long general conditioning to weightlessness might present special difficulties when the time came for the abrupt transition back to a normal gravity field.

Some writers have speculated on the possibility of a gradual build-up of fear and apprehension in the strange zero-gravity state, or, perhaps, a tendency to hallucinations. Psychological research has already established that a state of prolonged sensory deprivation tends to produce hallucinations, and certainly weightlessness is, among other things, a state of sensory deprivation. Schock has observed that sensory deprivation while asleep may lead to dreams of falling, which, in turn, might produce a "dread of sleep with its disturbing fancies."[56] And this does not exhaust the list of problems that may arise once prolonged exposure to weightlessness becomes a reality. On the other hand, it is well to note that some of the early fears appear to have been dispelled already by the experiments conducted so far. A case in point is the hypothesis of Otto Gauer and Heinz Haber, mentioned in a previous chapter, that in a zero-gravity state the operation of the Weber-Fechner law might produce sensations grossly disproportionate to the actual stimuli received. It should not require prolonged exposure for this effect to become evident, but, in fact, it has not been observed.[57]

If worst comes to worst, weightlessness can be avoided by rotation of the space ship or by constant rocket acceleration. There is no conclusive evidence so far, however, that this will be necessary.

PART FOUR

The Radiation Hazards

11

Cosmic Rays

COSMIC radiation is perhaps the least understood of all the major problems man will encounter in space. The name itself has a vaguely sinister ring, suggesting a mysterious and possibly deadly hazard. No one knows precisely where cosmic rays come from, or how they acquire the particular qualities that make them unlike any other known form of radiation. As for their potential danger to space travelers, though studies of their effects on living matter have been going on for 30 years, no clear-cut picture has emerged. Most investigators are inclined to believe that the exposure to cosmic rays in space flight need not exceed tolerable limits. But unfortunately it will not be easy to establish just how much exposure is tolerable or "safe."

Radiation of one kind or another is an everyday condition of man's environment. He is continually exposed to light rays, ultraviolet rays, radioactivity from the earth (*i.e.*, alpha, beta, and gamma rays), and some cosmic radiation. All this environmental radiation is well within the accepted limits of human tolerance; man has become accustomed to live with it. Indeed, the Swiss scientist Jakob A.G. Eugster, a leading authority on the biological effects of cosmic rays, reported that organisms kept in an environment almost wholly free of ionizing radiation did not develop as well as those exposed to the normal amount. He reached the conclusion—which not all of his fellow scientists accept—that a certain amount of environmental radiation is beneficial to living organisms.[1]

Cosmic rays contribute roughly 27 per cent of the ionizing radiation regularly present at the earth's surface. This despite the fact that our atmosphere is equivalent in shielding power to a lead wall more than one yard thick.[2] Some cosmic-ray particles even penetrate far underground. According to one estimate, to be completely shielded against cosmic radiation a laboratory would have to be covered by 700 feet of earth or a lead roof 49 feet thick.[3] To conduct his experiments in a place comparatively free of cosmic radiation, Eugster chose a point in the Simplon Tunnel 8,000 feet below the crest of the Alps.[4]

DISCOVERY OF COSMIC RAYS

The discovery of cosmic rays came as a by-product of research on the earth's normal environmental radiation in the early part of the twentieth century. It was known that the soil and rocks were radioactive, but detection instruments showed a surprising amount of ionizing radiation to be present even over bodies of water. Where did it come from? Experimenters measuring radioactivity high in the air (*e.g.*, in balloons and at the top of the Eiffel Tower) began to ask a similar question, for they found that ionizing radiation did not diminish as much as it should have as one moved away from the ground. Then, just before World War I, the Austrian physicist Victor F. Hess showed that at still higher altitudes the radiation actually increased. In balloon-borne experiments in the years 1911 to 1913, he found that at 1,500 meters ionization became as intense as at ground level, and it continued to increase rapidly as measurements were taken still higher up. He therefore concluded that a hitherto unknown form of radiation must be coming from above, presumably from outside the earth and its atmosphere. He also found that this radiation did not diminish during an eclipse of the sun, so apparently it did not come from the sun, at least not in a straight line as rays of visible light do.[5]

World War I seriously interfered with research on this "cosmic radiation," as it later came to be known. But after the war Hess and other scientists in Europe and America took it up again with vigor.[6] Among other things, they learned that the intensity of cosmic radiation varied with latitude. To be exact, it varied with geomagnetic latitude, that is, with relation to the magnetic poles rather than the poles of the earth's axis. Thus it became clear that the cosmic radiation was deflected by the earth's magnetic field, and therefore it must consist, at least in part, of electrically charged particles, such as protons. Further research showed that the amount of cosmic radiation coming into the earth's atmosphere increases steadily from the equator to about 55 to 60 degrees north or south geomagnetic latitude.[7] From there to the geomagnetic poles, the radiation appears to level off, for reasons not yet understood.

The high-altitude balloon ascents of the 1930's brought more information. In 1935 the Explorer II balloon flight took equipment for the measurement of cosmic rays to 72,395 feet, and unmanned sounding balloons went even higher. After World War II the introduction of scientific research rockets and constant-level polyethylene balloons gave tremendous help to cosmic-radiation studies. So did the development of special emulsions for recording cosmic-ray tracks, introduced by Ilford in Great Britain and Eastman Kodak in the United States. These thick photographic plates proved more satisfactory for cosmic-ray analysis than the cloud chambers and other measuring devices previously used.[8]

Among the discoveries made with the improved research techniques, the most sensational was the announcement in 1948 that not only protons (nuclei of hydrogen atoms) and alpha particles (helium nuclei) but also the nuclei of considerably heavier elements had been found in the primary cosmic radiation. They included iron nuclei and occasionally even heavier elements.[9] These particles were far less numerous, but they possessed a disproportionate share of the total cosmic-ray energy.

After some 40 years of research by cosmic-ray physicists, the over-all picture that now emerged was one of "a sea of rapidly moving nuclei, stripped of their electrons and converging incessantly on the earth homogeneously from each direction in space. Protons are most abundant, while the frequency of particles diminishes with increasing atomic number. Neutrons, electrons, and gamma rays are largely absent; at least they are not found in the primary component near the top of the atmosphere."[10] To be more specific, protons make up about 80 per cent of the cosmic-ray particles. Together with alpha particles, they form possibly 99 per cent of the total.[11]

At this point it should be noted that if cosmic radiation were defined as including *all* radiation of extra-terrestrial origin, the foregoing description would be incomplete. One would have to include ordinary sunlight, ultraviolet, solar X-rays, radio waves from outer galaxies, and the Van Allen belts of radiation around the earth discovered in 1958. But all these radiations are another problem; any hazards they present probably can be by-passed or warded off by shielding. The same cannot be said of the radiation specifically called cosmic rays. A protective hull of lead seems impracticable for a space ship. Thus the problem is not so much to try to find means of complete protection or evasion as to learn how much cosmic radiation human beings can tolerate.

Although the cosmic rays approach "homogeneously" from all directions in space, they do not display quite the same homogeneity in time of arrival. Periodic changes in their intensity have been observed, notably in conjunction with variations in solar activity. There are cyclical changes, and there are also sudden increases associated with the appearance of solar flares. A giant flare of February 1956 was followed by a twentyfold increase in cosmic-ray intensity at many points on the earth's surface; there is reason to suspect that outside our atmosphere the burst of intensity was very much greater. Of course, this observation tends to confirm that the sun is the source of at least part of our cosmic radiation, but other evidence indicates that most of the cosmic-ray particles raining into our atmosphere come from outside the solar system.[12]

The increase in cosmic radiation after a giant solar flare might well prove catastrophic for travelers caught out in space at the time. Fortunately, such flares are rare, and the other observed jumps in cosmic-ray intensity are less extreme. But even the average or "normal" cosmic-ray dosage—if such a thing can be said to exist—raises some real problems. When a space traveler reaches the top of the atmosphere, thousands of cosmic-ray particles will enter his body every second.[13] In terms of the total flux of energy, the exposure is moderate, but we must reckon with the phenomenal energies possessed by some of the individual particles.

Cosmic-ray particles approach the atmosphere with kinetic energies ranging from 200 million electron volts up to 100 million billion electron volts per nucleon. (The term "nucleon" is a general name for either proton or neutron; a heavy nucleus will contain a great many nucleons.) No terrestrial radiation is remotely comparable; and though it is theoretically possible to accelerate nuclei in a laboratory to cosmic-ray energies, this has not yet been achieved with the heavier nuclei.[14]

PRIMARIES AND SECONDARIES

As soon as the primary cosmic-ray particles enter the upper atmosphere, they begin to lose energy gradually by grazing encounters with the orbital electrons in air atoms. That is, they lose a little energy in stripping an electron from an atom (ionization) or in "exciting" an electron from a lower to a higher level. The cosmic particle's rate of energy loss is low at first, but as it gradually slows down, it grazes an increasing number of atoms and spends more and more of its energy. Finally it may give up what it has left in a burst of intense ionization followed by rapid tapering down to a complete halt. This process is called "thindown," from the appearance of the dying cosmic particle's track in a photographic plate (see Plate X).

Before it reaches the thindown stage, a primary cosmic particle may collide directly with another atomic nucleus; in that case it produces an explosion which scatters debris in all directions. The debris consists of fragmented nuclei, electrons, mesons, neutrons, and other elementary particles. In this process, the energy of the incoming cosmic particle is transferred to the "secondary" particles. In an emulsion recording such an event, the explosion and the scattering of the secondary particles form a "star" (see Plate XI).

Each secondary particle possesses substantially lower energy than the original primary, but the secondaries are still capable of producing further ionizations and "stars" before they are absorbed completely. Technically one can speak of "tertiary" radiation, denoting the by-products of nuclear collision with a secondary particle; this leads to "quaternary" radiation, and so forth. For convenience, it is well to place all nonprimary cosmic radiation under the general heading of secondary particles. And most primary cosmic radiation is extinguished before it reaches the 70,000-foot level; from there on down, cosmic radiation is predominantly secondary.[15]

Between about 70,000 and 80,000 feet lies the region of the heaviest ionization and the largest number of particles, mostly secondary. It does not necessarily follow that this is the area of greatest hazard from cosmic rays. A few heavy hits may well have a greater biological effect than the scattered ionization caused by many secondaries, and few heavy primaries reach this region (iron nuclei, for instance, usually penetrate no lower than 115,000 feet). David G. Simons of the United States Air Force explains the situation by comparing a heavy nucleus to a cannon ball and a proton to a bullet: if both are fired into a forest with the same speed and direction, the cannon ball will have a far higher chance of hitting wood, and therefore will be stopped sooner, than the bullet.[16]

A further complication in estimating cosmic-ray hazards is that the structure of a space vehicle will give rise to secondary particles as it absorbs some of the primary rays. In theory, the walls of a space vehicle might be made thick enough to stop most of the cosmic radiation, but this is an extremely difficult engineering feat, and *too little* shielding, just slowing primaries to the thindown range, might be worse than none at all. In some types of vehicles, adequate shielding might be provided by arranging the vehicle's fuel and supplies along the hull as a lining; such an arrangement has been suggested by several researchers.[17] Another possibility would be the deflection of cosmic-ray particles by means of an artificial magnetic field created around the space vehicle. This device, which has been proposed on both sides of the Iron Curtain,[18] seems rather questionable as protection against cosmic rays, but it might work against some other types of space radiation.

After a satellite or space vehicle has left the earth's atmosphere, its magnetic field, and its "shadow" (the earth's bulk blocks off almost half the incoming radiation from any given point even high in the atmosphere), the ship will be nakedly exposed to the full flux of primary cosmic-ray particles in space. This flux may be more hazardous than observations near the earth indicate. All the primary cosmic radiation we detect has an energy of at least 200 million electron volts per nucleon, but it is quite possible that in space there are great numbers of particles with slightly lower energies—particles still energetic enough to be dangerous.

Finally there are the variables in biological sensitivity to radiation. Some tissues, such as skin, are comparatively resistant because they easily replace destroyed or damaged cells. Nerve tissue is nonregenerative, but with certain exceptions it can afford fairly heavy losses, because the number of neural cells is much more than sufficient for most purposes. On the other hand, reproductive and embryonic cells are peculiarly sensitive to radiation, because a single damaged cell can affect so many others, directly or indirectly. In assessing the biological effects of radiation one must also distinguish between specific, functional injuries and more general, long-range damage, which may take such forms as a slight shortening of life. An aging effect might be expected, for instance, from the destruction of nerve cells that are surplus to a body's immediate requirements but irreplaceable in the long run.[19]

With so many variables involved, scientists have been understandably reluctant to commit themselves as to the precise biological significance of cosmic rays. One radiation expert, Cornelius A. Tobias of the University of California, has ventured the estimate that a space traveler leaving the protection of the earth's atmospheric and magnetic shielding (and presumably its "shadow") will receive from cosmic rays alone four times what is considered a maximum permissible radiation exposure.[20] This would be no insuperable obstacle for short trips, provided they were followed by periods of exposure to a minimum radiation environment. Longer expeditions might be a different matter, unless adequate shielding can be devised. But all estimates of the cosmic-ray hazard are still largely guesswork, particularly because there is too little experimental evidence on how cosmic rays compare with other forms of radiation in "relative biological effectiveness."

BIOLOGICAL RESEARCH

Before World War II, stratosphere balloons were used in a few cases to expose test specimens to cosmic rays, but most studies of biological exposure were conducted at ground level. They were limited to exploring the effects of secondary cosmic radiation, notably by exposing animals and other specimens to the cosmic-ray "showers" that are produced when such radiation strikes a metal plate of the right thickness.[21]

Probably the foremost early investigator of biological effects of cosmic rays was Jakob Eugster, whose experiments were mentioned at the beginning of this chapter. Setting out "to study the influence of total [environmental] radiation on biological processes, with special attention to cosmic radiation,"[22] he exposed seeds, bacteria, and small mammals at various locations in Central Europe, including the research station at 11,000 feet on the Jungfrau. Exposure times had to be long, because of the low intensity of ground-level radiation even in the Alps. Eugster reported some positive results which he attributed to cosmic radiation. After prolonged exposure of seeds to cosmic-ray showers, the plants that grew were noticeably stunted; and rabbits after similar exposure proved incapable of normal reproduction.

Other researchers in the years before World War II reported similar results from experiments of their own. None of these tests was capable of correlating specific biological effects with particular cosmic-ray hits. They indicated, essentially, a general inhibitory action—or, in the case of genetic experiments with fruit flies and laboratory cultures, a certain increase in the number of mutations. In no case were the results so striking and clear-cut as to suggest that cosmic radiation would be a barrier to travel at high altitudes or in space. Some later investigators have been rather skeptical about the test procedures and analyses used in these experiments. Moreover, the studies left virtually untouched the problem of primary cosmic radiation.[23]

After World War II, the research branched out in several new directions. V-2 rockets fired from the White Sands Proving Ground carried biological samples far into the upper atmosphere. An experiment in December 1946, sponsored by the National Institutes of Health, exposed fungus spores, but it ended in failure because the lucite cylinders containing the spores were not recovered. Experimental techniques improved, however, and in the following year a container of fruit flies was carried to an altitude of 106 miles and successfully parachuted back to earth. The flies were recovered alive and in apparent good health.[24] Later rocket flights from White Sands and from neighboring Holloman Air Force Base, made primarily to explore the effects of weightlessness on mice and monkeys, also served to expose the test subjects to cosmic radiation. The altitudes attained took the specimens fully into the region of primary cosmic particles, but the subjects showed no sign of radiation damage.

THE SHIFT TO BALLOONS

Rocket flights such as these allow only a few minutes' exposure in the upper atmosphere—too brief an interval to expect appreciable effects from cosmic rays. They also entail exposure to multi-*g* acceleration and other complicating factors which may conceivably affect the test results. So interest turned to balloons. The late J.M. Beal of the University of Chicago sent up several kinds of seeds with clusters of rubber balloons, launched from the athletic field of the University. One flight in November 1947, which ultimately ended in Lake Erie, lasted eight hours and reached over 100,000 feet; other flights were conducted at lower altitudes, expressly to study secondary radiation. In no case did the seeds show any effect of their exposure to the radiation.[25]

A more significant program of cosmic-ray research flights was inaugurated at Holloman in the summer of 1950. It used the newly-developed constant-level balloons made of polyethylene, which were sturdier and more reliable than rubber balloons. The Air Force balloon flights began at a highly opportune moment, for the whole problem of cosmic-ray hazards had recently been put in new perspective by the discovery of the heavy primaries. Scientists who had seen no major reason for alarm in the results of Eugster's rabbit experiments now began to talk of "deadly atomic particles" and to wonder whether cosmic rays might not turn out to be a critical hazard after all.[26]

Like the early rocket flights staged with mice and monkeys, these balloon flights at Holloman were directed by the Aero Medical Laboratory at Wright Field. Holloman was chosen as the launch site because it was becoming the main Air Force flight center for research ballooning. In the first flight bearing animals, on September 8, 1950, the balloon reached only 47,000 feet, and the "14 or 16" mouse subjects died, because the capsule leaked and lost pressure. But on September 28, 1950, a balloon took eight mice to 97,000 feet and brought all back alive. One mouse died en route back to the base after landing, but autopsy indicated that its death was due to a pulmonary inflammation rather than to cosmic rays.[27]

By the end of 1952, Holloman's Balloon Branch had launched 21 more research flights for the cosmic-ray program. Some carried non-biological payloads, such as track-recording emulsions and experimental equipment.

On live flights, the subjects included mice, hamsters, fruit flies, cats, and dogs. The usual flight plans called for altitudes in the neighborhood of 90,000 to 100,000 feet, with durations all the way up to 28 hours. About half the flights experienced either balloon failure (complete or partial) or other equipment trouble. In others, the equipment functioned properly but the animals died on the ground while awaiting recovery. In fact, out of 11 flights with animal subjects, only two could be counted wholly successful, although others enjoyed partial triumphs. Such problems were inevitable in a young art like plastic research ballooning, and above all in the biomedical branch of that art, which presented special complications.[28]

One complication shared by all the flights that required long duration was the difficulty of keeping the balloon at the desired altitude overnight, because the gas cooled and contracted. This could be overcome by dropping ballast, but with unmanned vehicles the operation was not easy. Another complication was the need to provide a controlled environment for the test animals. This required careful balancing of many factors. For example, the animals had to be kept reasonably warm at night; this could be accomplished simply by putting enough animals in the capsule, but that called for more oxygen and made it harder to keep the subjects cool in the daytime. The apparatus for controlling their environment also presented problems of bulk and weight. Last but certainly not least, the animal flights required unusual precision in recovery to bring the specimens back alive. The equipment at hand normally was not adequate both to protect the specimens in flight and to sustain them for any considerable length of time after landing.[29]

People from the Wright Field laboratory and from the Holloman balloon organization worked hard to bring these and related problems under control. Yet, valuable as all this work was in developing research techniques and experience, the early flights did not produce much useful biological information. The animal subjects showed no apparent signs of radiation damage, but this gave no real assurance, especially because it was becoming apparent that Holloman was too far south in geomagnetic latitude to obtain any significant exposure to thindown hits by heavy primary particles, which are likely to produce the greatest biological effect.[30]

Meanwhile other experiments were going on, at ground level and in balloons, but with similar limitations and ambiguous results. Frank H. J. Figge of the University of Maryland Medical School had reported in 1947 that the "rate of induction" of cancer in mice rose when they were exposed to cosmic-ray showers (under a lead plate). However, a group of British scientists, in experimenting at the Jungfrau and in London, failed to confirm Figge's finding,[31] and the hazard of secondary cosmic radiation remained far from clear. (The best current estimate is that even in the region of its greatest concentration in the atmosphere this radiation would amount to less than the maximum permissible radiation dose for "continuous industrial exposure."[32])

Dr. Eugster, the Swiss investigator, expanded his experimentation. He persuaded mountain-climbers to take biological specimens with them to the upper slopes of Mount Everest. In Switzerland he sent up specimens with meteorological sounding balloons to altitudes as high as 100,000 feet, where they were exposed to appreciable primary cosmic radiation. Eugster did not attempt to control the environment of his subjects by enclosing them in a capsule; he simply selected hardy organisms, such as the eggs of *Artemia salina* (brine shrimp), which could stand the thin air and extreme temperatures at high altitude. He put the tiny eggs in perforations in a special plate, sandwiched the plate between nuclear emulsions to record the cosmic-ray exposure, and attached the sandwich to a balloon. His findings suggested that the right kind of cosmic-ray hit was capable of killing an *Artemia* egg.[33]

But Eugster's weather balloons could carry only a small payload, allowed only a short exposure, and were launched at a geomagnetic latitude (50° north) which, though farther north than Holloman, just touched the borderline for exposure to heavy nuclear thindowns. What cosmic-radiation studies now needed was an intensified program of high-altitude flights with plastic research balloons at more northerly latitudes.

12

The Edge of Space

EVEN before the successful launching of the first man-made satellite, there was a growing awareness that man was on the eve of the Age of Space, and one of the clearest signs was a sharp increase in research on the biological effects of cosmic radiation. From 1953 on, a great amount of effort was devoted to this research. The techniques were constantly improved, and researchers began to come to grips with the problem of measuring the effects of heavy primary cosmic particles.

The heavy primaries are considered particularly dangerous for several reasons. They carry a major share of the total cosmic-ray energy, and their heavy electrical charge gives them high ionizing power. To be sure, an individual nucleus traveling with very high energy may actually be less dangerous than a slower one. A primary with a kinetic energy of more than one billion electron volts (*bev*) per nucleon may go right through the body without inflicting any major damage. Moreover, it usually ends in a direct collision with a nucleus, producing a "star," or explosion of secondaries, which have not so far been found to be a critical hazard. On the other hand, a slower-moving primary (less than one *bev* per nucleon) has a higher probability of stripping electrons from atoms by grazing hits. It may spend its entire energy in such ordinary ionizations without ever encountering a nuclear collision; that is to say, it is more likely to end in the thindown process. In doing so, a heavy primary produces dense ionization; at the peak, the ionization track may be one millimeter long and more than 20 microns wide. This is wide enough to envelop entire cells.

A single thindown hit by a heavy nucleus may deliver an amount of energy, measured in roentgen units, which is many times what would be a lethal dose if the same energy were absorbed by the whole body. Fortunately, the hit is lethal only to cells in the particle's track. If they happen to be reproductive cells, a heavy hit may be less serious in ultimate consequences than a lighter one, for it is likely to kill the cells outright instead of producing harmful mutations to be transmitted to later generations.

Nonetheless, the heavy cosmic particles traveling slowly enough to produce ionization by thindown hits are reckoned to be the greatest single cosmic-ray hazard to space travelers. Herman Yagoda of the Air Force Cambridge Research Center has estimated that a flier at the top of the atmosphere would be exposed to thindown ionizations from about 28 medium or heavy nuclei per cubic centimeter of tissue per day. Farther out, beyond the zone where the earth shields off part of the cosmic radiation by the "shadow" effect, the number would of course be substantially greater.[1]

Because the low-energy particles are most susceptible to deflection by the earth's magnetic field, they are seldom encountered by research balloons save at the higher geomagnetic latitudes. In 1953, therefore, the Air Force began to launch its cosmic-ray balloon flights farther north. Holloman Air Force Base was still used as a launch point for equipment tests and control flights, and it continued to serve as headquarters for all the flights, but certain changes were made in the organization and personnel of the Air Force's cosmic-radiation program. In January, 1953, the program ceased to be conducted by officers assigned from the Aero Medical Laboratory at Wright Field; it became instead an activity of the Air Force Missile Development Center at Holloman. These administrative changes assured the cosmic-ray program of somewhat greater and more continuous support than it had enjoyed when it was just one small, physically separated activity of the huge Wright Field organization.

The program benefited further from improvements in flight performance, due in part to the fruition of previous efforts and in part to continuing research and development by aeromedical scientists, balloon technicians, and others. Radio-equipped panel trucks on the ground supplemented aircraft in tracking the balloons. Improved antenna systems permitted the payload capsule to send out reliable signals even after it landed, thus helping search parties to find it. Improvements in tracking and recovery were of course particularly important for space biology flights, which required prompter recovery than most. It did little good to get back a lost balloon capsule months after a flight (in response to the $25 reward offered), for by then all the biological specimens had perished.

Another noteworthy development was a method of terminating balloon flights by radio command. Two different devices for this purpose were inaugurated in 1953—one developed at Wright Field, the other provided by the aeronautical laboratories of General Mills, the nation's largest manufacturer of plastic research balloons. This new radio method supplemented the earlier pre-set timer, which had been inadequate by itself because it might automatically let down a balloon capsule during a thunderstorm or drop it in an inaccessible area. At least now the flight would be shortened if these difficulties were anticipated.[3]

The environmental controls for sealed animal capsules likewise improved. One of the most ingenious developments was the use of boiling water as a coolant—a system developed at Holloman and successfully flight-tested on balloon missions in the fall of 1953. With decreasing atmospheric pressure, water boils at lower temperatures: at an altitude of about 112,000 feet, for example, its boiling point is 32 degrees Fahrenheit—the freezing temperature at sea level. At high altitudes, therefore, water can be made to boil simply by placing it in a container vented to the low outside atmospheric pressure. Now if the air in the animal-bearing capsule is circulated around this container, the water will absorb its heat and the vapor of the boiling will carry off the heat through the vent.[4]

During 1954 and 1955 the weight of the standard animal capsule was reduced from 165 pounds to about 70. The weight of balloon-borne instrumentation also was sharply reduced. As a result, it became possible to attain significantly higher altitudes with the same balloons and biological payloads.[5]

There were also improvements in balloon-launching methods, designed principally to protect the balloons from high winds during inflation. To be sure, these and other innovations in balloon techniques were not developed solely for space biology. Of some 1,000 plastic-balloon flights launched by the Holloman Balloon Branch from 1950 through 1958, only a small fraction were for cosmic-ray studies of Holloman's Aeromedical Field Laboratory. But the space-biology flights made use of all the major technological advances, including those developed by balloon specialists of the Air Force Cambridge Research Center and by the private balloon firms that handled most of the northern launchings in the cosmic-ray program.[6]

Meanwhile the balloons themselves were growing bigger and better. One landmark was the introduction of two-million-cubic-foot plastic balloons. The first to be used on a biological cosmic-radiation flight was launched from Fleming Field in South St. Paul, Minn., in July 1955. It reached an altitude of over 120,000 feet.[7] Two years later the research program was using three-million-cubic-foot balloons, and in 1958 David G. Simons and his Holloman co-workers tried a balloon with a capacity of five million cubic feet—almost equal to that of the ill-fated dirigible *Hindenburg*. The giant new vehicle was to have taken biological specimens to an altitude of 135,000 feet, but several attempts failed to produce a successful flight. Notwithstanding this failure, there was general improvement during these years in balloon performance, flight techniques, and post-flight recovery. One successful innovation was an installment plan for lengthening the exposure of specimens to cosmic rays: the same organisms were sent up again and again. For example, in 1954 a batch of radish seeds was exposed on consecutive flights for a total of 251 hours above 82,000 feet, and some animal subjects were exposed for more than 74 hours at the same altitude.[8]

However, the very first flight in the cosmic-radiation program after Dr. Simons assumed its direction indicated that there was still room for human error. The flight was launched at Holloman on February 12, 1953, with the objective of exposing hamsters to the effects of radiation at about 90,000 feet. Tracking crews lost the balloon, but the capsule was found the next day near Whiting Naval Air Station in Florida. Unhappily, the teletypewriter message that the naval authorities promptly sent to the Aeromedical Field Laboratory was not delivered until six days later—a minor duration record in itself. The Laboratory quickly put in a telephone call to the Florida finders asking them to open the capsule. Because hamsters are very hardy, all seven passengers were still alive, but one hamster died the next day and another later was cannibalized by its fellows.[9]

This memorable flight was followed by six launched from the Vernalis Naval Air Station in California. They were cross-country flights designed by the Air Force Cambridge Research Center to study high-altitude wind fields; Holloman's Space Biology Branch took the opportunity to send along 600 fruit flies (*drosophila*) in sealed tubes on each flight. But the journeys in this project were too long for effective tracking, and only 12 flies out of several thousand came back to Holloman alive.[10]

NORTHERN FLIGHTS

The first flight from a northerly location took place on March 26, 1953. Launched at Tillamook, Ore., it carried a variety of test subjects. In June and July four flights took off from the Great Falls Air Force Base in Montana. Five were launched in October and November from Pierre, South Dakota, under a contract with General Mills, which supplied the balloons and took full responsibility for the flight operations, although a number of Holloman people, including Dr. Simons, were also on hand.[11]

In the following year another contractor, Winzen Research, conducted a new series of northerly flights. After one preliminary launching at Fleming Field in South St. Paul, the main series took place at Sault Sainte Marie, Mich., a location at 57½ degrees north geomagnetic latitude. Winzen supplied the balloons and the launch crew, under the direction of Ed Lewis, who has also launched propaganda balloons across the Iron Curtain in Europe. The eight flights from Sault Sainte Marie carried specimens ranging from radish seeds to monkeys. Two sets of monkeys were lost because of technical difficulties, but the next pair flew successfully on two separate occasions.[12] Six Holloman flights in the fall of 1954 and the first part of 1955 set the stage for a series of 11 launchings from South St. Paul and International Falls, Minn., in the summer of 1955. Winzen Research again directed flight operations under contract. On several occasions, uninvited tracking assistance was received from jet fighters of the Air Defense Command, which were in the air investigating flying-saucer reports inspired by the balloon flights.[13]

During 1956 and 1957 the Holloman cosmic-radiation program

received less emphasis. One reason was Holloman's absorption in preparations for the manned-balloon program, Project Man-High. In this project, cosmic-radiation studies were secondary to the objective of testing a sealed-cabin environment for man. Another reason for the slackening pace in cosmic-ray research was simply that the Human Factors Division of the Air Research and Development Command was limited in funds and gave higher priority to other projects. In the fiscal year 1957, the Holloman cosmic-ray program received no "in-house" operating funds at all, and all related research by outside investigators had to be funded through the Air Force Office of Scientific Research in Washington. The latter negotiated only one contract, with the University of Texas. It was assumed that test flights of the Man-High balloon capsule could provide whatever direct cosmic-ray exposures were needed under the Texas contract and two other outside contracts carried over from an earlier period.

All this should have about finished cosmic-radiation research as a separate program of the Aeromedical Field Laboratory, but Simons did not give up easily. During fiscal 1957 he kept Harold H. Kuehn assigned as a cosmic-ray task scientist under his own direction, although Kuehn could not do much more than think things over. Then on July 1, 1957, the Aeromedical Field Laboratory regained its right to negotiate contracts related to cosmic-ray research. "In-house" funds were also authorized once more, but it was some time before the program regained momentum.[14]

During 1956 and 1957 just two balloon flights were made specifically for biological cosmic-ray research. Both were launched from Holloman early in 1956, in large part as controls for the International Falls flights of 1955. Certain experiments were also carried out with guinea pigs in April 1957, in conjunction with an unmanned flight test of the Man-High capsule from South St. Paul. Finally a group of cosmic-ray experiments was conducted during Simons' flight of August, 1957, which was launched from an open-pit iron mine in Crosby, Minn. It lasted 32 hours and reached an altitude of 102,000 feet, the record for a manned balloon.

Two containers of pink bread mold (*Neurospora crassa*) were flown underneath Simons' capsule for study of the genetic effects of cosmic radiation. This fungus is well suited for such studies, because of its relatively simple cell organization and short-lived "generations." Simons himself also served as a subject for cosmic-ray research (among many other things) on this flight. Three nuclear track plates were attached to his body to monitor his cosmic-ray exposure, and samples of his blood were examined before and after the flight for the possible appearance of bilobed lymphocytes as an effect of cosmic radiation. It had been planned to send a monkey along with Simons in the capsule, not so much to keep him company as to squeeze in another cosmic-ray experiment. Webb Haymaker, Chief of the Neuropathology Section of the Armed Forces Institute of Pathology, had actually selected the monkey and had it shipped from Washington to Wright Field in Ohio to take part in a pre-flight test of the capsule. But at this point the animal was firmly grounded by order of Colonel Stapp, Chief of the Aeromedical Field Laboratory.[15]

Haymaker was to have had a chance to expose several small primates to cosmic radiation in six balloon flights scheduled by the Aeromedical Field Laboratory in the summer of 1958. These flights were to use the newly designed balloons of five-million-cubic-foot capacity. The plans even called for frogs and goldfish to take part—the goldfish to travel in plastic-bag containers for a special study of the effects of radiation on their pigmentation. But only one batch of specimens—a monkey, a goldfish, *drosophila* larvae, and some *Neurospora*—was actually assembled, and in three attempts from International Falls and Crosby this cargo never managed to get above 63,000 feet. The summer's flight program was cancelled, on the ground that more work was needed to perfect the balloon vehicle.[16]

In fact, the whole program of animal balloon flights was terminated, so that the Aeromedical Field Laboratory could better carry out a new mission emphasizing operational support of United States biosatellite activities. Simons was reassigned to the Air Force School of Aviation Medicine in January 1959, and the future outlook for biological cosmic-ray research by the Air Force is not wholly clear. Presumably satellites will in due course play an important part in studies of biological effects of cosmic radiation.

The last flight in the Man-High project, launched from Holloman in October 1958 with Clifton M. McClure, III, as pilot, was at least partly concerned with cosmic-ray research. It was hoped that McClure's flight would serve as a "control" for more northerly flights entailing exposure to heavy-primary thindowns. Unfortunately, premature termination of his flight, due to overheating of the capsule, impaired its significance for cosmic-ray studies, either as a control or otherwise.[17]

Of course the experiments with animals, seeds, and other organisms had been fully backed up with control tests. The biological subjects flown at northern latitudes were compared with specimens flown in balloons from Holloman or with "ground controls" in a chamber which simulated all the test conditions except exposure to cosmic rays.[18]

BLACK MICE AND GRAY HAIRS

So far as finding any effects of cosmic radiation is concerned, the results of most of the animal and seed experiments were either negative or inconclusive. The same applies to the exposure of Simons himself in his record flight of August 1957. He later pointed with pride, half seriously, to certain gray hairs on his arm which he attributed to primary cosmic rays. Hair graying, as we shall see, is a definitely established effect of radiation, but since Simons already had some gray hairs before he left the ground, it would be hard to prove that the new ones were really due to bombardment from outer space.[19]

Much of the Air Force program of research on cosmic-ray effects was performed by academic investigators on a contract basis. Berry Campbell of the University of Minnesota had a contract to examine the effects on neural tissue, but he received too few exposed animal specimens to arrive at any conclusive findings. He attempted to get a "model of cosmic-ray events" by irradiating hamsters in the University of California 184-inch cyclotron; the results were unsatisfactory, but this method served as a precedent for later biological experiments at Berkeley, seeking to parallel cosmic-ray exposures.[20]

Herman B. Chase of Brown University had more success later in a study of the effects of cosmic radiation on skin and hair; his subjects were mice and guinea pigs that had been flown at northern locations. Professor Chase and his associates were able to report the most clear-cut effects of cosmic radiation to date: a statistically significant increase in white or gray hairs on black mice and guinea pigs, presumably due to destruction of hair-pigmentation cells by cosmic rays. These cells are few in number (at least few per hair) and not replaceable, and they are excellent indicators of cosmic-ray damage because the evidence of their destruction is magnified and made visible by the appearance of a nonpigmented hair. What is more, the investigators found that gray streaks were up to ten times wider than would be expected from a thindown hit by a heavy primary, which suggested the possibility of an "unidentified mechanism" capable of spreading the radiation damage.[21] (In the unsophisticated days of 1950, when the balloon flights with animals at Holloman began, only *white* mice had been used!)

Another notable research contract, partly financed by the Atomic Energy Commission, provided physiological and psychological testing for the two monkeys flown from Sault Sainte Marie in 1954. After their 74 hours in the balloon capsule at 82,000 to 90,000 feet and higher, these monkeys were delivered to Harry F. Harlow of the University of Wisconsin for behavioral studies. They received the Wisconsin Appetite Test to detect possible changes in their fondness for peanuts and raisins and were subjected to many other tests. After six months they were returned to Holloman and kept for some time under less intensive observation. No evidence of harm from cosmic rays was ever established.[22]

Eugster in Switzerland also collaborated with Holloman; in fact, part of his research was financed under contract with the Air Research and Development Command. He shipped a number of specimens to Holloman to be flown in its balloon program and analyzed them after their exposure. His subjects included seeds, *Artemia* eggs, and most exotic of all, slices of animal skin, plus some skin of his own. After these bits of skin had been exposed to cosmic rays, he reimplanted them in their donors. Some of the implants developed small tumors, but apparently none of the effects of the exposure was really serious. Plants grown from seeds flown for Eugster on various northern flights showed evidence of poor development as compared with plants grown from controls; there were also three cases of apparent color mutations.[23]

Wilson S. Stone of the University of Texas and A. Gib DeBusk, formerly at Texas and now with Florida State University, have shown a special interest in the genetic effects of cosmic rays. *Neurospora crassa* molds were flown on their behalf during the 1955 International Falls flights, and they reported some "significant" increases in the number of back mutants after exposure to cosmic radiation. Later Stone and DeBusk received contracts to continue their genetic studies, and DeBusk was the contributor of the *Neurospora* samples which were attached to Simons' capsule on the historic Man-High flight of August 1957.[24]

Among the leading investigators taking advantage of the Holloman balloon-flight program was Webb Haymaker of the Armed Forces Institute of Pathology, who has already been mentioned. He continued Campbell's work on nerve tissue, working with other scientists in the United States and abroad. He used mice, guinea pigs, and various tissue cultures, and he detected one or two lesions, possibly caused by medium-weight cosmic-ray primaries, in the brains of guinea pigs that went on the unmanned test flight of the Man-High capsule in April 1957. This was the closest that anyone had come to finding evidence of nerve-tissue damage from cosmic rays. The flight in question was further notable as marking the first time that emulsion plates were successfully attached to the bodies of test animals in an attempt to correlate signs of damage with a record of specific cosmic-ray events.[25]

Other government scientists taking part in the program included Irwin Lebish, also of the Armed Forces Institute of Pathology, who looked for radiation effects such as leukemia, life-shortening, and genetic changes in mice;[26] Paul Cibis and Hubertus Strughold of the Air Force School of Aviation Medicine, who investigated possible eye damage;[27] and the late Howard Walton of the Argonne National Laboratory, who studied balloon-flown seeds and grasshopper eggs exposed to cosmic rays. Walton believed that he had found some signs of developmental aberrations in the grasshoppers, but this work was unfortunately cut short before its completion by his death.[28] In 1955 Herman Yagoda, then with the National Institutes of Health, contributed a notable experiment of quite another kind. To count the cosmic-ray hits that would impinge on a man's head, he mounted an emulsion on "a human skull padded with foam rubber to simulate soft tissue." This odd contraption was flown on one of the northern flights in the Holloman program.[29]

This by no means exhausts the list of government and academic researchers who participated one way or another in the Aeromedical Field Laboratory cosmic-radiation program. Some of them simply threw in small items as "hitchhikers" on the balloon flights; some served as valuable advisers on the general orientation of the program; some took part in actual flight operations. Dr. Haymaker has published a short article, "Operation Stratomouse,"[30] giving a lively picture of his own direct participation in the 1955 International Falls flights.

The net result of all this effort, however, has been a dearth of positive signs of cosmic-ray effects. To be sure, the negative findings may not be too significant, because the samples and exposures may have been inadequate, and delayed reactions may yet appear. Nevertheless, even with these qualifications, the experimental results have been rather encouraging. Hair-graying, the most striking effect that anyone discovered, would surely be a tolerable price to pay for the advantages of man's takeoff into space. The developmental effects that have been reported are mildly disturbing, but a human embryo might be less vulnerable to cosmic rays than grasshopper eggs, and anyway pregnant women could be left at home (except on multi-generation voyages through the galaxies).

The genetic effects, though no immediate health problem, do raise awkward questions, for while they would not injure the traveler himself, they might inflict disabilities upon innocent members of distant generations. But this risk is essentially no different from the one accepted by persons who regularly work in the vicinity of X-rays or other radiation. Considering the comparatively small number of persons likely to be engaged in space travel, the genetic danger to mankind as a whole is possibly less than that from occupational radiation exposure on earth. There is no doubt that cosmic rays will be a real hazard for space travelers, and that the hazard will increase steadily as longer trips into space are attempted, but it does not yet appear so great as to offset the positive advantages of exploring the vertical frontier.

FUTURE COSMIC-RAY WORK

Research on the hazard has really only begun. The tests that showed radiation effects, such as Chase's hair studies, might well be repeated with careful monitoring of the exposure by emulsions. A coordinated effort is being waged from California to Scandinavia to simulate primary cosmic rays, particularly the heavy particles, in accelerating machines.[31] And the Air Force has elaborate plans to measure the "whole-body radiation activity" of pilots returning from very high-altitude flights in the X-15 research aircraft.[32] The most pressing need is for even higher and longer exposure of test specimens. The plastic balloon can still help, because space biology has not yet fully exploited its potential ceiling of about 150,000 feet (where it runs out of air in which to float). But the "ultimate" test vehicle is the biosatellite. Sputnik II, with its passenger dog Laika, pointed the way, though its great drawback from the standpoint of radiobiology was the failure to bring Laika back for examination. The mere fact that the dog survived for a week may prove something about the biological hazards of space radiation, but the Russians readily admitted that the experiment offered no basis for any firm conclusions on this matter.[33]

The Soviet Union has excellent cosmic-ray physicists, but its work in space biology has given less attention to cosmic-ray exposure than to other problems. Researchers in Great Britain and India have explored cosmic rays with polyethylene balloons, but they have been interested primarily in studying the physical properties of the radiation; at least they do not appear to have loaded their balloons with seeds and animal test subjects.[34] Nor have other foreign scientists, with the notable exception of Eugster in Switzerland, performed work in recent years at all similar to that of the United States Air Force with its high-altitude balloon research on the biological effects of cosmic rays.

In the summer of 1958 the United States Navy started work along the same lines. Its Stratolab balloon, piloted by Malcolm Ross and M. Lee Lewis to 80,000 feet on July 26-27, carried a collection of 10,000 insects ranging from fleas to honey bees. This phase of experimentation was under the charge of scientists representing the United States Department of Agriculture and Howard University, and the purpose was to look for cosmic-ray influences on the rate of mutations. The results were inconclusive.[35] The Navy later flew seeds with unmanned research balloons and turned them over to Republic Aviation for planting in its "lunar garden," where effects on the germination and growth of the specimens were to be studied.[36]

Meanwhile, some cosmic-ray experimentation has continued in rocket shots. The Jupiter missile launched from Cape Canaveral on May 28, 1959, carried not only the monkeys Able and Baker but also a large number of smaller test items—fruit fly larvae, mustard seeds, human blood, yeast, sea urchin eggs, etc. Most of these specimens were sent along to test the effects of radiation rather than weightlessness.[37] In September, 1959, a Jupiter similarly loaded with biological samples—this time including pregnant mice—had to be destroyed by the range safety officer just after launching.[38] And there have been other recent rocket flights with animals in the United States, not to mention those launched by the Soviet Union. However, ordinary rocket shots do not offer much information on cosmic-ray effects. The successful Jupiter shot of May 28, 1959, for example, allowed an exposure measured only in minutes, though it did reach an altitude of 300 miles.

Attempts to pursue cosmic-ray research in biosatellites really began in June 1959, when the United States Air Force tried to send up a Discoverer satellite with a cargo of black mice from the Vandenberg Air Force Base in California. Elaborate arrangements were made to recover the capsule after a few revolutions around the earth. Unfortunately, the satellite failed to go into orbit, but presumably this was only a forerunner of further attempts.[39] In the long run, such experimentation as this may permit a definitive answer as to whether cosmic radiation will limit man's exploration of space.

13

Other Radiations in Space

WE HAVE already referred to the fact that the cosmic rays are only one of the potentially troublesome radiations in space. The others range from ordinary sunlight to the so-called "Van Allen radiation." Research on these has not been altogether neglected.

One of the first radiation problems to engage the serious attention of writers dealing with the prospect of manned space flight was that posed by the sun's heat radiation. Heat, however, is a familiar phenomenon, and the studies of this problem have been concerned with cabin insulation, rather than the radiation *per se*. Much the same is true of the sun's visible-light radiation. Because in space sunlight is not diffused, as it is in the earth's atmosphere, objects exposed directly to it will be so bright as to create an uncomfortable glare or even actual danger to the eyes. This problem was discussed by Hubertus Strughold at the Tenth Annual Congress of the International Astronautical Federation in London in 1959. But again it is a matter to be dealt with largely in terms of space-cabin (and space-helmet) design. Likewise, cabin arrangements, and possibly preconditioning of the crew, will have to deal with the absence of a day-night cycle on long voyages.[1]

Radiation studies *per se* first became a significant concern of space biology with the growth of research and speculation on the effects of cosmic rays, and of the heavy primaries especially. However, ultraviolet rays and solar X-rays did get mentioned at early symposia on space medicine, such as one held in Chicago in March 1950 under the auspices of the University of Illinois.[2] They occasioned some discussion, but by and large no great alarm.

Against the sun's ultraviolet rays, the ozone layer in our atmosphere (extending from about 12 to 25 miles up) suffices to protect us. In space, these rays could burn the skin and cause conjunctivitis. But the hull of a space craft would ward them off just as effectively as the ozone layer does, and the windows or observation ports could be made opaque to ultraviolet. Anyone leaving the vehicle (*e.g.*, to assemble an orbital space station or to explore an ozone-less celestial body) could be protected by a space suit and helmet.[3]

Solar X-rays present a slightly more complicated problem. The sun, especially during flares, emits appreciable quantities of X-rays—both "soft" (*i.e.*, easily screened off) and "hard." The latter, which can penetrate our atmosphere down to perhaps the 30-mile level, are not as abundant as the soft component but may be intense enough to be damaging. It is possible that measurements of this radiation will show that shielding will be needed. If so, the shielding will have to be very carefully designed, for one must bear in mind in this connection that a wrong amount of shielding, as pointed out in a previous chapter, may actually increase the hazard from cosmic rays.[4]

THE VAN ALLEN RADIATION

The sun also emits potentially dangerous streams of electrons and low-energy protons—the streams that create magnetic storms and auroral displays in our atmosphere. (The aurorae also contain X-rays, generated by the electrons on striking the upper air.)

The auroral radiation has been studied extensively in recent years, by such scientists as James Van Allen of Iowa State University, using research rockets, high-altitude balloons, and "rockoons" (rockets launched from balloons). The investigators found that the energy of the "primary" electrons and protons is usually less than 0.5 mev (million electron volts) and that the secondary X-rays have energies in the range of 10 to 100 kev (thousand electron volts). The total intensity of the auroral radiation is estimated to be "at least 1,000" times that of the cosmic radiation. But Hermann J. Schaefer of the United States Naval School of Aviation Medicine, a leading authority on the biological significance of cosmic and other space radiations, believes that shielding against this relatively "soft" radiation would be no problem. Just one millimeter of Alclad hull would greatly reduce the intensity of the auroral X-rays, and clothing would offer still further protection. Schaefer emphasized, too, that the auroral radiation is irregular and mainly confined to high latitudes, so that the proportion of time spent within it would be small for any kind of satellite orbit. In fact, it would be perfectly possible to avoid the auroral zones altogether.[5]

Schaefer's analysis, the first important discussion of the auroral radiation from a radiobiological standpoint, was published in the *Journal of Aviation Medicine* in July 1958. But when it appeared, his conclusions were slightly anticlimactic, for a new radiation danger had just been discovered. It was announced in newspaper headlines such as this: SCIENTISTS DISCLOSE SPACE DANGER—Radioactive Belt Revealed as Threat to Human Travel.[6] One news report spoke of "a mysterious band of extremely intense radiation" some 600 miles in space which raised a "new obstacle to manned space flight."[7]

The cause of all the excitement was a series of special reports to the National Academy of Sciences on the results of the first two successful United States satellite experiments: Explorer I, launched January 31, 1958, and Explorer III, launched on March 26. Geiger counters aboard the satellites had detected a new band of radiation "1,000 times as intense" as the known cosmic radiation. To be sure, this figure was at best an approximation; it was really impossible to say just how intense the radiation was, because it had "jammed" the measuring instruments. The new belt of radiation appeared to start about 600 miles up and showed no signs of tapering off at the highest point reached by the satellites (about 1,700 miles).[8]

The experts were understandably cautious in speculating as to the precise nature and origin of the new-found radiation. But Dr. Van Allen, chief designer of the Explorers' radiation experiments, distinguished "this new radiation" from the "cosmic rays themselves." He and his co-workers believed that it was probably attributable to ionized gas shot out from the sun, and that it consisted of electrons and/or protons. They surmised further that the radiation "must at least initially be associated with plasmas which seriously perturb the earth's magnetic field," and that "this plasma is closely related to geomagnetic storms and aurorae."[9] Scientists speculated on the need for, and feasibility of, some kind of artificial shielding in manned flight through the radiation zone,[10] but they were careful to reserve final judgment pending clarification of the nature of the phenomenon.

The next step was to send up a satellite expressly designed to study this "mysterious" radiation. Explorer IV, launched on July 26 from Cape Canaveral, carried two Geiger counters, one of which was shielded to keep out low-energy radiation.[11] Preliminary results released in August gave rise to more alarm. "Space Radiation Found Deadlier," said a caption in the conservative *New York Times*.[12] In effect, the data transmitted from Explorer IV seemed to indicate that the radiation doubled with every 60-mile increase in altitude, starting from about the 250-mile level, and that it became "harder," or more penetrating, the higher the measurements were taken. Some calculations now put the exposure for a human space traveler as high as 100 roentgens per hour—and the lethal dose for man is about 450 roentgens.[13] Explorer IV thus led Albert R. Hibbs, of Caltech's Jet Propulsion Laboratory, to predict that man's first journey into space was indefinitely postponed.[14]

Explorer IV, it developed later, also was designed to record the radiation created by the secret Project Argus—a series of atomic explosions set off in August-September 1958 around 300 miles up. A principal objective of this experiment was to determine whether radiation resulting from the explosion would be trapped by the earth's magnetic field—and trapped it was. The experiment served to demonstrate that certain forms of radiation could be caught in the magnetic field and held in a belt around the planet.[15]

GETTING THROUGH

When the Ninth Annual Congress of the International Astronautical Federation met in Amsterdam in August 1958, space radiation was one of the foremost topics of discussion. The Russians pointed out that the existence of the new radiation zone had also been clearly detected by Sputnik II (launched May 15, 1958).[16] But the radiation paper that attracted the widest attention was one entitled "Some Consequences of a Theory of the Radiation Belt," by

S. Fred Singer of the University of Maryland. Singer described the radiation belt as consisting of particles trapped by the earth's magnetic field, which he termed "a good 'container' for *charged* particles of not too high energy." In discussing a possible "injection mechanism" by which particles might enter this "container," Singer observed:

> Primary cosmic rays smash into the earth's atmosphere in the vicinity of 20-25 kilometers (70,000 feet) and disintegrate atmospheric nuclei. Neutrons are released with energies up to several 100 Mev, many of which travel upwards (and are therefore called cosmic-ray "albedo").
>
> Being uncharged, the neutrons travel along straight lines, right through the earth's magnetic field, out into space. But free neutrons are radioactive. A minute fraction of them change into protons while traveling through the field (about 10^{-13} per centimeter, or about one in a million in 100 miles). These protons immediately spiral around the lines of force; a fraction are lost immediately as they get back too deep into the atmosphere, but the rest are trapped.

Singer believed that the "lifetimes" of the trapped protons—"ranging to tens of years at high altitudes"—were long enough to produce a significant concentration even with the low injection rate. He gave a "preliminary calculation" of their energies as "from less than five Mev to perhaps 400 Mev, with a very large percentage of high energies." He added that reasonably complete protection might require an "impractical" amount of shielding. And after mentioning certain unconventional shielding methods which would afford a saving in weight if they proved feasible, he captured the imagination of reporters by suggesting the use of "space-sweeper" satellites, designed to " 'sweep out' a channel in the radiation belt, *i.e.*, remove the protons by absorbing those which hit [them]."[17]

The space-sweeper proposal was admittedly a radical solution, which some people greeted with skepticism. On the other hand, the concept of cosmic-ray albedo as an important component of the new-found radiation—an idea which appears to have been advanced independently by Soviet scientists—had fairly wide acceptance. Of course, it did not necessarily exclude particles from the sun as another component of the radiation.

Most scientists were still disinclined to offer any categorical conclusions as to the significance of the radiation zone for space flight. According to one report, at a space-medicine symposium sponsored by the British Interplanetary Society in October 1958 "it proved almost impossible to get any of the experts to talk" about the biological aspects of space radiation.[18] The experts apparently wanted more data on the nature of the new radiation.

A real breakthrough came with Pioneer III, the space rocket launched by the United States Army on December 6, 1958. Pioneer III did not attain its objective of escaping from the earth's gravitational field, but reached 63,580 miles before falling back, and it transmitted valuable radiation data on both the outbound and the inbound legs. It clearly established the fact, already suspected by some, that there was an inner zone of relatively hard radiation and a wider outer zone composed of softer, less energetic particles. Van Allen pictured two separate belts of radiation around the earth, each roughly doughnut-shaped and each trapped by the action of the earth's magnetic field. Pioneer III also confirmed that the new radiation did not extend indefinitely into space—which eliminated some rather frightening possibilities.[19]

During 1959 radiation studies went ahead with the help of continuing satellite work, sun and moon probes, and miscellaneous rocket firings, both by the United States and by the Soviet Union. This experimentation filled in additional details, while confirming very broadly the radiation pattern indicated by Pioneer III.[20] Explorer VI, the "paddle-wheel" satellite launched in August 1959, produced findings which at first suggested to some writers that there were not two radiation belts but three, the third being carved out of territory previously regarded as lying just below the core of the hard inner belt. However, the picture that emerged from Explorer VI—which provided continuous readings over a wide range of altitude and latitude —was not quite so simple. It suggested that one should talk not so much about clear-cut radiation belts as about a general radiation field around the earth in which different types of radiation are peaked in different regions.[21]

In any case, it is clear that the particles of highest energy are concentrated in a fairly narrow region (of one or more peaks) starting about 1,000 miles above the earth. They include protons with energies up to several hundred Mev and probably electrons up to 13 Mev or more. These particles appear to be limited to low geomagnetic latitudes. Most likely they are derived, at least in large part, from cosmic-ray albedo.

Mixed with the high-energy particles is radiation of lower energy, and this is found also above and below the region of peak energies. The radiation in the outer zone is generally "soft;" apparently it consists of vast numbers of low-energy electrons and protons (a few Mev or less) originating in the sun, and its intensity and extent fluctuate greatly with the sun's activity. Pioneer IV, launched in March 1959 shortly after a major solar disturbance, recorded this radiation out to 52,000 miles, but it apparently did not extend so far at the time of Pioneer III. In geomagnetic latitude, the outer zone of radiation lies mainly between the 60-degree north and south latitudes: *i.e.,* it ends at the auroral regions and dips toward the earth there. The auroral displays are caused, presumably, by interaction of air atoms with particles from both ends of the radiation field.[22]

Further probing may change this picture of the "Van Allen radiation," but the general outline seems established. Just how great a hazard it will be to space travelers is still a matter of speculation. There has been almost no experimental information on exposure to it. Laika penetrated the lower part of the hard radiation zone, but never came back for examination, and the various animal rocket experiments conducted by the United States and the Soviet Union have generally been too low in altitude and too brief in duration to shed light on the problem. Studies in the laboratory may, however, because the Van Allen radiation seems to be comparable to artificial radiations on which physicists and radiobiologists have done a great deal of work. The difficulty is that laboratory tests cannot furnish any really reliable estimate of the hazard until there is more information on the density of this radiation in space, on the relative proportions of protons and electrons, and on their energies.

One fact that appears to be established beyond question is that prolonged exposure to the hard radiation of the inner zone would be very dangerous, although early estimates such as 100 roentgens per hour are now considered excessive. Singer recalculated in September 1959 that an hour's dose would be roughly equivalent to the maximum permissible exposure for one year.[23] This level of radiation would still be unacceptable for more than a very short time, and "brute-force" shielding with lead slabs would carry too great a penalty in weight.[24]

On the basis of later indications as to the energy of the particles, Singer has decided that the "space sweeper" he once suggested will not be necessary.[25] This leaves three other novel solutions that he has proposed at one time or another. One is "shadow shielding," which would use a shielding "ring" rather than a complete shell, on the theory that the particles in the belt would be "incident mainly perpendicular to the line of force" and would hit the vehicle from a particular direction. The second idea is to use a "magnetic screen"—that is, to deflect the particles by the generation of an artificial magnetic field.[26] His third proposal is known as the "club-sandwich" radiation shield.[27] The sandwich would consist of a "thin layer of lead on a sub-stratum of tin (also serving as a meteor bumper); the skin of the vehicle itself, made of aluminum, magnesium or titanium; and, finally, an inner layer of hydrocarbons (such as rocket fuel) to catch fragments."[28] Singer thought of these devices primarily in terms of protection against the hard Van Allen radiation, which he attributed to cosmic-ray albedo. But they would naturally be applicable against the soft outer-zone radiation, too, and some such form of "club sandwich" might conceivably be developed against the cosmic rays themselves.

The consensus is, however, that it would be best for space travelers to by-pass the hard Van Allen radiation entirely. This should not be too difficult, in view of its rather limited extent. Going to or from the moon or Mars, one might plow right through it at high speed, taking the calculated risk of a few minutes' exposure.

The outer-zone radiation will be harder to avoid, except of course in a low-flying satellite. But flights away from the earth may be able to miss it by using sufficiently high geomagnetic latitudes as their gateway. The spaceports of the future may thus be located in the Arctic or Antarctic. On the other hand, Schaefer has estimated that one could pass through the worst of the outer zone in about 15 minutes, provided the vehicle's course was a direct "radial shot." The calculated risk in this case would be less than for a similar plunge through the hard radiation. In the same discussion, Schaefer recommended that passengers going through either zone should roll themselves up into a "fetal position" behind shielding for minimum exposure.[29] With or without a "fetal position," effective shielding could be provided much more readily against the soft radiation of the outer zone, because the electrons and low-energy protons that populate it are easily stopped. The secondary X-rays generated by the electrons striking the space vehicle's hull offer a separate complication, but one which certainly can be solved.

On the whole, there has been a retreat from the expressions of alarm that first greeted discovery of the Van Allen radiation. Although it cannot be dismissed as unimportant, Robert Jastrow of the National Aeronautics and Space Administration expressed the prevailing view when he summed the matter up in mid-1959: "This problem may not be a major one in comparison with other uncertainties in the first space flights."[30]

FURTHER HAZARDS

The catalogue of potential radiation hazards in space still contains a few more items. It has even been speculated that the radio microwaves broadcast by distant stars might have some effects upon space travelers.[31] In fact, certain types of microwave exposure have been shown to produce injury in test animals, and the United States Air Force has studied possible biological effects of radar microwaves at its Rome Air Development Center.[32] Furthermore, other planets probably are surrounded by radiation belts; physicists have suggested that Jupiter, for instance, may have a zone of trapped radiation "a million times more intense than that of the earth."[33] Then again, if nuclear power is eventually used to propel space ships, astronauts will have to cope with the radiations of the rocket engine itself. Scientists of the Atomic Energy Commission have given considerable thought to this; one suggestion is to delay turning on the nuclear power plant until chemical propellants have raised the ship to ten or twelve miles above the earth, where "there would be little scattering of radiation by the atmosphere, and shadow shielding can be used for [the] crew compartment."[34] The ship's stores and equipment could naturally be arranged to help in the shielding and thus save weight.[35]

Protection against the hazards of radiation has been a major concern of medical science in the atomic and space age, and not merely in connection with man's coming venture into space. Already there has been some progress toward dealing with radiation exposure by means of injections, pills, and other medical expedients. For example, scientists at the Walter Reed Army Medical Center recently indicated that a combination of the chemicals mercaptoethylamine and cysteine might give some immunity to radiation damage; these substances seem to have helped dogs to live through radiation doses which would normally have been lethal.[36] Bone-marrow injections, parathyroid extract, and other techniques also have shown promise, either as treatments or prevention, against radiation effects. In fact, over the past 15 years there has been an enormous amount of research on the problem, and it will undoubtedly be expanded in the years to come. Naturally space medicine takes a very keen interest in this research, for it will be reassuring to have shots and pills to fall back on as fortification when man sets forth into the unpredictable hazards of radiation in space.

PART FIVE

Conclusion

14

The Impact of Astronautics

ONE of the aspects of astronautics and space technology which is seldom discussed is the impact of the age of space upon mankind in general—not just upon the men who will journey into outer space or the scientists and engineers who will put them there, but upon the world society of today and tomorrow. This aspect in many respects is probably the most important, for astronautics is bound to be one of the very few truly important stimuli in history which will affect all men's thoughts concerning the physical and spiritual universe in which the individual finds himself.[1]

This impact of astronautics is already beginning to exercise a profound influence upon almost the total range of man's attitudes toward himself as an individual and his role as a member of society, as well as his concept of the relationship between himself and totality. Because of this powerful influence upon his prevailing philosophy of life, the developing program of astronautical endeavor is beginning to force significant changes in his political, economic, and educational institutions. It is beginning to affect his religious and artistic concepts. It is making its influence felt in various of his professions having nothing directly to do with this onrushing program. It is even apparent in his modes of recreation and relaxation.

In short, astronautics is pushing man into a new era of human history. The transition from the old to the new will not be without considerable agony. Because all astronauts and their scientific and technical allies must share the responsibility for forcing this transition in our way of life, they would do well to consider these monumental side-effects of their endeavor. They must realize that the conquest of space is also the alteration of a human adjustment to life on earth which was at least partially successful in its compromise with reality, and which must be replaced with a new adjustment to an existence in a vastly magnified personal universe.

Over coffee at the student snack bar of Amsterdam's Municipal University during the Ninth Congress of the International Astronautical Federation in 1958, Herbert F. York, then Chief Scientist of the Advanced Research Projects Agency, denied that the social repercussions of scientific endeavor were the responsibilities of the scientists involved.[2] His attitude, scientifically correct, was that the scientist must pursue truth and let the chips fall where they may. And, indeed, this was the very spirit of the Scientific Revolution of the sixteenth through eighteenth centuries that turned man's quest for knowledge from the dictum of ancient authority to the methodical investigation of the unknown and to the revolutionary successes of modern science and technology.[3] This is the attitude which, in large part, has placed us today upon the threshold to space.

But this is also the attitude of those medical researchers and sanitary engineers who have freed underdeveloped areas of endemic diseases and who have brought the gift of life to literally millions of individuals. These scientists and technicians acknowledge their accomplishments in having stamped out yaws, yellow fever, malaria, trichinosis and other vicious afflictions. They generally refuse, however, to claim any share of credit for related major accomplishments —the creation of explosive overpopulation pressures, depressed per capita income, political unrest, and similar problems resulting in large measure from their otherwise wonderfully humanitarian scientific and technological successes. Of course, the responsibility for all of these accomplishments—the beneficial along with the less desirable—is also shared by politicians, administrators, economists, and many others, although this, the pure goals of science notwithstanding, does not free the scientist of partial responsibility for the nonscientific ramifications of his work. At least as an individual within society he might ponder the subject.

What will be the effects of astronautics upon society? As with the medical conquest of infested regions, they are immediately beneficial but also productive of long-range side effects. The scientific and technological rewards to be reaped from astronautics are many. They have been the subject of numerous proposals addressed to the elected representatives and military defenders of the celebrated man in the street. But the complex social ramifications, which will radically change our way of life, have received slight attention. Few of us, in spite of our innate distrust of radical change, would halt the brilliant progress of astronautics and rob ourselves of its many promised benefits. Some of us, however, might consider these accomplishments in broader perspective and be privileged to contribute toward easing the transition from today to tomorrow. The attempt to understand and evaluate the complexities of space technology's impact upon man, of course, will be the effort of scholars throughout all future generations. Because of its importance to the immediate future, however, it would be well to begin this study without delay, even though our efforts are based on nothing more than somewhat superficial evidence gathered from reports of current events.

PHILOSOPHICAL IMPLICATIONS

Already there are indications that astronautics is upsetting the familiar applecart in which for generations we have piled our most precious ideas and rationalizations which protect and comfort us in the midst of the sea of ignorance which is our true cosmic environment. What is more important is that the impact of astronautics is only beginning to be felt and that this influence will rapidly mushroom to almost infinite proportions. It will probably result in a significant reorientation of the prevailing general philosophy governing our attitude toward life, and this is the fundamental stimulus which ultimately gives identity to such social institutions as organized government, religion, and other basic facets of our pattern of existence. Astronautics will alter much of this.

How could astronautics affect man's fundamental philosophical attitude? Throughout his entire existence until now, man has never truly experienced any of the physical dimensions in a cosmic sense. Even the circumnavigation of the earth initiated by Magellan was, in this context, an accomplishment much the same as that of a small boy turning around without removing his foot from a chalk mark on the sidewalk. One of the immediate effects of astronautics is the demand for the common acceptance of radically different concepts of physical dimensions, of time, and of physical and psychological forces. What will be the effect of this upon contemporary thought? What is the power of an alien idea?

This multidimensional expansion of human awareness is certainly as catalytic as was the concept of a heliocentric solar system, of a universe governed by fixed and unchanging physical laws of nature, or of organic evolution. Before considering the evidence that astronautics is already exerting significant influence upon man's basic philosophy of life, it might be useful to challenge the original thesis by asking how such changes in thought can have any unusual importance. Perhaps we should ponder a moment, by analogy, some of the far-reaching ramifications of these other historic ideas which have affected man's thoughts concerning the universe and his position and purpose within it.

Nicolaus Copernicus was a mild-mannered man who blew the lid off man's egocentric concept of the universe by postulating that the sun was the pivotal feature of our solar system. This wasn't exactly an original idea—almost 2,000 years before, Heracleides of Pontos and Aristarchos of Samos had advanced the same theory.[4] Their suggestion had crumbled, however, before the relative superiority of Ptolemy's mathematics, and man remained at the center of God's creation for another 13 or 14 centuries. Copernicus fared much better, for his argument was confirmed beyond doubt by the more accurate observations of Tycho Brahe and the mathematical genius of Johannes Kepler.[5]

The impact of this simple astronomical theory published in 1539 was impressive. First of all, along with the pioneer work on anatomy of Andreas Vesalius published the same year, it launched the Scientific Revolution, which has led directly to our present invasion of outer space.[6] More than this, it was the first truly frontal attack upon the literal interpretation of the Scriptures.[7] Interestingly enough, the Lutheran Protestants were the first to resist this overturn of ancient authority, although the Roman church soon added fuel to the conflagration.[8] The fire of Giordano Bruno burning at the stake, however, only served to illuminate the matter for many others to see, although Francis Bacon and others continued to resist this so-called "fiction," which appeared to ignore every tenet of common sense.[10] But in spite of massive resistance in defense of the old way of life, the earth did turn on its axis and it did spin in its orbit about the sun. Gradually men of religion adjusted the doctrine of their faiths and men of learning began to use the new light to explore further the mysteries of the universe. But much had changed. And much will change because of astronautics.

The impact of astronautics should prove more powerful even than the physics of Isaac Newton. Newton's theories nailed the lid on the coffin of the old philosophical and theological cosmology, and pried open the Pandora's box leading toward our present concept of the greater universe. His chief contribution was a very rational and simple explanation of universal gravitation. By implication, however, he swept the heavens clean of the time-honored universe where the Littlest Angel and the others of the host were responsible for the proper movements of heavenly bodies. Instead, he substituted an orderly universe governed by fixed, unchanging physical laws.

Very directly, Newtonian physics set the pace for science for almost three centuries to follow. But his concepts of absolute values for time and space, of a universe responding to the pure harmony of the laws of nature, had a much greater effect upon human thought and action than only this.[11] The philosophical implications of his mechanical universe gave rise to the Enlightenment, that optimistic age when, in theory, reason ruled.[12] This new philosophy encouraged the rise of Deism, a sometimes rationalistic Christianity, a sometimes purely materialistic faith. It provided the climate that made it possible for a band of colonial revolutionaries to address their declaration of political independence to the world at large with confidence that men of reason everywhere would understand the motivating natural laws —the inalienable rights of man. The same spirit led to the rational adoption of the metric system in France, but also to the irrational excesses of Madame Guillotine. It wiped away a large percentage of astrological superstition but it substituted an egotistical smugness concerning human intellectual prowess which culminated in the pre-

Einsteinian pronouncement that every major scientific discovery had been made and that future generations would only be able to mop up by-passed areas in the wake of the great conquest.

The effect of the new cosmology of Copernicus and Newton upon thought in general and its specific impact upon one field of endeavor in particular have been considered by the music critic John M. Conly:

> In the 16th century (which was really not so very long ago; only six lifetimes) two gentle and demonic astronomers, by name Nicolaus Copernicus and Galileo Galilei, cracked Mankind's eggshell and let the Universe in. This was a dread event. Shocked churchly scholars foresaw its consequences and strove to stem them, but of course they could not. The small comfortable cosmos had been breached beyond mending. Man's world was no longer to be God's footstool, and Man no longer His special concern, not in the old, sure sense. The new universe was too immense for such intimacy. We were too small. . . .
>
> By the latter half of the 18th century, thoughtful men were lost in a welter of questions and almost hopeless for answers. The old mentors, Moses and Aristotle, still were at hand, but the trouble was that now we knew more than they ever had. And still not enough, not for the great quesion. *Why* were we here, with drives and dreams so urgent and lives so brutally short? . . .
>
> History gives us simultaneities which seem accidental, but aren't. . . . And the fantastic fact is that as the eighteenth century turned into the nineteenth music uncovered not one but *three* symphonists willing, and mightily able, to undertake this huge depiction of Man in his Cosmos, directly, deeply, and in all its aspects. These were Ludwig van Beethoven, Franz Peter Schubert, and Johannes Brahms.
>
> There can be no quibbling here about musical meanings. Beethoven was explicit to the point of using words in his finale, and the other two not only followed his approach but quoted him in salute as they did so.[13]

The reference to man's new position within the new mechanical universe introduces another major intellectual jolt that has affected his thought and his life—the concept of organic evolution. Although first suggested by Anaximandros of Miletos almost 600 years before Christ, this theory was not substantiated with explosive force until the publication in 1859—scarcely a hundred years ago—of *The Origin of Species* by that quiet observer of nature, Charles Darwin. The impact of evolution should rival that of astronautics, for of all the blows inflicted upon man's egocentric concept of himself and his purpose, this was the most personal. With man now considered the product of sexual selection and the survival of the fittest, repercussions upon man were unprecedented. To quote historian Henry Steele Commager:

The impact of Darwin on religion was shattering; his impact on philosophy was revolutionary. Evolution banished the absolute, supplanted special design, challenged not only the scriptural story of creation but creation itself, and revealed man not as the product of beneficent purpose but of a process of natural selection that . . . confounded the concept of omnipotence. Yet it was a blow to Man rather than to God who, in any event was better able to bear it, for if it relegated God to a dim first cause, it toppled Man from his exalted position as the end purpose of creation, the crown of Nature, and the image of God, and classified him prosaically with the anthropoids.[14]

The effect of evolution upon human thought had many far-reaching consequences. It fell like a bombshell. The entire first edition of *The Origin of Species* sold out the day of issue, although "judging from the storm which it caused, apparently only enemies bought it."[15] It was an exotic fuel dumped on the fire already smoldering in the quarrel between science and religion, a flame which had been kept alive by the recent rise of geology as a field of science, one which disagreed with the "catastrophists" who placed the antiquity of the earth at only 4004 B.C.[16] Darwin became a bulwark of the philosophy of Herbert Spencer, and together they upset the reigning transcendentalism and helped to blaze the "broad highway over which American thought traveled in the later years of the [nineteenth] century."[17] The new philosophy gave rise to the rather benevolent liberalism that dominated the late nineteenth and early twentieth centuries of the western world.[18] It led to the popular pragmatic and optimistic view of the universe of John Fiske and others.[19] At the same time it encouraged a more realistic interpretation of the geographical and social expansion of the United States, as opposed to the earlier romantic version of Mark Twain and Whitcomb Riley.[20]

Darwin himself concluded hopefully that, "as natural selection works solely by and for the good of each being, all corporal and mental endowments will tend to progress towards perfection."[21] But the theory of the survival of the fittest also led directly to a crassness in political, economic, and social life which tolerated stepping on the man who was down because he was obviously "unfit" to survive in the natural competition of life. On the whole, as two distinguished students of history, have observed, "the implications of evolution were incorporated into every field of thought—law and history, economics and sociology, philosophy, religion, and art."[22] And so will astronautics invade every corner of our lives.

Between the impact of organic evolution and that of astronautics appeared one other major influence which we may briefly consider, especially since it applies directly to certain aspects of our present scientific and technological exploration of space. Shortly after the turn of the twentieth century, an obscure employee in the Swiss Patent Office at Berne published the first of his papers on the theory of relativity. At once the universe of Newtonian absolutes began a major transformation. The long era of classical physics began to blend into what we call the modern. And in the wake of this exposition of relativity came an abandonment of the prevailing philosophy of life that had dominated since Newton, even though the new relationship between concepts of space and time seemed entirely contrary to the data immediately understandable to man's intuition.[23]

The impact of Einstein upon science and technology has been revolutionary, but so has been his influence upon many fields of thought related to other aspects of our current pattern of existence. One of the important side-effects—one completely erroneous and in no way really connected with the true theory of relativity—has been the concept which would imply a relativism of men's duties and rights, that moral conceptions should vary with the social class, ethnic group, or structure of civilization.[24] This sort of insidious relativism might condone the annihilation of a persecuted segment of society by a so-called master race, but the authorizing rationalization has no basis in fact nor is it supported in any manner by scientific theory. Such a concept is the complete perversion of one of the most brilliant accomplishments of human genius, the contribution of a very humane and considerate individual. It is, however, an example of the far-reaching effects of what would normally be considered a purely scientific development.

Along with this handful of other important influences that have altered the course of history by heavily pressuring men's thoughts and the various aspects of their lives must be considered astronautics. Just beginning to be felt, the exact nature and magnitude of its effects upon our lives are impossible to identify fully or to measure with any degree of precision. Nevertheless, the data accumulated from our preliminary ventures into outer space include much more than an indication of reasonable technological progress. Indeed, they include evidence which indicates that astronautics will have important general effects upon our basic philosophy of life, as well as an impact upon specific aspects of our routine patterns of existence.

THE INFLUENCE ON RELIGION

Already in the minds of men astronautics is beginning to challenge traditional concepts associated with religion. A recent conference held at the Pacific School of Religion in Berkeley, Calif., pointed out that the religious adjustment required by the cosmology of Copernicus and Newton was nothing compared to that required "by an open and traversable universe in which life, as sacred as man's, existed on perhaps billions of planets."[25] Concerned with the impact of science and technology upon man, the exiled Dalai Lama of Tibet has called on the world's religious leaders to "struggle forward, hand in hand," toward peace on earth by narrowing the gap between spiritual and material civilizations.[26] Faced with the rapid dissemination of astronautical thought, organized religions are already making the first overtures of rationalization.

The Roman Catholic church has given its official blessing to the concept of manned flight through the universe. In September 1956, for instance, Pius XII received in special audience delegates to the Seventh Congress of the International Astronautical Federation, including several from the Soviet Union and its political satellites. He told them that their efforts were "legitimate before God," and that God had not intended man's efforts to be limited to the earth alone but wanted them extended to the whole of creation. Efforts to explore outer space should be the concern of all humanity, he said, and "man has to make the effort to put himself in new orientation with God and His universe."[27] As for the implications of astronautics as a force upon religion, the Pope instructed the delegates that "it will not have escaped your attention, gentlemen, that an undertaking of such magnitude involves intellectual and moral aspects which it is impossible to overlook. Such a project involves a certain concept of the world, its meaning, and purpose."[28] And the following year Pius cautioned a group of leading astronomers to read in the stars a message written by God. He warned that the efforts of scientists, however disinterested and courageous they may be, will remain useless unless scientists see beyond the purely intellectual ends to the basic problem of conscience.[29]

As mentioned in connection with the conference at the Pacific School of Religion, the anticipation of encountering forms of intelligent life elsewhere in the universe, too, is receiving religious sanction. In San Francisco's Cow Palace in 1958 Billy Graham informed his rallied followers that "I personally believe there is life on other planets."[30] The Roman Catholic theologian Father George Van Noort wrote shortly after World War I that "a person would not violate the faith who would believe that there are certain rational creatures on other heavenly bodies."[31] All of which represents a considerable readjustment from the prevailing views that burned Giordano Bruno at the stake in 1600 for teaching the plurality of inhabited worlds.[32]

Some theologians apparently feel that astronautics—even the discovery of other forms of intelligent life on distant planets—will have no effect upon religion. In June 1959 the fathers of the Augustana Lutheran church (including Roy W. Johnson, who was then director of the Advanced Research Projects Agency) held their hundredth synod in Stamford, Conn. They adopted a resolution on behalf of their flock of 600,000 members to the effect that space exploration, including the discovery of life on other planets, will have no effect upon their religious concepts. Prominent laymen, including space-technology pioneers Wernher von Braun and Major General J. B. Medaris, have stated that the Ten Commandments are sufficient to govern the exploration of space and expect no upheaval as a result of this endeavor.[34] British astronomer A. C. B. Lovell, however, feels that as we unlock the secrets of the universe, fuller understanding of the origin of everything may present theology with a serious dilemma where it would be difficult to reconcile certain fundamental doctrines with our new knowledge.[35]

At lower levels of theological thought—the level of the man in in the street—there is already some confusion concerning astronautics. One writer, referring to common concepts of various religions, wonders whether the great percentage of the flock will still believe in the existence of a lofty realm with pearly gates, harplike music, and angels after man explores the physical heavens, or whether they will find a new faith in the profounder miracles of the very nature of things.[36]

Which way will heaven be then?
Up?
Down?
Across?
Or far within?

Both in England and the United States there have been pacifist demonstrations against the construction of launch sites for war rockets.[37] Newspapers have been barraged with letters protesting space exploration on religious grounds. "If the good Lord wanted us to go to outer space, He would have built a bridge," is one example.[38] P. E. Cleaton, founder of the British Interplanetary Society, was invited to renounce the whole idea and become a Christian, because "the enterprise is immoral and against God. He will never permit it."[39] One of the more interesting of these protests appeared recently in the London *Times*:[40]

THE MOON AND YOU.—Act NOW to divert the brains and energy of science into CREATIVE channels for the GOOD of humanity. You cannot stop progress, but you can stop it taking the black path of destruction. YOU can insist on public money, YOUR money, being well spent. More precise research against disease, new roads, better railways, &c. YOU can assist and actively promote progress on the white path of CREATIVE science, whereby we may learn to live without greed, envy, suspicion and fear. DOWN with the MOON MANIACS. Take action NOW in any way you can, towards a future where spiritual values come FIRST. Where the welfare of your fellow men matters more than curiosity about the Moon. Remember Pandora's Box! Public money is YOUR money, why spend it on being blown up? Public opinion is powerful, EXPRESS IT! Good example is a power, GIVE IT!—M

On the other hand, there are manifestations which indicate that man's personal religion will survive the strain and make the necessary adjustments. Recently the police of Farmington township, Michigan, received a flurry of alarming telephone calls.[41] One caller reported: "I was driving my wife home from shopping and I saw this guy carrying a huge rocket out of his garage. It must have been twelve feet long and he looked like he was headed for a nearby field." Another caller, a woman, related in haste that "I just saw a man setting up a big rocket in his driveway. I don't think he ought to shoot that thing up by all these houses. It must be 20 feet long."

Minutes later, the Reverend Arthur R. Parkin, Jr., assistant pastor of the Clarenceville Methodist church, and his 15-foot green-and-white rocket were confronted by the police. "It's for my church," he explained. "I'm a former sheet metal worker and I made it myself out of furnace pipes. It's going to sit on the church lawn as an advertisement for a vacation Bible school. Our theme is 'Exploring God's Wonders.' " Upon this man of religion, at least, the influence of astronautics would seem to rest as lightly as upon the celebrated early churchman who—according to the story—postulated that the Almighty, before creating heaven and earth, first made hell for those who stirred up such troublesome influences.[42] Upon religion itself, however, the impact promises to be tremendous.

THE EFFECT ON EDUCATION

The launching of Sputnik also launched a tidal-wave attack upon the educational system of the United States. In this important field the effects of astronautics and space technology are already becoming vividly apparent. One is quite familiar with the recent flood of comment to the effect that alleged Soviet superiority in astronautics, with the implied threat to our national security, is an indictment of our educational system. In 1954 John T. Rettaliata, president of the Illinois Institute of Technology, had warned of the Soviet technical buildup and called for 30,000 new engineers annually in the United States to keep our necks from under the shadow of the hammer and sickle.[43] The annual report for 1958 by the President's Committee on Scientists and Engineers found the United States dangerously short of trained technicians, engineers, and scientists, and predicted that the situation would rapidly become worse.[44] There has been a flood of articles with titles such as "U.S. Short 130,000 Experts," "Industry's Frantic Pursuit of Talent," "Great Hero Hunt," "150,000 Science Jobs Waiting for Graduates," "Bold Strategy to Beat Shortage," "Scientists Explain U.S. Technical Lag," and "Survey Ties R&D Cut to Scientist Shortage."[45]

Some educational leaders have soberly insisted that "school personnel must, today, develop a new outlook and new skills to meet the demands of an atomic and space age."[46] Others, however, have gone to the extreme of advocating the junking of 50 per cent of our high school teachers as not qualified to meet the challenge.[47] Unusual interest in the problem has been expressed by individuals from many walks of life. Much of the criticism has been constructive, although as John Gardner recently observed, "Characters we never heard of before went into orbit and started beeping" about the failure of our educational institutions.[48] Great emphasis has been placed upon the necessity of strengthening our curricula in science, mathematics, and engineering, although here, too, various extremes have been reached. A few months after Sputnik I, the *Saturday Review* commented upon the latter demands:[49]

> De-emphasize Humanities,
> Divert the college courses;
> Give us Nike instead of psych
> To meet the hostile forces.
>
> Languages and literature
> Let science supersede
> With stratagems, ICBMs . . .
> And nobody who can read.

The effect of this outcry has been felt in many ways by the colleges and universities of the nation, and not always to the benefit of either the nation or the educational institutions, and especially not to civilization in the broad sense. A critic has written that "the haste with which most of our people condemned the scapegoat education for the Russian lead in space affairs is the result of fright and injured national ego."[50] However exaggerated the outcry, though, the shortage of trained scientists and engineers does exist and serious steps have been taken to initiate the solution. The entire affair is another indication of the impact of astronautics upon our lives. We trust that the nontechnical aspects of our civilization will survive the sudden emphasis on science and technology within our educational system.

One approach to the educational problem has been the Science Education bill that became Federal law September 2, 1958. Under its provisions some 1,229 colleges and universities are already participating in the loan program which subsidizes students in science, mathematics, engineering, and foreign languages.[51] Other steps have been taken by the educational institutions themselves.

As early as 1939, Samuel Herrick began offering a course in interplanetary navigation at the University of California at Los Angeles. Since then the astronautics program there has expanded within the departments of astronomy, physics, mathematics, and engineering to where Ph.D. degrees may now be built around combinations of celestial mechanics, astrodynamics, aerodynamics, fluid mechanics, electromagnetic theory, structures, mechanics, and mathematics. In 1958 Robert M.L. Baker received the first doctorate, in space navigation.[52] UCLA also conducts summer sessions in fields such as astrodynamics, rocket navigation, and the fundamentals of rocket propulsion.[53] It presented a 24-lecture series on space technology for postgraduate students by leading experts at five different California locations; the series was a spectacular success, drawing more than 4500 persons. In fact, a television station has televised the entire course, reaching an even wider audience.[54] The university has also prepared a series of 16-mm films based on the original lecture series, totalling 45 hours of lectures by 36 of the nation's astronautical experts. The series, with printed lecture notes, has been used by many government agencies and industrial firms.[55] So strong has been the influence of astronautics upon UCLA that the 1958 Homecoming Committee adopted a space theme, devoted a day to lectures on outer space by UCLA professors, and exhibited special displays on astronautics—all in addition to the traditional football game in the Los Angeles Coliseum.[56]

At other institutions, too, the impact of astronautics is in evidence. The Polytechnic Institute of Brooklyn has launched a new curriculum leading to the master's degree in space technology; the program requires 34 graduate credits, two more than normally required in other fields.[57] At the Massachusetts Institute of Technology Charles S. Draper now heads the new department of aeronautics and astronautics. One of its first offerings was a lecture series featuring 12 afternoon lectures called a Space Environment Symposium, which was open to the public.[58] The University of Michigan, too, has changed the name of its aeronautical engineering department to the Department of Aeronautical and Astronautical Engineering.[59] During the summer of 1959, Pennsylvania State University offered seminars on missile engineering,[60] Yale presented a course on dynamical astronomy,[61] and the University of Connecticut held an Army R&D-sponsored institute on missile and rocket technology.[62] At the University of Illinois Grover J. D. Schock, then with the Aeromedical Field Laboratory at the Air Force Missile Development Center, earned a Ph.D. in space physiology.[63] At Goettingen in Germany, Welf Heinrich Prinz von Hannover received a doctorate in space law.[64] The University of Houston, with financial assistance from the Ford Foundation, is filming a series of 13 half-hour television programs on space medicine which will be distributed by the National Education TV Center of Ann Arbor, Michigan.[65] The new Community College of Alamogordo, N.M., is offering a course in space biology taught by Harald J. von Beckh, the subgravity and biodynamics expert at the nearby Air Force Missile Development Center.[66] A different sort of expression of the influence of astronautics on education is that of D.L. Biemesderfer, president of State Teachers College at Millersville, Pa., who has investigated the "Effect of Space on Education."[67] And so it goes.

It is, of course, no surprise to find a department of astronautics at the United States Air Force Academy, or that the cadets there are star-gazing in their new planetarium.[68] And it is natural that other Air Force educational and training institutions, such as the Air University at Maxwell Air Force Base in Alabama, and the technical schools at Lowery Air Force Base in Colorado, at Vandenberg Air Force Base in California, and at Cape Canaveral in Florida are producing rocket and astronautics experts in significant numbers.[69] Even the Reserve Officers Training Corps units scattered among the colleges and universities of the nation now include this type of indoctrination.[70]

At lower levels of education, too, space technology is exerting its influences. The American Rocket Society, with the cooperation of the Army Corps of Engineers and various industrial organizations active in astronautics, has started a course in Washington, D. C., for science teachers and students, stressing safe methods of high-school astronautical instruction.[71] The University of New Mexico, together with the New Mexico state board of education, sponsored a "space school" for 400 high school science students at the Air Force Special Weapons Center at Kirtland Air Force Base. Among the scheduled speakers was the chief scientist of the Army Missile Test Center at the White Sands Missile Range.[72] New York University hosted an Army "Teen-Age Rocket Seminar" for 800 high school students, at which leaders in astronautics addressed the youths.[73] The Dayton Section of the American Rocket Society attempted a Space Education Week for students, teachers, and the public-at-large, with the theme "Peaceful Use of Space."[74] The major government research-and-development centers are bombarded with letters from throughout the world from students constructing rockets and related astronautical devices as science projects.[75] One enterprising high school student sent a request for information directly to the Kremlin in Moscow; he received a reply in English and a bundle of pamphlets on Sputniks I and II—in Russian.[76]

Even in the lower grades of grammar school the initial impact of astronautics is apparent. In the fourth-grade *Gazette* of the West End School in Shippensburg, Pa., an editorial by young John Franklin, "Science Editor," compared Soviet and United States satellites and spoke of the advance in human knowledge derived from them. Another article by Robert McCann considered manned satellites and space stations which would "be little cities in themselves," and described the activities of the inhabitants.[77] In Long Beach, Calif., a first grader reported that "the world is something to come down to after you've been up in space."[78]

As early as 1954 the Boston Public Library children's summer reading program stressed space travel.[79] This type of program has been adopted elsewhere. In 1958 the summer reading program of the Alamogordo Public Library gave New Mexican youngsters an opportunity to win their "Space Explorers" navigation certificates for interstellar travel. Brief written reviews on books were logged in the Space Record Book, and the certificates were offered to those children reading and reporting on 20 or more books during the summer.[80] Certainly these activities are contributions toward creating the science-minded public which Joseph Kaplan, United States chairman for the International Geophysical Year, has said is needed to preserve the democratic process in the age of space.[81]

IMPACT ON GOVERNMENT AND POLITICS

In his political life, the citizen of the United States is responding to the influence of astronautics in many ways. The cumulative effect of this is already producing significant initial changes in the structure of his government at local and national levels, and in the political maneuvering of his elected representatives. Established institutions are performing new functions and new organizations are being created. Space topics have entered election campaigning and astronautical planks are appearing in political platforms.

The impact is obvious in the case of the creation of the National Aeronautics and Space Administration, and its influence is also apparent in the various branches of the Department of Defense. But even the staid Department of Commerce is responding, as its Bureau of Census grapples with the problem of identifying the new aerospace industries and its Weather Bureau explores the possibilities of weather satellites. In the Congress, both the Senate and House have established committees to handle space matters. Members of both branches are conducting investigations of the apparent lag in the missile and space race. All of them are involved in new types of legislation and gigantic appropriations for these programs. And even the highest offices of government have felt the initial impact of the age of space.

The pinnacle of the executive branch is the Presidency, and recently astronautics has been added to all the time-honored problems which have occupied the incumbent of that position. For the first time in history, the President has been forced to devote considerable time to reading books on outer space, selected from bibliographies prepared at his request by government scientists.[82] With this limited background, plus the conflicting solicited and unsolicited advice of many individuals both within and outside the government, he is required to make far-reaching decisions on a multitude of major problems generated by the growing influence of astronautics. These decisions range from restricting the national space program within arbitrary budget limits[83] to intervening in interagency disputes such as the recent conflict between the National Aeronautics and Space Administration and the Department of the Army over the fate of the Jet Propulsion Laboratory and the Army Ballistic Missile Agency.[84] And in the role of spokesman for the national program of missiles and space technology, he must periodically report to the sometimes-impatient public in defense of what frequently appears to them as a second-best effort.[85]

More important than the effect of astronautics upon the activities of this busy individual, however, is the fact that the structure of the Executive Office itself has already begun to change somewhat as a result of this powerful influence. It now includes a host of new officials, advisory groups, and technical committees—all established as a result of the advent of the age of space and all capable of exerting considerable influence upon the lives of university professors, dog-catchers, or housewives at any supermarket.

For instance, the President now has a Special Assistant for Science and Technology who can recommend the allocation of a multimillion-dollar pool of scientific research instrumentation to universities and other institutions, who can encourage the expenditure of funds for a program to improve weather forecasting using satellite-gathered data, and who can oppose a crash program aimed at achieving an early operational capability in nuclear-powered aircraft and space vehicles.[86] The Presidential office also includes a Science Advisory Committee, which has been powerful enough to oppose the creation of a Department of Science with cabinet rank and which was instrumental in establishing a new Federal Council for Science and Technology, an agency to oversee government programs already totaling $5 billion and increasing rapidly.[87] The President has revised the charter of the Civilian-Military Liaison Committee, which coordinates space programs between the Advanced Research Projects Agency and the National Aeronautics and Space Administration, to permit it to mediate civilian-military space disputes on its own initiative.[88] And he has established a host of other groups, such as the Science Information Service in the National Science Foundation, which coordinates government and private scientific information. On the whole, the activities of the President have been altered considerably by the impact of astronautics, and the character and power of his office have begun to change in response to this stimulus.

ECONOMIC INFLUENCE

The economic impact of astronautics and space technology is already greater than many suspect. For the individual, personally, this is reflected in his direct and indirect taxes, in new job opportunities, in stock-market activities, and in many other ways. As taxpayers, we have paid an estimated $1 million for each pound of Vanguard satellite payload tossed into orbit. It is a relief to learn that the Explorer payload has cost only $80,000 to $100,000 per pound, and that the price in the future is expected to decline ultimately to only $100 through the application of new propulsion devices.[90] But of course the number of pounds will soar to staggering totals. The aggregate cost of space technology, which is still in its infancy, is already astronomical. Dan E. Kimball, president of the Aerojet-General Corporation, has said that in order to sustain the conquest of space an entirely new means of financing besides money may be required.[91] Pentagon figures have indicated that more than $17 billion had already gone into missiles alone between World War II and the end of 1957, all but a half-billion since the beginning of the Korean conflict.[92] Since 1957 the total has continued to swell. One observer has estimated that the cost of missiles and space flight will total far beyond $170 billion for the period 1960 through 1975.[93] In 1958 the Air Force Ballistic Missile Division alone was reportedly spending $30 a second, 24 hours a day, every day of the year.[94] This is quite a bite on the individual citizen. In fact, in May 1958 the National Science Foundation sponsored a conference on Research and Development and Its Impact on the Economy to look into the matter.[95]

During 1958, 15 stocks prominently identified with missiles and space technology gained a phenomenal 71 per cent in value—well over twice the soaring stock market's average.[96] Even when the entire market dipped, the simple announcement that a new series of satellites would go into orbit was enough to rally investors.[97] Scientists and other specialists in astronautics have banded together to launch a Missile-Jets-Automation Fund, a mutual investment firm for the man in the street, whose advisers include such astronautic experts as Theodore von Karman, Andrew G. Haley, Wernher von Braun, C.C. Furnas, Edwin R. Gilliland, and Athelstan Spilhaus.[98]

Most of the money poured into missiles and astronautics goes, probably by necessity, to the leading, well-established industrial firms. The Boeing Airplane Company has replaced General Motors as the top holder of military contracts. One hundred organizations have received 63.5 per cent of all the prime contracts.[99] Astronautics, therefore, is also a potent economic force for further centralization of industry. The Senate Small Business subcommittee estimated that small firms received less than 2 per cent of the $5 billion spent on prime missile contracts during fiscal year 1959.[100]

Several regional economies are tied directly to the invasion of space. Brevard county in Florida, the area of the Cape Canaveral complex, had a 98 per cent per capita increase in income during the years 1950-1956, compared to a 30 per cent increase for all Florida.[101] Business and political leaders in the county, alarmed that newer launching facilities in California might draw Federal money away from Cape Canaveral, have exerted coordinated political pressure upon Washington to avoid a local economic slump.[102] The Florida Development Commission has reported that 296 new industrial plants or major expansions of existing facilities were built in the state during the first seven months of 1958.[103] More than 10,000 new jobs were added, over a quarter of them in electronics. A significant percentage of the total is related to guided missiles and space technology. Similar booms have started in many other areas of the nation, as documented in a long series of articles by William E. Howard and others.[104]

During the 1957 economic recession, the post-Sputnik spending program in astronautics played a significant role in national economic recovery.[105] Labor leaders strongly supported the concept that Federal space-technology contracts should be channeled into so-called distressed areas to minimize the effects of industrial layoffs.[106] On the other hand, technological advances within the rocket and missile industry can have important economic effects upon employment. In Los Angeles, for instance, North American Aviation announced that 15,000 workers would be released after the cancellation of the Navaho missile program, although the company later revised its estimate to 12,000.[107] The transition from aircraft to missile production at the Douglas plant in Santa Monica caused a payroll reduction of about 22,500 men.[108] The winning of a large subcontract by Boeing for a space-scraping chemical-powered bomber was hailed in Seattle as a boon to the unemployment problem in that city.[109] In Texas, however, the cancellation of the Regulus II project brought about the immediate layoff of 1,500 employees at Chance Vought, with the total expected to rise.[110]

As the nation's aeronautical industry has managed to dominate the transition to astronautics, it has replaced the automotive industry as the largest commercial employer in the country, with missiles and space technology rapidly becoming the more important aspect of the new partnership. In fact, the Aircraft Industries Association of America changed its name to Aerospace Industries Association.[111] Certainly the economic impact of astronautics and space technology upon the individual and the nation is powerful and complex. The entire subject is worthy of intensive investigation by qualified economists and sociologists.

MUSIC, ART, AND LITERATURE

Skipping over the important influence of astronautics upon some other aspects of our organized existence, consider the available evidence which indicates that this powerful stimulus is also affecting our aesthetic notions and the media of their expression. Consider music, for instance, whether classical, jazz, or rock-and-roll. This indeed would seem an unusual medium for the expression of astronautical influence, but it is there.

At the Royal Opera House in Stockholm, the opera *Aniara* had its première in June 1959. Written by avant-garde Swedish composer Karl-Birger Blomdahl and playwright Erik Lindegren, *Aniara* is based on a "space cycle" by the Swedish poet Harry Martinson.[112] It is a lengthy allegory about man's journey through life in a spiritual void, ending inevitably in his own destruction. The entire opera takes place aboard a gigantic space ship on an abortive mission to Mars, and some of the implications of space flight figure deeply in both the story and the music. Three months after its first performance it again created controversy in musical circles when performed at King's Theatre in Edinburgh.[113] The advent of *Aniara* came less than a year after the concert series in London's Festival Hall billed as the Hoffnung Interplanetary Music Festival, which enjoyed standing-room-only prestige during its two-day run.[114]

In popular music there is a swarm of long-playing recordings presented to the buying public in dust jackets depicting moonscapes and other surrealistic astronautical scenes. Some of these, such as *Destination Moon* by the Ames Brothers[115] or *Other Worlds, Other Sounds* by the Mexican maestro Juan García Esquivel,[116] are merely familiar earth-bound compositions in new and sometimes brilliant arrangements. Others, however, reveal more truly the impact of astronautics. *Adventures in Sound and Space* by Marty Gold and his orchestra—which are exactly that—include such numbers as "Blastoff," "Free Fall," "Space Station," and "Mars and the Secret of the Canals."[117] *Space Songs,* a collection written by Hy Zaret and Lou Singer, with vocals by Tom Glazer, includes items such as "Planet Minute," "Ballad of Sir Isaac Newton," "Constellation Jig," and "Zoom-a-Little-Zoom," the latter related to methods of rocket propulsion.[118] Even the long-dead Alexander Borodin has not escaped a posthumous romance with astronautics. Some of his music, with lyrics supplied, was adapted by Robert Wright and George Forrest for the stage-and-screen success *Kismet,* and Borodin's "Dance of the Slave Maidens" became the "Stranger in Paradise" who found himself suspended in outer space.

Nor has painting escaped the impact of astronautics. At a recent art exhibition in Connecticut a depiction of a space-vehicle blastoff entitled "5-4-3-2-1-zero" caused a stir—mostly because it had been hung 90 degrees from its proper orientation and had been greatly admired by many as a representation of a fleet of sail boats.[119] A more serious manifestation of the impact of space technology has been mentioned by Woodi Ishmael, the New York illustrator, who has observed that astronautics is introducing new forms and concepts into his profession.[120] In fact, art received a reinforcement from the missile industry when Frank J. Malina, one of the pioneer founders of the famous Jet Propulsion Laboratory and recipient of the REP-Hirsch International Prize for rocketry development, abandoned missilry and went to Paris to explore three-dimensional painting involving electronic instrumentation, lights, and physical motion to depict his aesthetic notions of outer space.[121] And along with the avant-garde of music and painting comes modern dance. A recent New York dance production, *Symbols of Now,* presented dances called "Fall Out" and "Missile," purporting to "focus on the current code of SPACE VIOLENCE."[122]

The movies, of course, discovered astronautics long ago. Screen stories of this type began with George Méliès' *A Trip to the Moon*[123] and Fritz Lang's *The Girl in the Moon.*[124] Walt Disney and Wernher von Braun have done a film called *Man In Space*. When it was shown at the 1955 International Astronautical Federation meeting in Copenhagen, it made an impression on Soviet Academician Leonid Sedov (who later became president of the Federation for 1959-1960).[125] Another American astronautical film, *Destination—Moon,* evoked a different kind of comment from Soviet N. A. Varnarov, who saw in it evidence that the United States wants to convert the moon into a source of profit for capitalistic monopolies and a military base from which to conquer the earth.[126]

The main point, however, is that the space theme has invaded the motion picture theaters and that this is just another indication of the broad scope of the influence of astronautics. Some of the recent films are honest efforts to depict modern research-and-development accomplishments, as in *On the Threshold of Space;* others are purely speculative, like *Conquest of Space*. Still others are grade-B exploitations of the advent of the age of space, such as *Teenagers from Outer Space* (who "blast the flesh off Humans!"), *First Man Into Space* ("Yesterday he was a handsome test pilot. . . . Did the deadly Gamma Rays turn him into a MONSTER?", or *The Space Children* ("Slowly . . . and with horror the parents realized their children were the slaves of

'The Thing' from outer space!"). And of course there are many more, like *I Married a Monster from Outer Space* and *Forbidden Planet.* Even Charlie Chaplin is said to be resurrecting his famous "tramp" character, after a long retirement, for a film which will take him on a trip to the moon.[127]

Literature, too, has experienced the influence of astronautics with added force. J. Douglas Bush, Guerney Professor of English Literature at Harvard, ridicules the possibility that astronautics could exert an influence upon education or other aspects of our current cultural pattern—"as if outer space had anything to do with the quality of human life," he challenges.[128] Quoting Robert Frost, he continues:

> They cannot scare me with their empty spaces
> Between the stars—on stars where no human race is.

But even Bush's own profession is being affected more than before by the influence of astronautics, and it seems incredible that he is unaware of this. In fact Robert Frost, the very poet he quoted in support of his position, has stated that "the only *event* in all history is science plunging deeper into matter. We have plunged into the smallness of particles and we are plunging into the hugeness of space—but not without fears that the spirit shall be lost."[129]

However one may interpret this "plunge" into space, the enlargement of man's personal universe is an inexorable fact which more and more will come to dominate his literature—as well as his philosophy, education and other aspects of his life. As documented in the opening chapter, the desire to explore beyond the confines of the earth has been a recurring theme in literature from the earliest times. And now the realization of this ancient urge is beginning to be woven into the warp and woof of every aspect of our lives.

In countless ways astronautics impinges directly upon the man in the street. Museums, old and new, already depict the step-by-step progress of man's invasion of outer space.[130] New words and phrases have enriched our vocabulary.[131] Blue-sky entrepreneurs are already buying and selling titles to land on the moon and planets.[132] Postage stamps have appeared in many countries hailing astronautical achievement.[133] Scientists and engineers have used space technology as an excuse to push for the universal adoption of the metric system.[134] Volunteers for space flight are legion.[135] South African Zulu tribesmen have coined new words for space technology advances.[136] Women's fashion shows feature the theme of rocketry and space exploration.[137] Wherever he goes, the individual fails to escape the mushrooming impact of astronautics. In the toy stores he buys his children moon rockets or replicas of actual missiles with a Cape Canaveral play set.[138] In possible desperation, he might seek escape from the world (and other worlds, too) by going to the races—only to have Outer Space, daughter of Saggy-Supersonic, win the Bed O'Roses Handicap at Jamaica by a length and a half over the favorite.[139]

Man indeed is going into space. Although still earth-bound, he is learning more and more each day—through the strenuous research efforts reviewed in this book—about solving the problems of human space flight. Ultimate success is certain. And success in the exploration of alien portions of the universe will change the very nature of our lives.

Notes

CHAPTER 1

1. A brochure issued in February 1959 by the Library of Science, advertising the four-volume *Illustrated Library of the Natural Sciences,* published under the auspices of the American Museum of Natural History.
2. *Voyages to the Moon* (The Macmillan Co., 1948). Miss Nicolson is also author of, among other books, *World in the Moon* (Smith College, 1936), as well as many pertinent articles which appeared in *Smith College Studies in Modern Languages, Smith College Classical Studies, Journal of the History of Ideas, Studies in Philology, English Literary History, Annals of Science,* and *Modern Philology.*
3. James R. Newman, in a book review published in *Scientific American,* April 1958, p. 148, presents an intriguing challenge to explore further the relationship of the social environment to the progress of science.
4. Harry G. Armstrong, *Principles & Practice of Aviation Medicine* (3rd ed., Williams & Wilkins Co., 1952), p. 12, citing José de Acosta, *Historia natural y moral de las Indias* (Sevilla, 1590); George Sarton, *Six Wings: Men of Science in the Renaissance* (University of Indiana Press, 1957), pp. 7-8.
5. A. R. Hall, *The Scientific Revolution, 1500-1800: The Foundation of the Modern Scientific Attitude* (The Beacon Press, 1954), p. 227 and note 1.
6. Armstrong, *op. cit.,* p. 8, citing Gaston Tissandier, "Le voyage à grande hauteur du ballon 'Le Zenith,'" *Nature* (Paris), May 1, 1875, pp. 337-344.
7. Scientific results announced by David G. Simons and James E. Cook, Aeromedical Field Laboratory, Air Force Missile Development Center, Holloman Air Force Base, New Mexico, and reported in *Aviation Week,* August 25, 1958, pp. 41, 43.

8. Report by James A. Van Allen, University of Iowa, presented before a joint symposium of the National Academy of Sciences and the American Physical Society in Washington, D.C., *Washington Evening Star,* May 1, 1958.
9. George S. Duncan, *Prehistoric Man: An Introduction to Anthropology* (Stratford Co., 1931), p. 31; William Howells, *Back of History: The Story of Our Own Origins* (Doubleday & Co., 1954), pp. 95-100.
10. Nicolson, *Voyages to the Moon,* p. 67.
11. *Ibid.,* p. 10. (The quotation can be found in Psalms, 55:6.)
12. *Ibid.*
13. George Sarton, *A History of Science: Ancient Science Through the Golden Age of Greece* (Harvard University Press, 1952), p. 243.
14. Sir William Cecil Dampier, *A Shorter History of Science* (Cambridge University Press, 1944), p. 17.
15. Sarton, *History of Science,* p. 176.
16. *Ibid.,* p. 291, quoting the third-century *Philosophumena* of St. Hippolytos (translated by F. Legge and published in London in 1921), I, 48.
17. Nicolson, *op. cit.,* p. 16.
18. Heinz Gartmann, *The Men Behind the Space Rockets* (David McKay Co., 1956), p. 20; Patrick Moore, *The Story of Man and the Stars* (W. W. Norton & Co., 1954), p. 25; and Hubertus Strughold, *The Green and Red Planet: A Physiological Study of the Possibility of Life on Mars* (University of New Mexico Press, 1953), p. 1. All supply interesting comments on the role of Aristotle in astronautics.
19. Nicolson, *op. cit.,* pp. 8, 66. Another interesting discussion of the works of Lucian, apparently drawing upon Miss Nicolson's study, appears in a book by Frank Ross, Jr., entitled *Space Ships and Space Travel: The Scientifically Accurate Story of Man's Attempts and Plans to Travel into Interplanetary Space* (Lothrop, Lee & Shepard Co., 1954), pp. 1 ff.
20. W. Randolph Lovelace, 2d, of the Lovelace Foundation for Medical Education and Research, was involved in crew selection for Project Mercury and for manned-satellite programs in general. *Albuquerque Journal,* January 28, 1959.
21. Nicolson, *op. cit.,* pp. 10, 16.
22. *Ibid.,* pp. 8, 14.
23. *Ibid.,* pp. 10-13.
24. Ariosto began his chivalric epic about 1506, published the first 40 cantos in 1516 and enlarged it to 46 in the 1532 edition. Nicolson, *op. cit.,* discusses the journey of Astolfo on pages 19-20.
25. Nicolson, *op. cit.,* p. 35.
26. Hall, *op. cit.,* p. 364.

27. Nicolson, *op. cit.,* pp. 41-47, discussing Kepler's *Somnium,* remarks that "no important later voyage will employ so fully the supernatural, yet none will be more truly 'scientific.' . . ." Commentary on the other authors can be found on pages 18-19, 56, 67.
28. *Webster's Biographical Dictionary* (G. & C. Merriam Co., 1951), p. 1349.
29. *El Paso Herald-Post,* October 15, 1958, quoting from an article in the London *Spectator* which announced negative results in a contest requiring entrants to find lines in Shakespeare's works appropriate for comment on the United States Pioneer I moon probe, which had just reached almost 80,000 miles into space.
30. Nicolson, *op. cit.,* treats Donne on pages xi and 48, Kircher on page 57, Burton on pages 19-20, Bergerac on page 19, and Wilkins on pages viii-ix, 93. See also Ross, *op. cit.,* pp. 4-5.
31. Ross, *op. cit.,* pp. 2-4; Nicolson, *op. cit.,* p. 45.
32. Nicolson, *op. cit.,* p. 60.
33. *Ibid.,* p. 64.
34. *Ibid.,* p. 57; Strughold, *Green and Red Planet,* p. viii.
35. Nicolson, *op. cit.,* p. 87.
36. *Ibid.,* p. ix.
37. Beryl Williams and Samuel Epstein, *The Rocket Pioneers: On the Road to Space* (Julian Messner, Inc., 1955), p. 31, call attention to this fact.
38. Ross, *op. cit.,* p. 5.
39. The Mercury capsule and other rocket and space-vehicle cabins are discussed in chapters 3 and 4.
40. *Holloman Monthly News Bulletin* of the Holloman Section, American Rocket Society, October 1957, p. 9.
41. Nicolson, *op. cit.,* p. ix.
42. See P. M. Ashburn's *The Ranks of Death: A Medical History of the Conquest of America* (Coward-McCann, Inc., 1947).
43. This discussion is based primarily upon "Tsiolkovsky—the Pioneer Schoolmaster of Kaluga," by Heinz Gartmann, *op. cit.,* pp. 26-34.
44. Letter, G. Harry Stine to James Stephen Hanrahan, White Sands Proving Ground, March 1957, published in the *Holloman Monthly News Bulletin,* April 1957, p. 2.
45. The broadcast was on October 31, 1938. The script was later published by the Princeton University Press (Nicolson, *op. cit.,* pp. x-xi).
46. *New York Times,* May 1, 1955.
47. Such as the *New York Times,* December 18, 1954.
48. Quoted by Pius XII, *L'osservatore romano,* September 22, 1956.
49. Borodin's music, with lyrics supplied, was adapted by Robert Wright and George Forrest for the stage-and-screen success *Kismet.*

Chapter 2

1. Remarks by Dr. Strughold at the Aero Medical Association meeting, Washington, D. C., March 26, 1958.
2. The nature and symptoms of caisson disease are described in medical reference works such as *Blakiston's New Gould Medical Dictionary* (The Blakiston Co., 1949) under "Disease, caisson" (p. 303).
3. H. Shirley Smith, "Bridges and Tunnels," in Charles Singer *et al.*, eds., *A History of Technology* (Oxford University Press, 1958), V, 514-515.
4. *Ibid.*, pp. 519-520.
5. Eric Burgess, *Satellites and Spaceflight* (The Macmillan Co., 1957), pp. 35-38.
6. A. R. Hall, *The Scientific Revolution, 1500-1800: The Formation of the Modern Scientific Attitude* (Beacon Press, 1954), p. 227 and note 1.
7. Harry G. Armstrong, *Principles & Practice of Aviation Medicine* (3d ed., William & Wilkins Co., 1952), p. 12, citing José de Acosta, *Historia natural y moral de las Indias* (Sevilla, 1590); Edward Whymper, in his *Travels Amongst the Great Andes* (John Lehmann, 1949), pp. 265-266, quotes the actual passages of Acosta.
8. Preston E. James, *Latin America* (Odyssey Press, 1942), p. 294.
9. George Sarton, *Six Wings: Men of Science in the Renaissance* (University of Indiana Press, 1957), pp. 7-8.
10. The unknown author of "The White Monkey," in *Famous Chinese Short Stories,* retold by Lin Yutang (Pocket Library, 1954), pp. 23-42, referred to persons and events of the late sixth century, and made reference to the atmosphere becoming rarefied at high mountain elevations (p. 31). The translator volunteers that he has supplied additional material concerning the aborigines of southern China from three documents dating from the Tang and Sung dynasties. Unless he also supplied the data on atmospheric pressure, which would appear unlikely, the tale indicates that even literary men of sixth-century China were familiar with this atmospheric phenomenon.
11. James, *op. cit.,* p. 150 and *passim.*
12. *Ibid.,* p. 161.
13. School of Aviation Medicine Report No. 56-1, *Mechanisms of Natural Acclimatization: Studies on the Native Resident of Morococha, Peru, at an Altitude of 14,900 Feet,* by Alberto Hurtado *et al.* (School of Aviation Medicine, March 1956), pp. 1-2.
14. Armstrong, *op. cit.,* pp. 13-14.

15. *Ibid.*, p. 13.
16. *Ibid.*
17. Whymper, *op. cit.*, pp. 15, 17, 257-272.
18. Armstrong, *op. cit.*, p. 52.
19. S. M. Tenney *et al.*, "Adaption to High Altitude: Changes in Lung Volumes During the First Seven Days at Mt. Evans, Colorado," *Journal of Applied Physiology* (1953), pp. 607-613.
20. School of Aviation Medicine, *op. cit.*, p. 38.
21. *Time*, November 24, 1958, p. 77.
22. School of Aviation Medicine, *op. cit.*, p. 59.
23. *Ibid.*, p. 26.
24. *Ibid.*, p. 60.
25. *Ibid.*, p. 61.
26. *Aviation Week*, July 28, 1958, p. 51.
27. Observations by James Stephen Hanrahan during a visit to the peak August 5, 1958; *Aviation Week*, July 28, 1958, p. 51; *Time* [Atlantic Edition], August 25, 1958, p. 36.
28. *Denver Post*, August 5, 1958.
29. *Missiles and Rockets*, September 28, 1958, p. 28.
30. Bruno Balke, "Experimental Studies on the Conditioning of Man for Space Flight," *Air University Quarterly Review*, Spring, 1959, pp. 65-66; *Holloman Rocketeer*, October 17, 1958.
31. *Time* [Atlantic Edition], August 25, 1958, p. 37.
32. *Denver Post*, August 5, 1958.
33. *Holloman Rocketeer*, October 17, 1958.
34. Hermann Oberth, *Man Into Space* (Harper & Brothers, 1957), p. 6.
35. "Space Medicine," *Missiles and Rockets*, February 1958, p. 186.
36. The voyage of the *Skate* is described in the *Alamogordo Daily News*, September 23, 1958, and that of the *Seawolf* in *Time*, October 20, 1958, p. 23.
37. Washington *Evening Star*, September 8, 1958; *Missiles and Rockets*, September 15, 1958, p. 19.
38. Armstrong, *op. cit.*, p. 16.
39. William R. Anderson, " 'Nautilus' Transpolar Cruise," *1959 Britannica Book of the Year* (Encyclopaedia Britannica, Inc.), pp. 474-475. Commander Anderson was skipper of the *Nautilus* during this cruise.
40. This early submarine pioneer is apparently no family relation to the co-author of this volume who bears the identical name.
41. These and other historical facts are featured cleverly in an advertisement of the General Dynamics Corporation published on the back cover of *Scientific American*, November 1959.
42. *Alamogordo Daily News*, March 31, 1959.
43. *New York Times*, January 24, 1960.

44. Interview of Dr. Early by James Stephen Hanrahan at the Space Medicine Branch meeting of the Aero Medical Association in Washington, D. C., March 26, 1958.
45. *Time,* October 20, 1958, p. 23.
46. C. H. Gibbs-Smith, *A History of Flying* (Frederick A. Praeger, 1954), p. 81.
47. *Ibid.,* pp. 81-82, 99.
48. *Ibid.,* p. 80. Gibbs-Smith is quoting an unacknowledged source.
49. Peter W. Brooks, "Aeronautics," in Singer *et al., op. cit.,* V, 395.
50. Gibbs-Smith, *op. cit.,* p. 76.
51. Jeremiah Milbank, Jr., in his *The First Century of Flight in America: An Introductory Survey* (Princeton University Press, 1943), pp. 4-6, cites letters of Franklin to Banks, dated August 30 and November 21, 1783, reproduced in A. H. Smyth, *The Writings of Benjamin Franklin,* (1906), IX, 79-85 and 113-118.
52. Armstrong, *op. cit.,* p. 3.
53. *Ibid.,* pp. 2-10, discussing the early period of balloon flight.
54. *Ibid.,* p. 5.
55. Hubertus Strughold, "Basic Environmental Problems Relating Man and the Highest Regions of the Atmosphere as Seen by the Biologist," in Clayton S. White and Otis O. Benson, Jr. (eds.), *Physics and Medicine of the Upper Atmosphere: A Study of the Aeropause* (University of New Mexico Press, 1952), p. 27. Plate V(b), at the end of the volume, shows a candle burning in nearly pure oxygen at a simulated attitude of 59,055 feet.
56. Armstrong, *op. cit.,* p. 5.
57. *Ibid.,* containing an extensive quotation in English translation from J. Glaisher *et al., Voyages aériens* (Paris, 1870).
58. *Ibid.,* quoting an extensive English translation from G. Tissandier, "Le Voyage à grande hauteur du ballon 'Le Zenith,'" *Nature* (Paris), May 1, 1875, pp. 337-344.
59. *Air Force,* February 1953, p. 16.
60. Hansjörg Kolder of the Department of Physiology at Emory University objects to the term explosive decompression unless restricted only to conditions where severe lesions and/or fatalities are anticipated because of the pressure drop *per se,* and not as a result of other accompanying conditions, such as anoxia. His objections are stated in a letter to *Aerospace Medicine,* June 1959, p. 454.
61. A photograph of the XC-35 can be found in volume two of the *Encyclopaedia Britannica,* facing p. 805.
62. Burgess, *op. cit.,* p. 38.
63. Strughold, *op. cit.,* pp. 28-29.
64. D. I. Fryer, "Consequences of Loss of Cabin Pressure," in *Collected Papers on Aviation Medicine Presented at Aeromedical Panel Meetings of the Advisory Group for Aeronautical Research*

and Development (NATO), *Palais de Chaillot, Paris* (Butterworth's Scientific Publications, 1955), p. 69.
65. James P. Henry, "Problems of Escape During Flight above 50,000 Feet," in White and Benson, *op. cit.*, p. 517.
66. Ari Shternfeld, *Soviet Space Science* (Basic Books, 1959), p. 179.
67. *Astronautics,* November 1958, p. 5.
68. Marjorie Hope Nicolson, in her *Voyages to the Moon* (The Macmillan Co., 1948), pp. 3-4, cites this article.
69. *Alamogordo Daily News,* May 2, 1958.
70. *Astronautics,* September 1958, p. 10.
71. *Ibid.,* August 1958, p. 8.
72. Shternfeld, *op. cit.,* p. 180.
73. *Aviation Week,* June 8, 1959, p. 30.
74. *Washington Sunday Star,* August 16, 1959.
75. Strughold, *op. cit.,* p. 30.
76. Burgess, *op. cit.,* p. 40.
77. Julian E. Ward, Jr., then with the School of Aviation Medicine, USAF, files an objection to the term "boiling" when used in this context. He pointed out that this low-pressure, low-temperature vaporization is a physical process and does not include chemical reactions in the tissues, as occur in the boiling of food during which protein coagulates. He suggests the substitute term "embullism" in *Missiles and Rockets,* July 1957, p. 167.
78. Strughold, *op. cit.,* pp. 29-39; Burgess, *op. cit.,* p. 40, citing the work of U. C. Luft.
79. Letter of H. E. Ross to the editor, *Journal of the British Interplanetary Society,* March 1950, p. 1; Michael W. Ovenden, "The Nature and Distribution of Meteoritic Matter," *ibid.,* September 1947, pp. 172-173; F. Whipple, "Meteoritic Phenomena and Meteorites: The Conquest of Interplanetary Space," in White and Benson, *op. cit.,* pp. 137-170.
80. *Missiles and Rockets,* October 1956, p. 75.
81. *Aviation Week,* July 27, 1959, p. 23.
82. *Vought Vanguard,* July 24, 1959, p. 1.
83. Eugene B. Konecci, "Human Factors and Space Flight," a paper presented at the meeting of the Institute of Aeronautical Sciences in Tulsa on November 12, 1957, p. 3.

CHAPTER 3

1. Frank Ross, Jr., *Space Ships and Space Travel: The Scientifically Accurate Story of Man's Attempts and Plans to Travel into Interplanetary Space* (Lothrop, Lee & Shepard, 1954), pp. 2-3. For more erudition in an evaluation of Kepler's story, see Marjorie

Hope Nicolson, *Voyages to the Moon* (The Macmillan Co., 1948), pp. 41-47.

2. A brief, clear account of this cycle is given by Benjamin Holzman in "The Hydrologic Cycle" in *Climate and Man: Yearbook of Agriculture, 1941* (U. S. Government Printing Office, 1941), pp. 532-536.
3. A detailed account of the evolution of man's knowledge of this relationship is given by Leonard K. Nash in "Plants and the Atmosphere," in James Bryant Conant (ed.), *Harvard Case Histories in Experimental Science* (2 vols., Harvard University Press, 1957), II, 323-436.
4. Harry G. Armstrong, *Principles & Practice of Aviation Medicine* (3rd ed.; Williams & Wilkins, 1952), p. 22.
5. "Air Conditioning Problems of Rocket Travel," *Bulletin of the British Interplanetary Society,* November 1946, pp. 49-52.
6. K. E. Schaefer, "Selecting a Space Cabin Atmosphere," *Astronautics,* February 1959, pp. 28-29, 104, 106.
7. *Aviation Week,* July 27, 1959, p. 23.
8. *Astronautics,* June 1959, p. 110.
9. *Astronautical Sciences Review,* April-June 1959, p. 31.
10. U. C. Luft, "Physiological Limitations in Cabin Environments and Human Adaptations," in Clayton S. White and Otis O. Benson, Jr. (eds.), *Physics and Medicine of the Upper Atmosphere: A Study of the Aeropause* (University of New Mexico Press, 1952), pp. 567-568.
11. Ari Shternfeld, *Soviet Space Science* (2d ed.; Basic Books, 1959), p. 206.
12. *Ibid.,* p. 207.
13. I. S. Balakhovskii and V. B. Malkin, "Biological Problems of Interplanetary Flights" [translated from *Priroda,* August 1956, pp. 15-21], in F. J. Krieger, *A Casebook on Soviet Astronautics: Part II* (U. S. Air Force Project Rand Research Memorandum RM-1922, June 21, 1957), p. 92; David G. Simons and Druey P. Parks, "Climatization of Animal Capsules During Upper Stratosphere Balloon Flights," *Jet Propulsion,* July 1956, p. 567.
14. David G. Simons and Erwin R. Archibald, "Selection of a Sealed Cabin Atmosphere," p. 5 of a paper accepted by the *Journal of Aviation Medicine* in November 1957.
15. George P. Kidera and John P. Marbarger, "Effects of Oxygen on Freshly Applied Lipstick and Chapstick," *Aerospace Medicine,* June 1959, pp. 431-432.
16. Eugene B. Konecci, *Human Factors and Space Flight,* a paper presented at the Tulsa Section Meeting, Institute of Aeronautical Sciences, November 12, 1957, pp. 2, 3, and 8; F. L. Dickey, *Dynamic Testing of a Space Cabin as Related to Human Factors,* a paper presented at the 5th Annual Human Engineering Confer-

ence, Office of Naval Research, Tulsa, Oklahoma, September 26-27, 1957.

17. Schaefer, *op. cit.,* pp. 29, 104.
18. Shternfeld, *op. cit.,* p. 207.
19. Frank K. Everest, Jr. (as told to John Guenther), *The Fastest Man Alive* (E. P. Dutton, 1958), p. 111.
20. Air Force Missile Development Center, *History of Research in Space Biology and Biodynamics . . .* (Holloman AFB: Historical Office, 1959), pp. 20, 26.
21. Charles E. Dryden *et al., Artificial Cabin Atmosphere Systems for High Altitude Aircraft* (Wright Air Development Center TR-55-353, November 1956), p. 39.
22. *Ibid.;* S. F. Cook and H. A. Leon, *Physiological Effects of Inert Gases* (AFMDC TR-59-26, June 1959), p. 25.
23. *Ibid.,* pp. 12, 19.
24. "Human Orientation During Travel in the Aeropause," in White and Benson, *op. cit.,* pp. 488-493.
25. "Cabin Conditioning System Weighed," *Missiles and Rockets,* October 5, 1959, pp. 26-27.
26. Rozenblat, "Before Flight into the Cosmos" [translated from *Nauka i zhizn,* November 1956, pp. 25-28], in Krieger, *op. cit.,* II, 142.
27. Hitchcock, "Some Considerations in Regard to the Physiology of Space Flight," *Astronautica Acta,* Vol. II, No. 1 (1956), p. 21.
28. Balke, "Experimental Studies on the Conditioning of Man for Space Flight," *University Quarterly Review,* Spring, 1959, pp. 68, 72.
29. Cited in Luft, "Physiological Limitations in Cabin Environments," pp. 569-570.
30. Rozenblat, *op. cit.,* p. 142.
31. Hubertus Strughold, "Space Medicine," *Missiles and Rockets,* September 1957, p. 60; the *Washington Star,* March 24, 1958, reporting on a paper presented by Strughold at the March 1958 convention of the Aero Medical (Aerospace Medical) Association.
32. Hitchcock, *op. cit.,* p. 21.
33. Eugene B. Konecci, "Hazards of Sealed Cabins," *Astronautics,* February 1959, pp. 40-41, 48-51.
34. Maurice K. Hanson, "The Payload on the Lunar Trip. Being an Account of the Equipment, Supplies, etc., Taken on the First Voyage to the Moon as Far as it is Possible to Detail Them at the Present Stage of the Society's Researches," *Journal of the British Interplanetary Society,* January 1939, p. 10.
35. Shternfeld, *op. cit.,* p. 208.
36. Article by Eugene B. Konecci abstracted in *Aerospace Medicine,* June 1959, p. 459.
37. Dryden, *op. cit.,* pp. 8, 30.
38. Shternfeld, *op. cit.,* p. 209.

39. John Adriani, "The Removal of Carbon Dioxide from Rebreathing Appliances," *Journal of Aviation Medicine,* December 1949, pp. 304-309.
40. Hanson, *op. cit.,* p. 11.
41. Tomaso Lomonaco, "The Evolution of Italian Aeronautical Medical Thought During the Last Twenty-Five Years," *Journal of Aviation Medicine,* October 1954, pp. 473-475.
42. N. J. Bowman, "The Food and Atmospheric Control Problem on Space Vessels. I: Chemical Purification of Air," *Journal of the British Interplanetary Society* (1953), pp. 118-123.
43. *Space/Aeronautics,* July 1959, p. 32.
44. "Item on Interplanetary Communications" (in the large Soviet encyclopedia *Bol'shaya sovetskaya* [2d ed.; 1954], Vol. 27, pp. 51-53) in Krieger, *op. cit.,* I, 67.
45. Hubertus J. Strughold, "Space Medicine," *Missiles and Rockets,* February 1958, p. 186.
46. *Alamogordo Daily News,* September 3, 1959; *New York Herald Tribune* (Paris edition), September 4, 1959.
47. *Albuquerque Journal,* February 20, 1959.
48. *Alamogordo Daily News,* August 26, 1958.
49. *Baltimore Sun,* September 11, 1958; *Missiles and Rockets,* September 22, 1958, p. 39.
50. Frank Ross, Jr., "Green Plants as Atmosphere Regenerators," *Bulletin of the British Interplanetary Society,* January 1947, p. 7.
51. *Aviation Week,* September 9, 1957, p. 65.
52. Nash, *op. cit.,* p. 433.
53. Eugene B. Konecci, "Human Factors and Space Cabin Development," a manuscript prepared for presentation at the 12th annual meeting of the American Rocket Society, New York, December 2-6, 1957, pp. 18a-22.

CHAPTER 4

1. *Vought Vanguard,* September 4, 1959, pp. 1, 6.
2. "The Payload on the Lunar Trip. Being an Account of the Equipment, Supplies, etc., Taken on the First Voyage to the Moon as Far as it is Possible to Detail Them at the Present Stage of the Society's Researches," *Journal of the British Interplanetary Society,* January 1939, p. 12.
3. "Before Flight Into the Cosmos," translated from *Nauka i zhizn,* November 1956, pp. 25-28, in F. J. Krieger, *Casebook on Soviet Astronautics,* (U.S. Air Force Project Rand Research Memorandum, RM-1760, June 21, 1956), p. 141.
4. "The Road Into the Cosmos," translated from *Nauka i zhizn,* November, 1955, pp. 33-37, in Krieger, *op. cit.,* p. 226.

5. *Alamogordo Daily News,* February 17, 1959; *Astronautics,* April 1959, p. 6.
6. *Aeronautics,* January 1959, p. 43.
7. An Associated Press release published in the *Alamogordo Daily News,* March 17, 1958, quoting from an article by Edson in the *Bulletin of the Atomic Scientists.*
8. *Aviation Age,* April 1958, p. 175; *Missiles and Rockets,* April 1958, p. 109.
9. *Aeronautics,* August 1958, p. 39.
10. *Astronautics,* September 1959, p. 12.
11. *Air Force Times,* November 12, 1958.
12. *Airman,* January 1959, p. 24.
13. *Jet Propulsion,* April 1957, p. 434.
14. *Missiles and Rockets,* January 1958, p. 67.
15. *Aviation Week,* May 25, 1959, p. 23.
16. *Missiles and Rockets,* June 15, 1959, p. 28.
17. *Astronautics,* August 1959, p. 4.
18. Reported by Albert Parry in *Missiles and Rockets,* September 8, 1958, pp. 91-92.
19. *New York Times,* August 22, 1958.
20. Letter from James W. Roach, Vought Astronautics, to James Stephen Hanrahan, November 24, 1959; *Vought Vanguard,* September 18, 1959, pp. 1, 8. The authors received a sample of these cookies and found them tasty and attractive, in spite of their green color.
21. *Vought Vanguard,* September 4, 1959, pp. 1, 6.
22. *Missiles and Rockets,* October 1957, p. 142.
23. *Aviation Week,* August 25, 1958, p. 43.
24. *Astronautics,* June 1959, p. 6.
25. *Air Force Times,* November 25, 1959.
26. Carsbie C. Adams, "Nutrition in Space Flight," *Missiles and Rockets,* November 1957, p. 107.
27. *Washington Daily News,* December 29, 1958.
28. *Astronautics,* September 1959, p. 16.
29. *Missiles and Rockets,* July 20, 1959, p. 29; *ibid.,* November 2, 1959, p. 49.
30. *Astronautics,* October 1959, p. 12.
31. Brochure distributed at the semiannual meeting of the American Rocket Society at San Diego, California, in June 1959.
32. *Air Force Times,* November 25, 1959.
33. J. S. Butz, Jr., "Development of Food-Waste Cycle Goal of Space Flight Researchers," *Aviation Week,* March 31, 1958, pp. 26-27.
34. *Ibid.; Astronautics,* May 1958, p. 8.
35. James Baar, "Space Feeding: Big $ Market," *Missiles and Rockets,* June 15, 1959, pp. 28, 32; *Astronautics,* June 1959, p. 6.
36. *Aviation Week,* September 7, 1959, p. 23.

37. *Air Force Times,* November 25, 1959.
38. *Space/Aeronautics,* June 1959, p. 29.
39. F. A. Hitchcock, "Some Considerations in Regard to the Physiology of Space Flight," *Astronautica Acta,* Vol. II, No. 1 (1956), p. 21.
40. Butz, *op. cit.,* p. 26.
41. Hanson, *op. cit.,* p. 11.
42. N. J. Bowman, "The Food and Atmospheric Control Problem on Space Vehicles. I. Chemical Purification of Air," *Journal of the British Interplanetary Society,* May 1953, pp. 118-123.
43. "Water Recovery in a Space Cabin," *Astronautics,* February 1959, pp. 34-35.
44. Douglas Aircraft Co., Inc., Tulsa Div., *Proposal for a Research and Development Program for a Sealed Environmental Cabin.* Report TU-28178, December 16, 1957, p. 14.
45. *Aviation Week,* August 17, 1959, p. 59.
46. Adams, *op. cit.,* pp. 105-107.
47. Hanson, *op. cit.,* pp. 13, 16.
48. *Jet Propulsion,* October 1956, p. 902; *ARDC Newsreview,* July 1959, p. 7.
49. Baar, *op. cit.,* pp. 28, 32.
50. *Aviation Week,* August 17, 1959, p. 59.
51. Walter Dornberger, *V-2* (Viking Press, 1954), p. 143.
52. *Time,* June 15, 1959, p. 50.
53. *Aviation Week,* July 27, 1959, p. 23.

Chapter 5

1. John Paul Stapp, "Acceleration: How Great a Problem?" *Astronautics,* February 1959, p. 38.
2. *Alamogordo Daily News,* May 2, 1958.
3. Harry L. Gephart, "Satellite Re-entry and Recovery," *Holloman Monthly News Bulletin,* September 1958, pp. 6-7; *Aviation Week,* November 17, 1958, p. 27.
4. Otto Gauer, "The Physiological Effects of Prolonged Acceleration," in *German Aviation Medicine, World War II* (two vols., U. S. Government Printing Office, 1950), Vol. I, p. 556.
5. *Ibid.,* p. 557; Harry G. Armstrong and J. W. Heim, "The Effect of Acceleration on the Living Organism," *Journal of Aviation Medicine* (hereafter cited as *JAM*) *9*:201-202, 205-211 (December 1938); *Astronautics,* July 1932; George C. Ham, "Effects of Centrifugal Acceleration on Living Organisms," *War Medicine, 3*:39, 41-46, 55 (1943).
6. Ham, *op. cit.,* p. 38; Gauer, *op. cit.,* p. 557; William G. Clark and Ralph L. Christy, "Use of Human Centrifuge in the Indoctrination

of a Navy Fighter Squadron in the Use of Antiblackout Equipment," *JAM 17*:394 (October 1946); Earl H. Wood *et al.*, "Effects of Acceleration in Relation to Aviation," in Federation of American Societies for Experimental Biology, *Federation Proceedings 5*:330 (1946).

7. John Lott Brown and Carter C. Collins, "Air-to-Air Tracking During Closed-Loop Centrifuge Operation," *JAM 29*:794 (November 1958); Carl C. Clark and James D. Hardy, "Preparing Man for Space Flight," *Astronautics,* February 1959, pp. 18-19.
8. John L. Brown and Marian Lechner, "Acceleration and Human Performance: A Survey of Research," *JAM 27*: 32-35 (February 1956); Ham, *op. cit.*, pp. 32-33, 40-41.
9. Brown and Lechner, *op. cit.*, p. 35; Siegfried J. Gerathewohl, "Physics and Psychophysics of Weightlessness: Visual Perception," *JAM 23*:382-387 (August 1952).
10. Brown and Lechner, *op. cit.*, p. 40; Neville P. Clarke and Stuart Bondurant, *Human Tolerance to Prolonged Forward and Backward Acceleration* (Wright Air Development Center [WADC] Technical Report 58-267, July 1958), p. 6.
11. Ham, *op. cit.*, pp. 38, 41; E. L. Beckman *et al.*, "Some Observations on Human Tolerance to Accelerative Stress, Phase II. Preliminary Studies on Primates Subjected to Maximum Simple Accelerative Loads," *JAM 24*:378 (October 1953); interview with Harald J. von Beckh by David Bushnell, November 4, 1959.
12. Stuart Bondurant *et al.*, *Human Tolerance to Some of the Accelerations Anticipated in Space Flight* (WADC Technical Report 58-156, April 1958), p. 12.
13. *Washington Post and Times-Herald,* August 9, 1958.
14. Bondurant *et al.*, *op. cit.*, pp. 3-6; F. C. Sheffield, " 'G' Men of the Air," *Flight,* February 12, 1942, abstracted in *Aeronautical Review,* April 1942, p. 29; Ham, *op. cit.*, p. 50.
15. J. C. Guignard, *The Physiological Effects of Transient Mechanical Forces: A Review of Their Relevance to Astronautics* (abstract of paper presented to Space Medicine Symposium sponsored by the British Interplanetary Society, October 1958), p. 3; Edwin P. Hiatt, "Biodynamics of Space Flight," *Astronautics,* February 1959, p. 70.
16. Wood *et al.*, *op. cit.*, pp. 337-342; Harry G. Armstrong, *Principles and Practice of Aviation Medicine* (3rd ed., Williams & Wilkins, 1952), pp. 377-379; E. A. Daley, "Aviation Medicine Progress in Australia over Twenty-Five Years," *JAM 25*:253-254 (October 1954); Charles F. Gell and Doris Cremore, "Dislocation of Organs and Tissues of Rats Exposed to Acceleration Stress," *JAM 27*:502 (December 1956).
17. Lew Zarem, "WADC Airman Accelerates Moon Travel," *ARDC Newsreview,* June 1958, p. 3.

18. Martin G. Webb, "Some Effects of Acceleration on Human Subjects," *JAM 29*:880-883 (December 1958).
19. H. E. Ross and J. H. Edwards, "The Firing Control of the B.I.S. Lunar Spaceship," *Journal of the British Interplanetary Society,* July 1939, p. 4.
20. Otto Gauer and Heinz Haber, "Man Under Gravity-Free Conditions," in *German Aviation Medicine, World War II,* I, 641-643.
21. Paul A. Campbell, "Human Orientation During Travel in the Aeropause," in Clayton S. White and Otis O. Benson, Jr. (eds.), *Physics and Medicine of the Upper Atmosphere* (University of New Mexico Press, 1952), p. 491.
22. E. R. Ballinger, "Human Experiments in Subgravity and Prolonged Acceleration," *JAM 23*:320-321 (August 1952); E. R. Ballinger and C. A. Dempsey, *The Effects of Prolonged Acceleration on the Human Body in the Prone and Supine Positions* (WADC Technical Report 52-250, July 1952).
23. H. Preston-Thomas *et al.,* "Human Tolerance to Multistage Rocket Acceleration Curves," *JAM 26*:390-398 (October 1955).
24. Rufus R. Hessberg, Jr., "Acceleration Forces Associated with Leaving and Re-entering the Earth's Gravitational Field," *Journal of Astronautics IV*:6 (Spring, 1957).
25. Zarem, *op. cit.,* p. 3.
26. Bondurant *et al., op. cit.,* pp. 2, 8, 10; Clarke and Bondurant, *op. cit.,* pp. 17, 23, 25; interview with Neville P. Clarke by David Bushnell, June 9, 1958.
27. *Aviation Week,* June 8, 1959, pp. 52-53, 55, 59.
28. Bondurant *et al., op. cit.,* pp. 1-2.
29. *Ibid.,* pp. 11-12; Hugh Miller *et al.,* "Duration of Tolerance to Positive Acceleration," abstract, *JAM 29*:243 (March 1958).
30. Carl C. Clark and James D. Hardy, "Preparing Man for Space Flight," *Astronautics,* February 1959, p. 90.
31. Bondurant *et al., op. cit.,* p. 10 and *passim;* Clarke and Bondurant, *op. cit.,* pp. 5, 7, 18; R. Flanagan Gray and Martin G. Webb, "High G Protection," abstract, *JAM 30*:185-186 (March 1959); Neville P. Clark, *Human Acceleration Effects for Rocket Flight* (American Rocket Society preprint 804-59, June 1959).
32. *Some Physiological and Pathological Effects in Chimpanzees Exposed to 40 Transverse G for 15 and 60 Seconds* (Aviation Medical Acceleration Laboratory Report, August 1957); *Effect of Positioning in Exposure of Chimpanzee to 40 Transverse G for 60 Seconds* (Aviation Medical Acceleration Laboratory Report, November 1957); interview with Alice M. Stoll, Aviation Medical Acceleration Laboratory, by David Bushnell, June 6, 1958; Alice M. Stoll and John D. Mosely, "Physiologic and Pathologic Effects in Chimpanzees during Prolonged Exposure to 40 Transverse G," *JAM 29*:575-586 (August 1958).

33. Interview with John P. Stapp by David Bushnell, February 11, 1958.
34. Below, pp. 144-145.
35. Bondurant *et al., op. cit.,* p. 10.
36. Hessberg, *op. cit.,* p. 7. Subjects in these tests used harnessing and, in one case, an anti-*g* suit.
37. Zarem, *op. cit.,* p. 3; Bondurant *et al., op. cit.,* p. 6; Clarke and Bondurant, *op. cit.,* pp. 15-16, 20.
38. Clarke and Bondurant, *op. cit.,* p. 8. See also pp. 14-15 of the same report.
39. *Aviation Week,* June 9, 1959, p. 59.
40. Clarke, *op. cit.,* pp. 2-3.
41. Clarke and Bondurant, *op. cit.,* pp. 22-23; Bondurant *et al., op. cit.,* p. 10.
42. *Aviation Week,* April 28, 1958, p. 23; Clark and Hardy, *op. cit.,* pp. 17, 19-21, 88, 90.
43. Clark and Hardy, *op. cit.,* p. 90; interview with Carl C. Clark by David Bushnell, June 6, 1958; Carl C. Clark and C. H. Woodling, "Centrifuge Simulation of the X-15 Research Aircraft," abstract, *JAM 30*:179 (March 1959).
44. Richard C. Kaehler, "Human Pilot Performance during Boost and Atmospheric Reentry," *Aerospace Medicine 30*:481-486 (July 1959); *Aviation Week,* May 11, 1959, p. 31.
45. *Aviation Week,* July 6, 1959, p. 89.

CHAPTER 6

1. Letter from A. Howard Hasbrouk, Director of Aviation Crash Injury Research, Sky Harbor Airport, Phoenix, Arizona, to the editor, *Aviation Week,* June 2, 1958, p. 90.
2. D. I. Fryer, "Passenger Survival in Aircraft Crashes," *Aeronautics,* April 1959, p. 31; J. H. Mathewson and D. M. Severy, "Automobile Impact Research," in National Safety Council *Transactions 28*:93-101 (1954). The United States Air Force crash research program at the Air Force Missile Development Center is discussed in some detail in *History of Research in Space Biology and Biodynamics at the Air Force Missile Development Center, Holloman Air Force Base, New Mexico, 1946-1958* (Historical Branch, Air Force Missile Development Center [AFMDC], December 1958), pp. 65-68, 81-85.
3. *New York Herald Tribune,* November 16, 1958.
4. Robert F. Rushmer *et al.,* "Internal Injuries Produced by Abrupt Deceleration of Experimental Animals," *Journal of Aviation Medicine* (hereafter cited as *JAM*) *17*:512-525 (December 1946); Siegfried Ruff, "Brief Acceleration: Less Than One Second," in

German Aviation Medicine, World War II (2 vols., U. S. Government Printing Office, 1950), 5, 587.

5. Ruff, *op. cit.,* pp. 585-586, 588-589; Sidney T. Lewis and John P. Stapp, *Experiments Conducted on a Swing Device for Determining Human Tolerance to Lap Belt Type Decelerations* (AFMDC Technical Note 57-1, December 1957); Committee on Interstate and Foreign Commerce, House of Representatives, 85th Congress, *Hearings Before a Subcommittee . . . on Crashworthiness of Automobile Seat Belts* (Washington, 1957), p. 39.
6. *Alamogordo Daily News,* February 8, 1959.
7. Walter S. Rothwell and Edward G. Sperry, "Escape from Aircraft by Downward Ejection," *JAM 24*:322-327 (August, 1953); A. Martin Eiband, *Human Tolerance to Rapidly Applied Accelerations: A Summary of the Literature* (NASA Memorandum 5-19-59E, June 1959), pp. 14-23.
8. Ruff, *op. cit.,* p. 586.
9. John P. Stapp, *Human Exposures to Linear Deceleration, Part I: Preliminary Survey of the Aft-Facing Seated Position* and *Part II: The Forward Facing Position and the Development of a Crash Harness* (Air Force Technical Report 5915, Wright Air Development Center, 1949-1951); H. G. Medlock and Everett E. Dodd, "Desert Sleigh Ride," *Air Force,* May 1953, pp. 81, 83; Irwin Hersey, "Our Chief Gravity Inspector," *Saturday Review,* December 13, 1958, pp. 49-50.
10. John Paul Stapp, *Human and Chimpanzee Tolerance to Linear Deceleration Forces* (n.d.), p. 9 and *passim,* and "Tolerance to Abrupt Deceleration," in Advisory Group for Aeronautical Research and Development, North Atlantic Treaty Organization, *Collected Papers on Aviation Medicine* (Butterworths Scientific Publications, 1955), pp. 123-131, 140-158.
11. Stapp, "Tolerance to Abrupt Deceleration," in *Collected Papers on Aviation Medicine,* pp. 124, 132-133, 162-169.
12. Committee on Interstate and Foreign Commerce, *Hearings Before a Subcommittee on . . . Crashworthiness of Automobile Seat Belts,* p. 25.
13. Address by Col. Stapp at Texas Technological College, Lubbock, October 3, 1955; Stapp, "Tolerance to Abrupt Deceleration," in *Collected Papers on Aviation Medicine,* p. 138; Hersey, "Our Chief Gravity Inspector," *Saturday Review,* December 13, 1958, pp. 49-50.
14. John Paul Stapp, "Biodynamics of Space Flight," in Kenneth F. Gantz (ed.), *Man in Space: The United States Air Force Program for Developing the Spacecraft Crew* (Duell, Sloan and Pearce, 1959), p. 67.
15. *History of Research in Space Biology and Biodynamics at the Air Force Missile Development Center,* pp. 46, 92; *Origin and*

Operation of the First Holloman Track (AFMDC Historical Branch, December 1959 [Vol. I, *History of Tracks and Track Testing at the Air Force Missile Development Center*]), pp. 9-19, 65-66.

16. John P. Stapp, "Effects of Mechanical Force on Living Tissues I. Abrupt Deceleration and Impact," *JAM 26*:269-270 (August 1955); *Origin and Operation of the First Holloman Track,* p. 67.
17. Stapp, "Effects of Mechanical Force on Living Tissues I.," *JAM 26*:273.
18. *Ibid.,* p. 274.
19. *Ibid.,* pp. 275-277; *History of Research in Space Biology and Biodynamics at the Air Force Missile Development Center,* pp. 46-47.
20. *History of Research in Space Biology and Biodynamics,* p. 47.
21. *Ibid.*
22. Stapp, "Effects of Mechanical Force on Living Tissues I," *JAM 26*:277-278; *Alamogordo Daily News,* December 28, 1954. The brick-wall comparison is quoted from a speech by Lt. General Samuel E. Anderson at a meeting of the American Rocket Society in Dallas, Texas, March 19, 1958.
23. Stapp, "Effects of Mechanical Force on Living Tissues I.," *JAM 26*:280.
24. *Ibid.,* p. 281.
25. Test report quoted in *History of Research in Space Biology and Biodynamics at the Air Force Missile Development Center,* p. 49.
26. Stapp, "Effects of Mechanical Force on Living Tissues I.," p. 286.
27. *Time,* September 12, 1955; *Alamogordo Daily News,* March 9, 1956; interview with Colonel Stapp by David Bushnell, March 31, 1958.
28. *Alamogordo Daily News,* March 4, 1956.
29. *Alamogordo Daily News,* August 26, 1955, and June 1, 1956. The description of the Cheney Award is quoted from *The United States Air Force Dictionary* (Air University Press, 1956), p. 112.
30. *History of Research in Space Biology and Biodynamics at the Air Force Missile Development Center,* p. 50.
31. *Alamogordo Daily News,* December 29, 1954, and January 4, 1955.
32. Cf. *Alamogordo Daily News,* June 17, 1956.
33. *History of Research in Space Biology and Biodynamics at the Air Force Missile Development Center,* p. 50.
34. *Ibid.,* pp. 51-52; John P. Stapp and C. D. Hughes, "Effects of Mechanical Force on Living Tissues II. Supersonic Deceleration and Windblast," *JAM 27*:407-413 (October 1956).
35. Burt Rowen, "Human-Factors Support of the X-15 Program," in Gantz, *op. cit.,* p. 221.

36. *History of Research in Space Biology and Biodynamics at the Air Force Missile Development Center,* pp. 50-51, 68.
37. *Ibid.,* p. 68; "Chimpanzees Pass Space Speed Test," *New York Times,* January 31, 1958; John P. Stapp, "Acceleration: How Great a Problem?" *Astronautics,* February 1959, p. 98; Stapp, "Biodynamics of Space Flight," in Gantz, *op. cit.,* pp. 67-68. Various figures have been given for the peak *g*-forces experienced in these tests, but the differences are never great enough to matter; the text has followed statistical data given in the *History of Research in Space Biology and Biodynamics.*
38. Cf. "Chimpanzees Pass Space Speed Test," *New York Times,* January 31, 1958.
39. Stapp, "Biodynamics of Space Flight," in Gantz, *op. cit.,* p. 68.
40. Cf. *El Paso Times,* November 6, 1959.
41. Some of these other experiments are described in *History of Research in Space Biology and Biodynamics at the Air Force Missile Development Center,* pp. 52, 53, 57-59, and in *Origin and Operation of the First Holloman Track,* p. 66.
42. W. H. B. Ellis, *Studies of Human Response to Linear Acceleration During Carrier Take-offs and Landings* (Flying Personnel Research Committee, Air Ministry, Report 905, June 1955), pp. 1-2.
43. Eli L. Beeding, Jr., *Daisy Track and Supporting Systems* (AFMDC Technical Note 57-8, June 1957); John P. Stapp and Wilbur C. Blount, "Effects of Mechanical Force on Living Tissues III. A Compressed Air Catapult for High Impact Forces," *JAM 28*:281-284 (June 1957); interview with Captain Erwin A. Archibald by David Bushnell, December 7, 1959.
44. Stapp and Blount, *op. cit.,* pp. 284-290; interview with Captain Beeding by David Bushnell, March 8, 1958.
45. *Hollomon Rocketeer,* May 23, 1958; below, pp. 107-108.

Chapter 7

1. Rodolfo Margaria, "Wide Range Investigations of Acceleration in Man and Animals," *Journal of Aviation Medicine* (hereafter cited as *JAM*) *29*:857-858 (December 1958).
2. Cf. *Holloman Rocketeer,* May 9, 1958.
3. Stuart Bondurant *et al., Effect of Water Immersion on Human Tolerance to Forward and Backward Acceleration* (Wright Air Development Center [WADC] Technical Report 58-290, July 1958), p. 1.
4. Martin J. Webb and R. Flanagan Gray, *Protection Against Acceleration by Water Immersion* (American Rocket Society preprint 805-59), pp. 2-3.

5. David P. Morris *et al.*, "Studies on the G Tolerance of Invertebrates and Small Vertebrates while Immersed," *JAM 29*:438 (June 1958); Harry G. Armstrong, *Principles and Practice of Aviation Medicine* (3rd ed., Williams & Wilkins Co., 1952), pp. 378-379.
6. Earl H. Wood *et al.*, "Effects of Acceleration in Relation to Aviation," in Federation of American Societies for Experimental Biology, *Federation Proceedings, 5*:337 (1946).
7. Morris *et al., op. cit.*, p. 438.
8. C. F. Code *et al.*, "Hydrostatic anti-blackout protection: the protection afforded man against effects of positive acceleration by immersion in water," *Federation Proceedings 4*:15 (1945).
9. Morris *et al., op. cit.*, p. 438.
10. Letter from Captain Herbert G. Shepler, Aviation Medical Acceleration Laboratory, to David Bushnell, July 2, 1958.
11. *Ibid.; Philadelphia Inquirer,* August 17, 1958; *Preliminary Study of G Tolerance of a Subject in the G-Capsule, Prone Position* (Aviation Medical Acceleration Laboratory, July 1958).
12. *Human Tolerance to High Acceleration Stress* (Aviation Medical Acceleration Laboratory, May, 1958).
13. Webb and Gray, *op. cit.*, pp. 3-5; *New York Times,* August 30, 1959.
14. Morris *et al., op. cit.*, pp. 438-442.
15. *Ibid.; Aviation Week,* March 31, 1958; *The Aquarium,* October, 1957, p. 328.
16. Bondurant *et al., op. cit.; Aviation Week,* May 12, 1958, p. 33; interview with Neville P. Clarke by David Bushnell, June 9, 1958; address by John P. Stapp to the Holloman Section of the American Rocket Society, May 5, 1959.
17. Interviews with Albert Zaborowski by David Bushnell, May 28, 1958, May 26, 1959 and November 2, 1959.
18. *Missiles and Rockets,* June, 1958, p. 34.
19. Rodolfo Margaria, "Le forze di accelerazione e la condizione di subgravità in volo," *Rivista di Medicina Aeronautica,* Anno XX, No. 2, pp. 175-186 (April-June 1957); Rodolfo Margaria *et al.*, "Protection Against Acceleration Forces in Animals by Immersion in Water," *JAM 29*:433-437 (June 1958); Morris *et al., op. cit.*, pp. 441-442.
20. Bondurant *et al., op. cit.*, p. 1.
21. Interview with Neville P. Clarke by David Bushnell, June 9, 1958.
22. Margaria, "Le forze di accelerazione," pp. 183-184.
23. *Aviation Week,* May 12, 1958, p. 33.
24. *Aviation Age,* June 1958, p. 163.
25. *Aviation Week,* September 14, 1959, p. 112.
26. Quax V, "Candid Comments," *Aeronautics,* November 1958, p. 45.

27. Cf. Bondurant *et al., op. cit.,* p. 12.
28. Robert F. Rushmer *et al.,* "Internal Injuries Produced by Abrupt Deceleration of Experimental Animals," *JAM 17*:512-525 (December 1946); James Roman, *Effects of Severe Whole Body Vibration on Mice and Methods of Protection from Vibration Injury* (WADC Technical Report 58-107, April 1958), pp. 19-21.
29. Roman, *op. cit.,* pp. 1, 15-16, 19-21; James Roman *et al.,* "Vibration, Buffeting, and Impact Research," *JAM 30*:123-124 (February 1959).
30. Harald J. von Beckh, "Multidirectional G Protection in Space Flight and during Escape: A Theoretical Approach," *JAM 29*: 335-341 (May 1958), and "Multidirectional G-Protection in Space Vehicles," *Journal of the British Interplanetary Society 16*:531 (September-October 1958); Harald J. von Beckh and Grover J. D. Schock, *Centrifuge Experiments on High-g Loads in Mice and Their Possible Alleviation by Multidirectional Anti-G Devices* (AFMDC Technical Note 58-10, August 1958).
31. Von Beckh and Schock, *op. cit.;* Harald J. von Beckh, *Physiology of Launching and Re-Entry Stress in Rodents* (AFMDC Technical Note 58-11, August 1958); interview with von Beckh by David Bushnell, August 28, 1959.
32. *El Paso Times,* February 26, 1959; *New York Times,* March 8, 1959.
33. Von Beckh and Schock, *op. cit.,* p. 3.
34. Von Beckh, *Physiology of Launching and Re-Entry Stress,* p. 5.
35. F. L. van der Wal and W. D. Young, *A Preliminary Experiment with Recoverable Biological Payloads in Ballistic Rockets* (Space Technology Laboratories, September 1958); interviews with Harald J. von Beckh by David Bushnell, June 18 and October 15, 1958; below, pp. 127-128.
36. Arthur C. Clarke, "Space Travel in Fact and Fiction," *Journal of the British Interplanetary Society 9*:221, 223 (September 1950).
37. Martin Gardner, *Fads and Fallacies in the Name of Science* (Dover Publications, 1957), pp. 92-100.
38. *Aviation Age,* May 1957, pp. 26-31; *Astronautics,* December 1957 p. 5, and April 1958, p. 5; *Missiles and Rockets,* October 1957, p. 64, and February 1958, p. 199; *Aviation Week,* March 31, 1958, p. 94; notes by James S. Hanrahan taken at American Rocket Society Meeting in Dallas, Texas, March 1958; *Space/Aeronautics,* September 1959, p. 30.

Chapter 8

1. Georges Ferry, *L'aptitude à l'aviation* (Paris, 1918), pp. 47-48.
2. Heinz Haber, "The Concept of Weight in Aviation," *Journal of*

Aviation Medicine (hereafter cited as *JAM*) *23*:594-596 (December 1952); Siegfried J. Gerathewohl, "Weightlessness," in Kenneth F. Gantz (ed.), *Man in Space: The United States Air Force Program for Developing the Spacecraft Crew* (Duell, Sloan and Pearce, 1959), pp. 112-113.

3. Hubertus Strughold, "Mechanoreceptors, Gravireceptors," *Journal of Astronautics IV*:61-63 (Winter, 1957). See also his contribution to *German Aviation Medicine, World War II* (two vols., U.S. Government Printing Office, 1950), II, 995-996.
4. *German Aviation Medicine, World War II,* II, 995.
5. Heinz Haber, "The Human Body in Space," *Scientific American 184*:17 (January 1951); C. R. Armstrong, "Space Physiology," *Journal of the British Interplanetary Society* (hereafter cited as *JBIS*) *12*:173 (July 1953).
6. Harry G. Armstrong, *Principles and Practice of Aviation Medicine* (3rd ed., Williams & Wilkins, 1952), pp. 284-291; Harald J. von Beckh, *Fisiología del vuelo* (Editorial Alfa, Buenos Aires, 1955), p. 89.
7. Otto Gauer and Heinz Haber, "Man Under Gravity-Free Conditions," in *German Aviation Medicine, World War II,* I, 643-644.
8. Edward J. Kendricks *et al., Medical Problems of Space Flight* (Special Report, U. S. Air Force School of Aviation Medicine, August 1955 [reprinted from *Instructors Journal,* Winter, 1954]), p. 17.
9. Heinz Haber and Siegfried J. Gerathewohl, "Physics and Psychophysics of Weightlessness," *JAM* 22:187 (June 1951).
10. *Ibid.*
11. Louis Gougerot, "Perspectives physiologiques soulevées par le problème astronautique," *Médicine Aéronautique 2*:70 (1947).
12. A. E. Slater, "The Balancing Mechanism of the Inner Ear," *JBIS 9*:18-23 (January 1950), and "Sensory Perceptions of the Weightless Condition," in *Annual Report of the British Interplanetary Society,* 1952, pp. 342-348. In the earlier paper Slater stated, as one possibility, that the otoliths might send impulses "at the rate characteristic for the normal position of the head," in which case no difficulty would arise. The special "frequency characteristic of weightlessness" was substituted for this alternative in the later version, but again no major difficulty was anticipated.
13. Gauer and Haber, *op. cit.,* p. 644.
14. *JBIS 14*:61-62 (January-February 1955).
15. Harry G. Armstrong *et al.,* "The Aero Medical Problems of Space Travel," *JAM 20*:400 (December 1949).
16. Cf. Derek F. Lawden, "The Simulation of Gravity," *JBIS 16*:134 (July-September 1957).
17. Slater, "Sensory Perceptions of the Weightless Condition," *loc. cit.*

18. Marjorie Hope Nicolson, *Voyages to the Moon* (The Macmillan Co., 1948), p. 77.
19. E. Jack Wilcox, "Psychological Consequences of Space Travel," *JBIS 16*:7 (January-March 1957); *Wall Street Journal,* October 2, 1958, citing remarks of Harald J. von Beckh.
20. Robert Esnault-Pelterie, *Considerations on the Results of Indefinite Decrease in Weight of Engines,* reprint translation (n.d.) of article originally published in *Journal de Physique,* March 1913.
21. H. F. Michielsen, "The Case for the Low Acceleration Spaceship," *Astronautica Acta,* Vol. III, Fasc. 2, pp. 130-152 (1957). This solution presupposes an equally low deceleration, by reverse rocket thrust, at the other end.
22. P. K. Isakov, "Problems of Weightlessness," in F. J. Krieger (ed.), *A Casebook on Soviet Astronautics* (U.S. Air Force Project Rand, Research Memorandum RM-1760, June 1956), p. 239; Pierre Bergeret, "La vie dans un milieu dans pesanteur," *Atomes,* July 1952, p. 224.
23. H. E. Ross, "The B.I.S. Space-Ship," *JBIS,* January 1939, p. 8.
24. R. A. Smith, "The Man-Carrying Rocket," *JBIS,* May 1948, p. 105.
25. Wernher von Braun, "Prelude to Space Travel," in Cornelius Ryan (ed.), *Across the Space Frontier* (Viking, 1953), pp. 38-41.
26. M. P. Lansberg, *Some Consequences of Weightlessness and Artificial Weight* (paper presented to British Interplanetary Society's Symposium on Space Medicine, October 1958).
27. Ari Shternfeld, *Soviet Space Science* (Basic Books, 1959), p. 175.
28. A. E. Slater, "Medical and Biological Problems," in D. R. Bates (ed.), *Space Research and Exploration* (Eyre and Spottiswoode, 1957), p. 176.
29. Heinz von Diringshofen, "Sensory-Physiological Observations During the Transition from Acceleration to Weightlessness," abstract, *Aerospace Medicine 30*:621-622 (August 1959); interview with Harald J. von Beckh by David Bushnell, February 17, 1958.

CHAPTER 9

1. David G. Simons, *Use of V-2 Rocket to Convey Primate to Upper Atmosphere* (Air Force Technical Report 5821, Wright-Patterson AFB, 1949), p. 1.
2. A popular account of the V-2 animal experiments is offered by Lloyd Mallan in his *Men, Rockets, and Space Rats* (Julian Messner, 1955), pp. 84-93. This should be read in conjunction with the technical report by Simons cited above and the article by James P. Henry *et al.,* "Animal Studies of the Subgravity State

during Rocket Flight," *Journal of Aviation Medicine* (hereafter cited as *JAM*) *23*:421-432 (October 1952). In the present chapter a few details have also been checked or filled in through an interview with David G. Simons by David Bushnell, December 13, 1957.

3. *New York Times Magazine,* March 23, 1958. Cf. Heinz Haber, "The Human Body in Space," *Scientific American 184*:17 (January 1951).
4. Henry *et al., op. cit.,* p. 428.
5. *Ibid.,* p. 425.
6. *Ibid.,* pp. 423-424, 429-431; *Final Report, USAF Aerobee No. 19* (Holloman AFB, February 1952); David G. Simons, "Review of Biological Effects of Subgravity and Weightlessness," *Jet Propulsion,* May 1955, p. 211.
7. Henry *et al., op. cit.,* pp. 425, 429.
8. *Ibid.,* p. 426; Simons, "Review of Biological Effects of Subgravity," p. 211.
9. Simons, "Review of Biological Effects of Subgravity," p. 211.
10. *Ibid.; Alamogordo Daily News,* December 1, 1957.
11. *New York Times,* March 23, 1952; *History of Research in Space Biology and Biodynamics at the Air Force Missile Development Center, Holloman Air Force Base, New Mexico, 1946-1958* (Historical Branch, Air Force Missile Development Center, December 1958), p. 9, note 15.
12. F. L. van der Wal and W. D. Young, *A Preliminary Experiment with Recoverable Biological Payloads in Ballistic Rockets, Project MIA* (Space Technology Laboratories, September 1958); "The Three 'Cadets' of Project MIA," *Space Age,* May 1959, pp. 30-31.
13. *Aviation Week,* December 22, 1958, p. 23, and December 29, 1958, p. 15.
14. *Alamogordo Daily News,* June 2, 1959; *Missiles and Rockets,* June 8, 1959, p. 28; *Time,* June 15, 1959, p. 78.
15. *Alamogordo Daily News,* May 29 and June 7, 1959; *Missiles and Rockets,* June 8, 1959, p. 28.
16. *Alamogordo Daily News,* September 16, 1959.
17. *New York Times,* December 6, 1959; *Alamogordo Daily News,* January 21, 1960.
18. Prof. Pokorovski (*sic*), *Study of the Vital Activity of Animals During Rocket Flights into the Upper Atmosphere* (Library Translation No. 625, Royal Aircraft Establishment, Farnborough, January 1957); "First Space Travelers," *Moscow News,* February 23, 1957; *Missiles and Rockets,* March 1958, p. 82; Andrei G. Kousnetzov, "Some Results of Biological Experiments in Rockets and Sputnik II," *JAM 29*: 781-784 (November 1958); B. G. Bugrov *et al., Investigations of the Vital Activity of Animals During*

Flights in a Nonhermetically-Sealed Rocket Cabin to an Altitude of 110 Kilometers (reprint translation, n. d.); *Astronautics,* February 1959, pp. 31, 80-81. These sources overlap considerably with one another, but all have been used in the general discussion of Russian animal flights.

19. Pokorovski, *op. cit.,* p. 4.
20. V. N. Chernov and V. I. Yakovlev, "Research on the Flight of a Living Creature in an Artificial Earth Satellite," *ARS Journal 29*: 736-742 (October 1959). All data on the Sputnik II experiment have been taken from this source, except for the reference to Laika's death, which is based on Kousnetzov, *op. cit.,* p. 784.
21. Quoted in *New York Times,* January 12, 1958.
22. *Alamogordo Daily News,* June 4, 1959.

Chapter 10

1. Fritz Haber and Heinz Haber, "Possible Methods of Producing the Gravity-Free State for Medical Research," *Journal of Aviation Medicine* (hereafter cited as *JAM*) *21*:395-400 (October 1950).
2. Edward J. Kendricks *et al., Medical Problems of Space Flight* (USAF School of Aviation Medicine Special Report, August 1955 [reprinted from *Instructors Journal,* Winter, 1954]), p. 17.
3. Siegfried J. Gerathewohl, "Weightlessness," in Kenneth F. Gantz (ed.), *Man in Space: The United States Air Force Program for Developing the Spacecraft Crew* (Duell, Sloan and Pearce, 1959), p. 109.
4. Siegfried J. Gerathewohl *et al., Producing the Weightless State in Jet Aircraft* (USAF School of Aviation Medicine Report 57-143, August 1957).
5. David G. Simons, "Review of Biological Effects of Subgravity and Weightlessness," *Jet Propulsion,* May 1955, p. 210; Kendricks *et al., op. cit.,* p. 18.
6. Kendricks *et al., op. cit.,* p. 18; Heinz Haber, *Man in Space* (Bobbs-Merrill, 1953), p. 172.
7. E. R. Ballinger, "Human Experiments in Subgravity and Prolonged Acceleration," *JAM 23*:319-320 (August 1952).
8. Kendricks *et al., op. cit.,* pp. 19-20; *Holloman Monthly News Bulletin,* September 1959, p. 2; interviews with Harald J. von Beckh by David Bushnell.
9. Harald J. von Beckh, *Fisiología del vuelo* (Editorial Alfa, Buenos Aires, 1955), pp. 103-107, and "Experiments with Animals and Human Subjects under Sub and Zero Gravity Conditions," *JAM 25*:235-241 (June 1954).
10. Harald J. von Beckh, "Gravity Changes in Aircraft and Ships," *Journal of the British Interplanetary Society* (hereafter cited as

JBIS) *15*:79 (March-April 1956); Von Beckh, *Flight Experiments About Human Reactions to Accelerations Which Are Followed or Preceded by the Weightless State* (Air Force Missile Development Center [AFMDC] Technical Note 58-15, December 1958), pp. 17-18.

11. Von Beckh, *Fisiología del vuelo,* p. 94; von Beckh, "Gravity Changes in Aircraft and Ships," *JBIS 15*:80.
12. *History of Research in Space Biology and Biodynamics at the Air Force Missile Development Center, Holloman Air Force Base, New Mexico, 1946-1958* (Historical Branch, Air Force Missile Development Center, December 1958), pp. 36-37; interview with Captain Joseph W. Kittinger, Jr., by David Bushnell, June 9, 1958.
13. *Holloman Rocketeer,* January 24, 1958; Grover John D. Schock, *Some Observations on Orientation and Illusions When Exposed to Sub and Zero-Gravity* (Ph.D. thesis, University of Illinois, 1958; copy from University Microfilms, Inc., Ann Arbor, Mich.).
14. *Alamogordo Daily News,* August 14, 1958.
15. Gerathewohl *et al., Producing the Weightless State in Jet Aircraft,* p. 6.
16. Siegfried J. Gerathewohl *et al.,* "Sensomotor Performance during Weightlessness: Eye-Hand Coordination," *JAM 28*:7 (February 1957), and *Producing the Weightless State in Jet Aircraft,* pp. 8-10.
17. Grover J. D. Schock, *Management Report, Subgravity Studies* (October 1957).
18. Haber, *Man in Space,* p. 172; Gerathewohl, *et al., Producing the Weightless State in Jet Aircraft,* p. 10; Grover J. D. Schock and David G. Simons, *A Technique for Instrumenting Subgravity Flights* (AFMDC Technical Note 58-4, February 1958); Schock, *Airborne Galvanic Skin Response Studies. A Preliminary Report* (AFMDC Technical Note 59-14, June 1959), pp. 2-5.
19. *History of Research in Space Biology and Biodynamics at the Air Force Missile Development Center,* p. 40.
20. *Missiles and Rockets,* April 1958, p. 129.
21. Siegfried J. Gerathewohl, "Personal Experiences during Short Periods of Weightlessness Reported by Sixteen Subjects," *Astronautica Acta, II*:205-212 (June 1956), and "Weightlessness," in Gantz, *op. cit.,* pp. 124-125.
22. Gerathewohl, "Personal Experiences during Short Periods of Weightlessness," pp. 206-207.
23. *Ibid.,* p. 210.
24. *Ibid.,* pp. 210-212.
25. Schock, *Some Observations on Orientation and Illusions,* pp. 57, 59, 74-75; interview with Captain Schock by David Bushnell, December 5, 1957; interview with Captain Joseph W. Kittinger,

Jr., by David Bushnell, December 12, 1957; *Aviation Week,* January 4, 1960, pp. 22-23.

26. Schock, *Some Observations on Orientation and Illusions*, pp. 54-56, 58; Gerathewohl *et al.,* "Sensomotor Performance during Weightlessness," *JAM 28*:7-11.
27. Julian E. Ward *et al.,* "Physiologic Response to Subgravity I. Mechanics of Nourishment and Deglutition of Solids and Liquids," *JAM 30*:151-154 (March 1959); *Los Angeles Times,* October 26, 1958.
28. Julian E. Ward *et al.,* "Physiologic Response to Subgravity II. Initiation of Micturition," *Aerospace Medicine 30*:572-575 (August 1959).
29. Siegfried J. Gerathewohl, "Physics and Psychophysics of Weightlessness: Visual Perception," *JAM 23*:373-395 (August 1952).
30. Grover J. D. Schock, *Apparent Motion of a Fixed Luminous Target During Subgravity Trajectories* (AFMDC Technical Note 58-3, February 1958).
31. Siegfried J. Gerathewohl and Herbert D. Stallings, "Experiments During Weightlessness: A Study of the Oculo-Agravic Illusion," *JAM 29*:504-515 (July 1958).
32. Von Beckh, *Flight Experiments,* pp. 9-14; *Missiles and Rockets,* July 7, 1958, p. 34.
33. Von Beckh, *Flight Experiments,* pp. 16-20; Schock, *Airborne Galvanic Skin Response Studies,* pp. 5-7.
34. Von Beckh, *Flight Experiments,* p. 15.
35. *Ibid.,* p. 16.
36. Siegfried J. Gerathewohl and Herbert D. Stallings, "The Labyrinthine Posture Reflex (Righting Reflex) in the Cat during Weightlessness," *JAM 28*:345-355 (August 1957); Grover J. D. Schock, *A Study of Animal Reflexes During Exposure to Subgravity and Weightlessness* (AFMDC Technical Note 59-12, June 1959); Schock, *Some Observations on Orientation and Illusions,* pp. 60-65, 75-77.
37. Grover J. D. Schock, *Sensory Reactions Related to Weightlessness and Their Implications to Space Flight* (AFMDC Technical Report 58-6, April 1958), pp. 2-3; Air Force Office of Scientific Research and Convair Division of General Dynamics Corporation, *Summary Session, Astronautics Symposium* (1957), p. 50; Hubertus Strughold, "Mechanoreceptors, Gravireceptors," *Journal of Astronautics, IV*:62 (Winter, 1957); Schock, *Some Observations on Orientation and Illusions,* p. 11; Rodolfo Margaria, "Wide Range Investigations of Acceleration in Man and Animals," *JAM 29*:856-860 (December 1958).
38. Leon A. Knight, "An Approach to the Physiology of Simulation of the Null-Gravity State," *JAM 29*:283-286 (April 1958).
39. Grover J. D. Schock, *Perception of the Horizontal and Vertical*

in Simulated Subgravity Conditions (AFMDC Technical Note 59-13, June 1959); Schock, *Sensory Reactions Related to Weightlessness,* p. 7; Schock, *Some Observations on Orientation and Illusions,* pp. 25-32, 37-53; interview with Captain Schock by David Bushnell, October 17, 1957.

40. Schock, *Sensory Reactions Related to Weightlessness,* p. 8.
41. *Aviation Week,* December 22, 1958, pp. 52-55; *Astronautics,* February 1959, p. 42, and June 1959, p. 28; *Holloman Rocketeer,* April 24, 1959.
42. Heinz Haber, "The Human Body in Space," *Scientific American 184*:18 (January 1951).
43. Washington *Evening Star,* April 2, 1959.
44. *Aviation Week,* January 13, 1958, pp. 26-28; *New York Times,* July 12, 1959.
45. Abstract of report by Johnson in *JAM 30*:189 (March 1959); interview with Dr. von Beckh by David Bushnell, June 24, 1958.
46. Cf. *Baltimore Sun,* January 14, 1958.
47. Interview with Dr. von Beckh by David Bushnell, October 28, 1959.
48. Margaria, *op. cit.,* pp. 860-863.
49. *JBIS 16*:45-46 (January-March 1957).
50. Howard Walton, Jr., "A Device for Artificial Production of Alternating Gravitational Forces," *JAM 28*:291-292 (June 1957).
51. H. J. Muller, "Approximation to a Gravity-Free Situation for the Human Organism Achievable at Moderate Expense," *Science 128*:772 (October 3, 1958).
52. C. L. Barker, Jr., *Space Flight Simulator* (Report No. DSP-TR-1-59, Army Ballistic Missile Agency, March 1959), p. i.
53. *Ibid.,* p. 33.
54. *ARDC Newsreview,* June 1958, p. 5.
55. Heinz von Diringshofen and Harald J. von Beckh, "Aspectos médicos de la astronáutica," *Revista Nacional de Aeronáutica* (Buenos Aires), November 1952, pp. 20-21.
56. Schock, *Sensory Reactions Related to Weightlessness,* pp. 4-8; *Missiles and Rockets,* May 1958, p. 171.
57. A. E. Slater, "Medical and Biological Problems," in D. R. Bates (ed.), *Space Research and Exploration* (Eyre and Spottiswoode, 1957), p. 175.

Chapter 11

1. Jakob A. G. Eugster, *Effects on Living Tissues by Primary Cosmic Ray Particles* (Air Force Office of Scientific Research, Technical Report 56-19, February 1956), pp. 3, 4, 17.
2. Hermann J. Schaefer, "Biological Significance of the Natural Back-

ground of Ionizing Radiation—Observations at Sea Level and at Extreme Altitude," *Journal of Aviation Medicine* (hereafter cited as *JAM*) *26*:453-462 (December 1955).

3. Frank H. J. Figge, "Cosmic Radiation and Cancer," *Science 105*: 323 (March 28, 1947).
4. Jakob A. G. Eugster, *Weltraumstrahlung* (Medizinischer Verlag Hans Huber, 1955), p. 52; Eugster, *Effects on Living Tissues by Primary Cosmic Ray Particles, passim.*
5. Victor F. Hess and Jakob Eugster, *Cosmic Radiation and Its Biological Effects* (2nd ed., Fordham University Press, 1949), pp. 3-7.
6. *Ibid.,* pp. 7-8.
7. *Ibid.,* pp. 9-10, 42; Hermann J. Schaefer, "Exposure Hazard from Cosmic Radiation at Extreme Altitude and in Free Space," *Journal of the American Rocket Society,* September-October 1952, p. 278. Despite the relation described between cosmic radiation and geomagnetic latitude, the "cosmic-ray equator" is not *quite* the same as the geomagnetic equator. This point must be noted for the record, although it makes little difference in space biology.
8. Hess and Eugster, *op. cit.,* p. 11; James A. Van Allen, "The Nature and Intensity of the Cosmic Radiation," in Clayton S. White and Otis O. Benson, Jr. (ed.), *Physics and Medicine of the Upper Atmosphere* (University of New Mexico Press, 1952), p. 249; Hermann J. Schaefer, "Evolution of the Present-Day Knowledge of Cosmic Radiation at Extreme Altitude in Terms of the Hazard to Health," *JAM 21*:379 (October 1950).
9. Phyllis Freier *et al.,* "Evidence for Heavy Nuclei in the Primary Cosmic Radiation," *Physical Review* 74:213-217 (July 15, 1948), and "The Heavy Component of Primary Cosmic Rays," *Physical Review 74*:1818-1827 (December 15, 1948).
10. Cornelius A. Tobias, "Radiation Hazards in Space Flight," included as appendix to Rudolf A. Hoffman, *Radiation Hazards of Primary Cosmic Particles* (Air Force Missile Development Center [AFMDC], Technical Report 59-32, July 1959), p. 97.
11. Eugster, *Weltraumstrahlung,* p. 10.
12. Hoffman, *op. cit.,* pp. 2-3, 9; Tobias, *op. cit.,* pp. 97-104; Hermann J. Schaefer and Abner Golden, *Solar Influences on the Extra-Atmospheric Radiation Field and their Radiobiological Implications* (preprint of paper for Second International Symposium on the Physics and Medicine of the Atmosphere and Space, sponsored by the U.S. Air Force School of Aviation Medicine at San Antonio, Texas, November 1958), pp. 12-14; Hermann J. Schaefer, "Cosmic Ray Dosage during the Giant Solar Flare of February 26, 1956," *JAM 28*:387-396 (August 1957).
13. Tobias, *op. cit.,* pp. 99-100.
14. Hermann J. Schaefer, "Optimum Altitudes for Biological Experimentation with the Primary Cosmic Radiation," *JAM 27*:519 (De-

cember 1956); "Remarks by Dr. Yagoda on Cosmic Rays," extract from a memorandum, supplied by Webb Haymaker of the Armed Forces Institute of Pathology in August 1958; Tobias, *op. cit.,* pp. 114-120.

15. Schaefer, "Exposure Hazard from Cosmic Radiation," p. 279.
16. *Ibid.,* pp. 279-280; David G. Simons, *Stratosphere Balloon Techniques for Exposing Living Specimens to Primary Cosmic Ray Particles* (AFMDC Technical Report 54-16, November 1954), p. 3.
17. Cf. Hermann J. Schaefer, *Theory of Protection of Man in the Region of the Primary Cosmic Radiation* (U.S. Naval School of Aviation Medicine, August 1953).
18. Alfred M. Mayo, "Environmental Considerations of Space Travel from the Engineering Viewpoint," *JAM 27*:386 (October 1956); *France Soir,* January 8, 1958 (Russian proposal).
19. Tobias, *op. cit.,* pp. 117-118; David G. Simons, *Military Aspects of Observed Biological Effects of Cosmic Ray Particles* (1956), pp. 9, 15, and *passim;* Berry Campbell, *Research on the Biological Effects of the Heavy Particle Cosmic Rays* (AFMDC Technical Report 55-8, 1955), pp. 4-6.
20. Tobias, *op. cit.,* p. 117.
21. Hess and Eugster, *op. cit.,* p. 97 and *passim;* A. T. Krebs, "Possibility of Biological Effects of Cosmic Rays in High Altitudes, Stratosphere, and Space," *JAM 21*:487-490 (December 1950).
22. Hess and Eugster, *op. cit.,* p. 87.
23. *Ibid.,* pp. 87-173; Hermann J. Schaefer, "Biological Effects of Cosmic Radiation," in White and Benson (ed.), *op. cit.,* pp. 310-311; Konrad Buettner, "Radiation Effects on Man in Space," *Bulletin of the American Meteorological Society 32*:183 (May 1951).
24. L. W. Fraser and E. H. Siegler, *High Altitude Research Using the V-2 Rocket March 1946-April 1947* (Johns Hopkins University Bumblebee Series Report No. 8, July 1948), p. 90; Kenneth W. Gatland, *Development of the Guided Missile* (2nd ed., Philosophical Library, 1954), p. 188.
25. J. M. Beal, "Negative Results Following Exposure of Several Kinds of Seeds to Cosmic Rays and Other Radiations at High Altitudes," *Botanical Gazette 112*:533-534 (1951); letter from D. M. Haskin, Department of Physics, University of Chicago, to David Bushnell, August 21, 1958.
26. Cf. Schaefer, "Evolution of the Present-Day Knowledge of Cosmic Radiation," *JAM 21*:376, 389, 390.
27. Simons, *Stratosphere Balloon Techniques,* pp. 11-12.
28. *Ibid.,* pp. 12-19.
29. *Ibid.,* pp. 1, 4-10, 51-59.
30. *Ibid.,* pp. 1-3.
31. Frank H. J. Figge, *op. cit.,* p. 323; E. P. George *et al.,* "Influence

of cosmic radiation in induced carcinogenesis in mice," *Nature, 164*:1044-1045 (December 17, 1949).

32. David G. Simons, *Biological Hazard of Space Radiations* (preprint of chapter to be included in volume edited by Otto Glasser on Medical Physics), p. 10, and "Observations in High-Altitude, Sealed-Cabin Balloon Flight," in Kenneth F. Gantz (ed.), *Man In Space: The United States Air Force Program for Developing the Spacecraft Crew* (Duell, Sloan and Pearce, 1959), p. 136.
33. Jakob A. G. Eugster, "Method for Demonstrating the Biological Effectiveness of Cosmic Radiation at High Altitudes," *JAM 24*: 222-226 (June 1953); Eugster, *Effects on Living Tissues by Primary Cosmic Ray Particles, passim;* Eugster, *Weltraumstrahlung,* p. 110; Simons, *Stratosphere Balloon Techniques,* p. 1.

CHAPTER 12

1. Hermann J. Schaefer, *Theory of Protection of Man in the Region of the Primary Cosmic Radiation* (U.S. Naval School of Aviation Medicine, August 1953) and "Exposure Hazards from Cosmic Radiation Beyond the Stratosphere and in Free Space," *Journal of Aviation Medicine* (hereafter cited as *JAM*) *23*:338-344 (August 1952); Herman B. Chase and Janice S. Post, "Damage and Repair in Mammalian Tissues Exposed to Cosmic Ray Heavy Nuclei," *JAM 27*:538-539 (December 1956); Rudolf Hoffman, *Radiation Hazards of Primary Cosmic Particles* (Air Force Missile Development Center [AFMDC], Technical Report 59-32, July 1959), p. 3 and *passim;* David G. Simons, *Biological Hazard of Space Radiations* (preprint of chapter to be included in a volume edited by Otto Glasser on medical physics), p. 18.
2. David G. Simons, *Stratosphere Balloon Techniques for Exposing Living Specimens to Primary Cosmic Ray Particles* (AFMDC Technical Report 54-16, November 1954), pp. 4, 8, 54-55; *Contributions of Balloon Operations to Research and Development at the Air Force Missile Development Center, Holloman Air Force Base, N. Mex.* (Historical Branch, AFMDC, March 1959), pp. 86-88, 93.
3. Simons, *Stratosphere Balloon Techniques,* pp. 7-9, 27, 39, 42-43, 50, 54; *Contributions of Balloon Operations to Research and Development,* pp. 90-92.
4. Simons, *Stratosphere Balloon Techniques,* pp. 41-42, 57; Hoffman, *op. cit.,* pp. 13, 19.
5. David G. Simons and Druey P. Parks, "Improved Techniques for Exposing Animals to Primary Cosmic Ray Particles," *JAM 27*: 318 (August 1956).

6. *Contributions of Balloon Operations to Research and Development,* pp. 75-85.
7. Aeromedical Field Laboratory, *Test Report on Aeromedical Field Laboratory Balloon Flights 61 and 62* (July 1955); Hoffman, *op. cit.,* pp. 63-64.
8. David G. Simons and C. H. Steinmetz, "The 1954 Aeromedical Field Laboratory Balloon Flights, Physiological and Radiobiological Aspects," *JAM 27*:105-106 (April 1956); Hoffman, *op. cit.,* p. 85.
9. Simons, *Stratosphere Balloon Techniques,* pp. 19-24; interview with Simons by David Bushnell, December 13, 1957.
10. Simons, *Stratosphere Balloon Techniques,* pp. 24-25; *Contributions of Balloon Operations to Research and Development,* pp. 25-29.
11. Simons, *Stratosphere Balloon Techniques,* pp. 25-49.
12. Simons and Steinmetz, *op. cit.,* pp. 100-110, and *Physiological and Radiobiological Aspects of the 1954 Aeromedical Field Laboratory Balloon Flights* (slightly different version of the same article, published separately, n.d.), p. 13; Webb Haymaker, "Operation Stratomouse," *Military Medicine 119*:154 (September 1956); Charles H. Steinmetz, *Experimental Material Flown on Aeromedical Field Laboratory Balloon Flights 46 Through 71* (AFMDC Technical Note 56-2, 1956, p. 7; Hoffman, *op. cit.,* pp. 31-42.
13. Haymaker, *op. cit.,* pp. 151-171; Steinmetz, *op. cit.,* pp. 1, 11; Hoffman, *op. cit.,* pp. 42-59.
14. Interviews with Harold H. Kuehn by David Bushnell, November 27 and December 2, 1957; interview with David G. Simons by David Bushnell, February 14, 1958.
15. Interview with Harold H. Kuehn by David Bushnell, November 27, 1957; Hoffman, *op. cit.,* pp. 59-63; Winzen Research, Inc., *Fact Sheet, Project Manhigh* (August, 1957).
16. Hoffman, *op. cit.,* pp. 10, 63-64; *Alamogordo Daily News,* July 30, 1958; *New York Times,* August 8, 1958; interview with Webb Haymaker by David Bushnell, August 5, 1958.
17. *Contributions of Balloon Operations to Research and Development,* pp. 12-13.
18. William J. Longmore, *Preparation of Control Specimens for the 1954 Aero Medical Field Laboratory Balloon Flights* (AFMDC Technical Note 55-6, May 1955).
19. Washington *Evening Star,* August 20, 1958; David G. Simons, "Observations in High-Altitude, Sealed-Cabin Balloon Flight," in Kenneth F. Gantz (ed.), *Man in Space: The United States Air Force Program for Developing the Spacecraft Crew* (Duell, Sloan and Pearce, 1959), pp. 154-155.
20. Simons, *Stratosphere Balloon Techniques,* pp. 5-6, 24, 36, 61-62; Berry Campbell, *Research on the Biological Effects of the Heavy*

Primary Cosmic Rays (AFMDC Technical Report 55-8, December 1955); Hoffman, *op. cit.,* pp. 27, 76, 115-116.

21. Steinmetz, *op. cit.,* p. 2; Simons, *Military Aspects of Observed Biological Effects of Cosmic Ray Particles,* pp. 19, 23; Herman B. Chase *et al., Effects on the Skin by Cosmic Ray Heavy Particles* (AFMDC Technical Report 55-2, May 1955); Chase and Post, *op. cit.,* pp. 533-540.
22. Harry F. Harlow *et al.,* "Exposure of Primates to Cosmic Radiation Above 90,000 Feet," *Journal of Comparative and Physiological Psychology 49*:195-200 (April 1956); Simons and Steinmetz, "The 1954 Aeromedical Field Laboratory Balloon Flights," *JAM 27*:105-106, 110.
23. Jakob A. G. Eugster, *Effects on Living Tissue by Primary Cosmic Ray Particles* (Air Force Office of Scientific Research, Technical Report 56-19, February 1956); interview with David G. Simons by David Bushnell, December 13, 1957; Jakob Eugster *et al., Effect of High Altitude Cosmic Radiation on Barley Seeds* (n. d.).
24. Hoffman, *op. cit.,* pp. 25, 76; interview with Harold H. Kuehn by David Bushnell, November 27, 1957.
25. Haymaker, *op. cit.,* pp. 151-171; Hoffman, *op. cit.,* pp. 79-85; interview with Webb Haymaker by David Bushnell, August 5, 1958; C. H. Steinmetz, *Techniques Used for Monitoring Biological Specimens on the 1954 and 1955 Aero Medical Field Laboratory Balloon Flights* (AFMDC Technical Note 57-1, 1957).
26. Hoffman, *op. cit.,* p. 68; Simons, "Observations in High-Altitude, Sealed-Cabin Balloon Flight," in Gantz, *op. cit.,* pp. 139-140.
27. Steinmetz, *Experimental Material,* pp. 3-4.
28. Hoffman, *op. cit.,* pp. 28, 85-86.
29. Simons and Parks, *op. cit.,* p. 320; Herman Yagoda, "Frequency of Thindown Hits by Heavy Primary Nuclei in Emulsion and Tissue," *JAM 27*:522-523 (December 1956).
30. Haymaker, *op. cit.*
31. Don Flickinger, "Biomedical Aspects of Space Flight," in Gantz, *op. cit.,* p. 54; Cornelius A. Tobias, "Radiation Hazards in Space Flight," included as appendix in Hoffman, *op. cit.,* pp. 108-117.
32. Burt Rowen, "Human-Factors Support of the X-15 Program," in Gantz, *op. cit.,* p. 219.
33. V. N. Chernov and V. I. Yakovlev, "Research on the Flight of a Living Creature in an Artificial Earth Satellite," *ARS Journal 29*: 752 (October 1959).
34. Interview with E. P. Ney, Department of Physics, University of Minnesota, by David Bushnell, July 1, 1958; interview with Bernard D. Gildenberg, Balloon Branch, Air Force Missile Development Center, by David Bushnell, December 14, 1959.
35. Washington *Evening Star,* July 21, 1958; *New York Times,* July 27, 1958; Sarah Bedichek Pipkin and William N. Sullivan, "A

Search for Genetic Change in Drosophila Melanogaster Exposed to Cosmic Radiation at Extreme Altitude," *Aerospace Medicine 30*:585-598 (August 1959).

36. *Astronautics,* October 1959, p. 12.
37. *Missiles and Rockets,* June 8, 1959, p. 28; *Aviation Week,* June 1, 1959, p. 37; *Alamogordo Daily News,* May 29, 1959.
38. *Alamogordo Daily News,* September 16, 1959.
39. *Alamogordo Daily News,* June 4, 1959.

CHAPTER 13

1. Hubertus Strughold, "Medical Problems Involved in Orbital Space Flight," *Jet Propulsion,* September 1956, pp. 746-747; Heinz Haber, "Manned Flight at the Borders of Space. The Human Factor of Manned Rocket Flight," *Journal of the American Rocket Society,* September-October 1952, p. 273; *Missiles and Rockets,* September 28, 1959, p. 34.
2. John P. Marbarger (ed.), *Space Medicine* (University of Illinois Press, 1951), pp. 56, 61; Eric Burgess, *Satellites and Space Flight* (Macmillan, 1957), p. 39.
3. Haber, *op. cit.,* p. 272; Hubertus Strughold *et al.,* "Where Does Space Begin?" *Journal of Aviation Medicine* (hereafter cited as *JAM*) *22*:345 (October 1951); Marbarger, *op. cit.,* p. 78.
4. Marbarger, *op. cit.,* pp. 61, 78; *Aviation Week,* October 5, 1959, p. 31.
5. Hermann J. Schaefer, "New Knowledge of the Extra-Atmospheric Radiation Field," *JAM 29*:495-499 (July 1958); Hermann J. Schaefer and Abner Golden, *Solar Influences on the Extra-Atmospheric Radiation Field and their Radiobiological Implications* (preprint of paper for Second International Symposium on the Physics and Medicine of the Atmosphere and Space, sponsored by School of Aviation Medicine, San Antonio, Texas, November 1958), pp. 16-18; David G. Simons, *Biological Hazard of Space Radiations* (preprint of chapter to be included in volume edited by Otto Glasser on medical physics), p. 19.
6. Washington *Evening Star,* May 1, 1958.
7. *New York Times,* May 2, 1958.
8. James A. Van Allen *et al.,* "Observation of High Intensity Radiation by Satellites 1958 Alpha and Gamma," *Jet Propulsion,* September 1958, pp. 588-592 (published in September but presented to a meeting of the American Rocket Society in June 1958); Washington *Evening Star,* May 1, 1958; *New York Times,* May 2, 1958.
9. Van Allen *et al., op. cit.,* p. 592.
10. Cf. A. R. Hibbs, *Scientific Results from the Explorer Satellites*

(Jet Propulsion Laboratory, External Publication No. 514, June 2, 1958), p. 14.

11. *Missiles and Rockets,* August 11, 1958, p. 20.
12. *New York Times,* August 22, 1958.
13. *Ibid. Aviation Week,* August 18, 1958, pp. 32, 33.
14. *Alamogordo Daily News,* September 17, 1958.
15. "The Argus Experiment—Q. and A. on the Basic Science Involved," *New York Times,* March 22, 1959, News in Review section, p. 6; *New York Herald Tribune,* March 22, 1959.
16. *Aviation Week,* September 1, 1958, pp. 21-22.
17. The quotations are from a preprint distributed at the Amsterdam meeting. A slightly amended version can be found in *Journal of the British Interplanetary Society,* November-December 1958, pp. 558-564.
18. A. E. Slater, "Space Medicine Symposium," *Space Flight,* January 1959, p. 17.
19. *Aviation Week,* December 8, 1958, p. 33; *Aviation Week,* January 5, 1959, p. 19; *Aviation Week,* May 11, 1959, p. 31.
20. On the Soviet contribution, cf. *Astronautics,* July 1959, pp. 23, 86-88, and *Aviation Week,* March 16, 1959, p. 32.
21. *Alamogordo Daily News,* September 30, 1959; *Aviation Week,* October 5, 1959, pp. 29-31.
22. S. F. Singer, "Artificial Modification of the Earth's Radiation Belt," *Journal of the Astronautical Sciences, VI*:5-7 (Spring, 1959); *Missiles and Rockets,* April 6, 1959, p. 40; *Missiles and Rockets,* June 15, 1959, p. 39, and July 20, 1959, pp. 43-47; *Aviation Week,* January 5, 1959, p. 19; *Aviation Week,* May 11, 1959, p. 31, and October 5, 1959, pp. 29-31.
23. *Aviation Week,* September 7, 1959.
24. Cf. Simons, *op. cit.,* p. 19.
25. *Aviation Week,* September 7, 1959.
26. S. F. Singer, *Some Consequences of a Theory of the Radiation Belt* (preprint of paper for 9th Annual Congress of the International Astronautical Federation, Amsterdam, August 1958), p. 6.
27. *San Antonio Light,* November 10, 1958.
28. *Astronautics,* January 1959, p. 10 (the quoted passage is in the words of the magazine writer).
29. Hermann J. Schaefer, "Radiation Dosage in Flight Through the Van Allen Belt," *Aerospace Medicine 30*:633-638 (September 1959).
30. *Missiles and Rockets,* July 20, 1959, p. 45.
31. Marbarger, *op. cit.,* p. 78; Konrad Buettner, "Radiation Effects on Man in Space," *Bulletin of the American Meteorological Society 32*:184 (May 1951).
32. *Missiles and Rockets,* July 7, 1958, p. 34.
33. *Astronautics,* August 1959, p. 6.

34. *Aviation Week,* August 4, 1958, p. 23.
35. Eugene B. Konecci and Robert Trapp, "Calculations of the Radiobiologic Risk Factors in Nuclear-Powered Space Vehicles," *JAM 30*:487-506 (July 1959).
36. *Astronautics,* June 1959, p. 6.

CHAPTER 14

1. Various aspects of this chapter's thesis have been developed and presented by the authors in a recent series of papers and lectures. David Bushnell, for example, considered *The Impact of Space Technology on Medical Research* in a presentation on November 19, 1959, at the 14th Annual Meeting of the American Rocket Society in Washington, D. C. (ARS preprint 1031-59). Other portions of the chapter have emerged from material presented by James Stephen Hanrahan, such as: "Space Technology and the Man in the Street," prepared for the ARS meeting in New York City March 20, 1959; *The Influence of Astronautics Upon Contemporary Thought,* presented at the ARS semiannual meeting in San Diego June 9, 1959 (ARS preprint 820-59); "Social Response in the United States to the Impact of Missile/Space Technology," prepared for the Tenth Congress of the International Astronautical Federation in London September 4, 1959; *Alterations in Cultural Patterns Resulting from the Developing Program of Astronautics,* presented at the 14th Annual Meeting of the ARS; and a series of lectures delivered at the United States Air Force Academy in October-December 1959.
2. Discussion between Herbert F. York and James Stephen Hanrahan, Amsterdam, August 29, 1958.
3. One of the most erudite surveys of this revolution in scientific thought is A. R. Hall's *The Scientific Revolution, 1500-1800: The Formation of the Modern Scientific Attitude* (Beacon Press, 1954).
4. George Sarton, *Six Wings: Men of Science in the Renaissance* (Indiana University Press, 1957), p. 54.
5. *Ibid.,* p. 67.
6. Hall, *op. cit.,* pp. 35-36; Lancelot Hogben, *Science for the Citizen: A Self-Educator Based on the Social Background of Scientific Discovery* (2nd ed., Alfred A. Knopf, 1938), p. 168.
7. Angus Armitage, *The World of Copernicus* (New American Library of World Literature, 1951), p. 25; Hall, *op. cit.,* p. 58.
8. Sarton, *op. cit.,* pp. 61-62, quoting from writings by Melanchthon and Martin Luther.
9. Hall, *op. cit.,* p. 103.
10. Philipp Frank, *Philosophy of Science: The Link Between Science*

and Philosophy (Prentice-Hall, 1957), pp. 33, 116, quoting works by Francis Bacon.

11. Albert Einstein, "The Mechanics of Newton and their Influence on the Development of Theoretical Physics," in his *Essays in Science* (Philosophical Library, 1934), pp. 28, 38. In one of these passages, Einstein refers to Newton as "this brilliant genius, who determined the course of western thought."
12. For an estimation of the effect of Newtonian physics upon American thought during this period, see Harvey Fish, *Society and Thought in Early America: A Social and Intellectual History of the American People Through 1865* (Longman's Green & Co., 1950), pp. 143, 168; Henry Steele Commager, *The American Mind: An Interpretation of American Thought and Character since the 1830's* (Yale University Press, 1950), p. 83.
13. *Great Music* (May 1959), pp. 1-3, issued by the Book-of-the-Month Club, Inc. John M. Conly is editor of *High Fidelity & Audiocraft.*
14. Commager, *op. cit.,* p. 83. See also Samuel Eliot Morrison and Henry Steele Commager, *Growth of the American Republic* (4th ed., two vols., Oxford University Press, 1950), II, 269; Vernon Louis Parrington, *Main Currents in American Thought: An Interpretation of American Literature from the Beginnings to 1920* (Harcourt, Brace and Co., 1930) III, 198, 204-206, 293, 323, and 352.
15. Quoted from the inside front cover of the book by Julian Huxley and James Fisher, *The Living Thoughts of Darwin* (Longman's, Green & Co., 1939).
16. Wish, *op. cit.,* p. 465.
17. Morrison and Commager, *op. cit.,* II, 269; Parrington, *op. cit.,* III, 198.
18. Parrington, *op. cit.,* III, 402.
19. Commager, *op. cit.,* pp. 82-83.
20. Parrington, *op. cit.,* III, 293.
21. Huxley and Fisher, *op. cit.,* p. 150.
22. Morrison and Commager, *op. cit.,* II, 269
23. Louis de Broglie, "A General Survey of the Scientific Work by Albert Einstein," in Paul Arthur Schilpp (ed.), *Albert Einstein: Philosopher-Scientist* (Tudor Publishing Co., 1951), p. 112.
24. Hans Reichenbach, in the chapter "The Philosophical Significance of the Theory of Relativity," in Schilpp, *op. cit.,* pp. 289-290, exposes the illegitimacy of this pseudo-relativism.
25. "Is God a Christian?," *Saturday Review,* February 28, 1959, p. 22.
26. *Alamogordo Daily News,* May 28, 1959.
27. *L'osservatore romano,* September 22, 1956; *New York Times,* September 21, 1956; *Missiles and Rockets,* October 1956, p. 30.

28. Eugen Sanger's contribution in *The Next Ten Years of Space,* a report issued by the United States Congress (U.S. Government Printing Office, 1959), pp. 158-172.
29. *New York Times,* May 21, 1957, reporting a week-long symposium on stellar galaxies sponsored at the Vatican by the Pontifical Academy of Sciences.
30. *Washington Daily News,* May 3, 1958.
31. Quoted in Hubertus Strughold, *The Green and Red Planet: A Physiological Study of the Possibility of Life on Mars* (University of New Mexico Press, 1953), p. 97, note.
32. Hall, *op. cit.,* p. 103.
33. *Alamogordo Daily News,* June 21, 1959.
34. *Ibid.,* July 19, 1959.
35. Robert A. Jonquil, "Can Science Prove When Time Began?," a review of Lovell's *The Individual and the Universe* (Harper and Bros., 1959), in *Saturday Review,* May 2, 1959, pp. 51-54.
36. David Greenfield in *Saturday Review,* July 4, 1959, p. 39.
37. *Denver Post,* September 10, 1958; *Army-Navy-Air Force Register,* December 27, 1958.
38. *Alamogordo Daily News,* February 2, 1959.
39. P. E. Cleaton, *Into Space* (George Allen & Unwin, 1953), p. 76.
40. London *Times,* September 2, 1958.
41. *Alamogordo Daily News,* June 10, 1958.
42. *Airman,* April 1959, p. 48.
43. *Air Force,* December 1954, p. 16.
44. *Missiles and Rockets,* February 9, 1959, p. 61.
45. These representative magazine articles are cited in a monograph on "Human Scientific and Technical Capabilities at Holloman Air Force Base: Their Origins and Development," by Theodore Saloutos of the University of California at Los Angeles, who prepared the study during the summer of 1958 while serving as consultant at the Air Force Missile Development Center.
46. Benjamin Fine, dean of the Graduate School of Education, Yeshiva University, quoted in *Saturday Review,* February 14, 1959, p. 30.
47. Herbert A. Smith, president of the National Teachers Association, cited in *Astronautics,* April 1959, p. 12.
48. Quoted by Edward D. Eddy, Jr., in "An Object Lesson," *Saturday Review,* May 24, 1958, pp. 39-40.
49. In the issue for April 5, 1958, p. 8.
50. Charles Calitri in *Saturday Review,* February 14, 1959, p. 27. See also "Light on the Human Predicament," by Paul Woodring, *Saturday Review,* February 2, 1959, pp. 23-24, which discusses the threat to the humanities posed by the technological emphasis on education.
51. Drew Pearson, *Alamogordo Daily News,* March 1, 1959.

52. *UCLA Alumni Magazine,* September 1958, p. 18.
53. *Missiles and Rockets,* July 14, 1958, p. 61.
54. *Astronautics,* March 1958, p. 5; *Missiles and Rockets,* June 1958, p. 181.
55. *Missiles and Rockets,* June 1958, p. 54; *Astronautics,* August 1958, p. 60.
56. *UCLA Alumni Magazine,* October 1958, p. 11.
57. *Astronautics,* September 1958, p. 86.
58. *Ibid.,* March 1959, p. 10.
59. *Ibid.,* May 1959, p. 9.
60. *Ibid.,* April 1959, p. 12.
61. *Missiles and Rockets,* April 13, 1959, p. 39.
62. *Ibid.; Astronautics,* May 1959, p. 9.
63. *Holloman Monthly News Bulletin* [of the Holloman Section, American Rocket Society], January 1958, p. 1.
64. *Ibid.,* December 1958, p. 1.
65. *Missiles and Rockets,* June 1957, p. 132, and February 1958, p. 186.
66. *Alamogordo Daily News,* February 9, 1959.
67. Letter from D. L. Biemesderfer to James S. Hanrahan, November 11, 1958.
68. *Holloman Rocketeer,* February 13, 1958; *Missiles and Rockets,* April 1958, p. 53.
69. *Air Force,* October 1951, p. 15; Holloman Rocketeer, June 6, 1958; *Aviation Week,* May 18, 1959, p. 82; *Air Force Times,* May 6 and May 27, 1959.
70. *Astronautics,* March 1959, p. 74.
71. *Missiles and Rockets,* November 10, 1958, p. 11.
72. *Alamogordo Daily News,* March 20, 1959.
73. *Astronautics,* April 1959, p. 12.
74. *Ibid.,* p. 58.
75. The Office of Information, Air Force Missile Development Center, for example, has a large file of such requests.
76. *New York Herald Tribune,* July 22, 1958.
77. The West End School's fourth-grade *Gazette,* April 30, 1956, pp. 1 and 6.
78. *Alamogordo Daily News,* June 19, 1958.
79. *New York Times,* August 26, 1954.
80. *Alamogordo Daily News,* June 9, 1958.
81. *UCLA Alumni Magazine,* October 1958, p. 13.
82. *U.S. News & World Report,* April 4, 1958, p. 29.
83. Washington *Evening Star,* December 11, 1958; *El Paso Times,* January 12, 1959.
84. *Aviation Week,* December 8, 1958; p. 30; *Space/Aeronautics,* January 1959, p. 9.

85. For example, the President's address to the nation November 13, 1957, on "Science and Security," which was designed to "stimulate the faith and confidence" of the American people in their own defense and space programs after the successful launching of the first Soviet artificial satellite.
86. *Astronautics,* April 1958, p. 8; *Aviation Week,* July 13, 1959, p. 25.
87. *Washington Post,* December 28, 1958; *U.S. News & World Report,* January 2, 1959, p. 5.
88. *Astronautics,* August 1959, p. 6.
89. *Ibid.,* February 1959, p. 8.
90. *Astronautics,* November 1958, p. 10.
91. *Alamogordo Daily News,* October 14, 1958.
92. *Astronautics,* February 1958, p. 14.
93. *Missiles and Rockets,* May 1958, p. 34.
94. *Ibid.,* June 1958, p. 183.
95. *Proceedings of a Conference on Research and Development and Its Impact on the Economy* (U.S. Government Printing Office. 1958).
96. *Astronautical Sciences Review,* January-March 1959, p. 27,
97. *El Paso Times,* December 4, 1958.
98. *Missiles and Rockets,* November 10, 1958, p. 16.
99. *Aviation Week,* September 15, 1958, p. 25.
100. *Missiles and Rockets,* October 13, 1958, p. 35.
101. *Space Age,* May 1959, p. 51.
102. *Missiles and Rockets,* December 22, 1958, p. 9.
103. *Ibid.,* October 20, 1958, p. 83.
104. Howard's articles, published in *Missiles and Rockets,* include "New England's Missile Boom" (July 6, 1959, pp. 13-15); "Boston—'Hub' of Space Research" (July 13, 1959, pp. 12-13); "East Fights for Missile Dollar" (August 17, 1959, pp. 17-18); "The Capital's Top Private Industry" (August 31, 1959, pp. 19-21); "Michigan Seeks Missile Comeback" (October 12, 1959, pp. 18-19); and "Explosive Growth in Great Lakes Area" (October 19, 1959, pp. 17-18).
105. *Washington Post and Times Herald,* June 30, 1958.
106. *Missiles and Rockets,* July 7, 1958, p. 33.
107. *Wall Street Journal,* July 30, 1957.
108. *Missiles and Rockets,* December 15, 1958, p. 67.
109. *Aviation Daily,* October 23, 1958.
110. *Missiles and Rockets,* December 29, 1958, p. 11.
111. *Ibid.,* January 1957, p. 118, and December 1957, p. 98; *Aeronautics,* October 1959, p. 49.
112. Reviewed in *Time,* June 15, 1959, p. 50.
113. London *Daily Mail,* September 4, 1959

114. *Saturday Review,* December 27, 1958, p. 33.
115. RCA Victor LPM-1680.
116. RCA Victor LPM-1753.
117. RCA Victor LBY-1013, and reviewed by Frederic Ramsey, Jr., in *Saturday Review,* January 17, 1959, p. 91.
118. Distributed by the Library of Science and advertised in a brochure received by mail in November 1959.
119. *Saturday Review,* August 15, 1959, p. 9.
120. Interview with Woodi Ishmael by James S. Hanrahan, Holloman AFB, N. Mex., June 2, 1959.
121. Interview with Frank J. Malina by James S. Hanrahan, Amsterdam, August 30, 1958.
122. *Reporter,* March 19, 1959, p. 7.
123. *Saturday Review,* June 27, 1959, p. 9.
124. Heinz Gartmann, *The Men Behind the Space Rockets* (David McKay, 1956), p. 63.
125. Interview with L. I. Sedov, *Pravda,* September 26, 1955, translated and published in F. J. Krieger, *A Casebook on Soviet Astronautics* [U.S. Air Force Project Rand Research Memorandum RM-1760, June 21, 1956], I, 210.
126. N. A. Varvarov *et al.,* "On the Way to the Stars," *Technikamolodezhi,* in Krieger, *op. cit.,* I, 73.
127. "Periscoping Movies," *Newsweek,* August 11, 1958.
128. The Harvard Foundation for Advanced Study and Research, *Newsletter,* September 30, 1959, p. 2.
129. Quoted from an interview with Robert Frost, published in *Saturday Review,* March 21, 1959, p. 17.
130. The Smithsonian Institution, for example, received the first Jupiter-C re-entry nose cone and a replica of Explorer I (*Missiles and Rockets*, December 1, 1958, p. 7; *Alamogordo Daily News,* January 29, 1959). New rocket and space technology museums have been created at Roswell, N.M., honoring Robert H. Goddard (*Astronautics,* March 1959, p. 48) and at the Air Force Missile Development Center at Holloman AFB, N.M. (where one of the authors is a member of the museum committee). The State of California is planning a permanent space-age museum at Sacramento (*Missiles and Rockets,* July 21, 1958, p. 9).
131. *Chicago Daily News,* December 22, 1958.
132. *New York Times,* November 22, 1955; *Missiles and Rockets,* February 1958, p. 199; *Cincinnati Enquirer,* August 13, 1958; *Alamogordo Daily News,* November 26, 1958.
133. *Missiles and Rockets,* October 20, 1958, p. 72.
134. *Space/Aeronautics,* December 1958, p. 8.
135. Air Force Missile Development Center, *The Beginnings of Research in Space Biology . . . 1946-1952* (Holloman AFB, 1958), p. 30; *Alamogordo Daily News,* January 12, 1959.

136. *Reporter,* January 22, 1959, p. 2.
137. *Alamogordo Daily News,* February 15, 1959.
138. *Space Age,* May 1959, p. 50; *Missiles and Rockets,* January 1957, p. 21; *Newsweek,* October 27, 1958, p. 69.
139. *Washington Post and Times Herald,* May 4, 1958.

Index